Welding and Fabrication Workbook

Cengage Learning and Skills2Learn

skills2learn
www.skills2learn.com
Experts in e-learning & virtual reality simulation

CENGAGE
Learning·

Australia • Brazil • Japan • Korea • Mexico • Singapore • Spain • United Kingdom • United States

Welding and Fabrication Workbook
Skills2Learn and Cengage Learning

Publishing Director: Linden Harris

Commissioning Editor: Lucy Mills

Development Editor: Claire Napoli

Project Editor: Alison Cooke

Production Controller: Eyvett Davis

Marketing Manager: Lauren Mottram

Typesetter: S4Carlisle Publishing Services

Cover design: HCT Creative

For product information and technology assistance,
contact **emea.info@cengage.com**.

For permission to use material from this text or product,
and for permission queries,
email **emea.permissions@cengage.com**.

British Library Cataloguing-in-Publication Data
A catalogue record for this book is available from the British Library.

ISBN: 978-1-4080-7885-3

Cengage Learning EMEA
Cheriton House, North Way, Andover, Hampshire, SP10 5BE,
United Kingdom

Cengage Learning products are represented in Canada by
Nelson Education Ltd.

For your lifelong learning solutions, visit **www.cengage.co.uk**

Purchase your next print book, e-book or e-chapter at
www.cengagebrain.com

Printed in China by RR Donnelley
1 2 3 4 5 6 7 8 9 10 – 14 13 12

Contents

Part 3 Engineering materials, metal fabrication and quality control

About the E-Welding & Fabrication Consortia

This Welding and Fabrication workbook is based on the interactive and immersive virtual reality e-learning programme developed by the E-Welding & Fabrication Consortium. Formed and led by Skills2Learn the consortium consists of Carnegie College, Cengage Learning, City & Guilds, City of Bristol College, College of North West London and Weldability SIF.

The consortium members are passionate about the welding and fabrication industry and are determined to enhance the learning experiences of people within the different trades that use these skills or those that are new to it. They have many years experience in the welding, fabrication, engineering and educational sectors and have created an interactive e-learning programme with the aim of:

- Providing accessible training to the different industries that use welding and fabrication.

- Bridging the gap between classroom based and practical based learning.
- Providing a concentrated set of improvement learning modules.
- Enabling learners to gain new skills and qualifications more effectively.
- Improving functional skills and awareness of sustainability issues within the industry.
- Promoting health and safety in the industry.
- Encouraging training and continuous professional development.

For more information about this workbook and the e-learning programme please visit: http://www.e-welding andfabrication.com, http://www.e-skillszone.com, or www. skills2learn.com.

E-learning

Introduction

This Welding and Fabrication workbook and e-learning programmes use a blended learning approach to train learners about welding and fabrication skills. Blended learning allows training to be delivered through different mediums such as books, e-learning (computer based training), practical workshops, and traditional classroom techniques. These training methods are designed to complement each other and work in tandem to achieve overall learning objectives and outcomes.

E-Learning

The welding and fabrication e-learning programmes that are also available to sit alongside this workbook offers a different method of learning. With technology playing an increasingly important part of everyday life, e-learning uses visually rich 2D and 3D graphics/animation, audio, video, text and interactive quizzes, to allow you to engage with the content and learn at your own pace and in your own time.

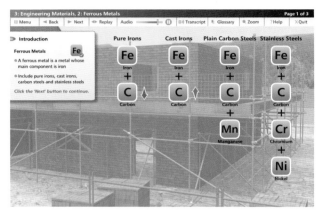

Materials, Fabrication and Quality Control

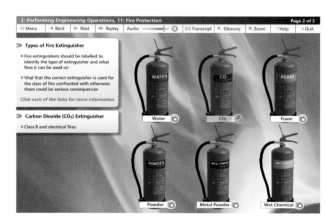

Performing Engineering Operations

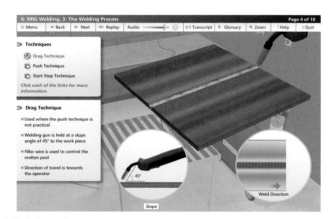

Welding Processes

E-Practical

The e-learning programme contains four interactive e-practical scenarios. This facility allows you to be immersed in virtual reality situations where the choices you make affect the outcome of your set job. Using 3D technology, you can move freely around the environment, interact with objects, carry out tests, and make decisions and mistakes until you have mastered the subject. By practicing in a virtual environment you will not only be able to see what you've learnt but also analyse your approach and thought process to the problem.

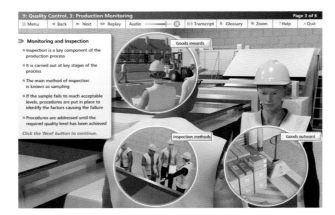

Material, Fabrication and Quality Control

Benefits of E-Learning

Diversity – E-Learning can be used for almost anything. With the correct approach any subject can be brought to life to provide an interactive training experience.

Technology – Advancements in computer technology now allow a wide range of spectacular and engaging e-learning to be delivered to a wider population.

Captivate and Motivate – Hold the learner's attention for longer with the use of high quality graphics, animation, sounds and interactivity.

Safe Environment – E-Practical scenarios can create environments which simulate potentially harmful real-life situations or replicate a piece of dangerous equipment, therefore allowing the learner to train and gain experience and knowledge in a completely safe environment.

Instant Feedback – Learners can undertake training assessments which feedback results instantly. This can provide information on where they need to re-study or congratulate them on passing the assessment. Results and Certificates could also be printed for future records.

On-Demand – Can be accessed 24 hours a day, 7 days a week, 365 days of the year. You can access the content at any time and view it at your own pace.

Portable Solutions – Can be delivered via a CD, website or LMS. Learners no longer need to travel to all lectures, conferences, meetings or training days. This saves many man-hours in reduced travelling, cost of hotels and expenses amongst other things.

Reduction of Costs – Can be used to teach best practice processes on jobs which use large quantities of or expensive materials. Learners can practice their techniques and boost their confidence to a high enough standard before being allowed near real materials.

Welding & Fabrication E-Learning

The aim of the e-lexarning programmes is to enhance a learner's knowledge and understanding of the welding and fabrication trades. The course content is aligned to units from Level 2 of the Fabrication and Welding Engineering National Occupational Standards (NOS) and Level 2 of the Performing Engineering Operations (PEO) NOS so can be used for study towards certification.

The programme gives the learners an understanding of the processes involved in welding and fabrication as well as looking at sustainability, health & safety and functional skills in an interactive and visually engaging manner. It also provides 'real-life' scenarios where the learner can apply the knowledge gained from the tutorials in a safe yet practical way.

By using and completing these programmes, it is expected that learners will demonstrate an understanding of:

- The welding and fabrication industry
- Health & safety in the welding and fabrication industry
- The processes when working in an engineering environment
- Communicating technical information
- Different materials used in welding and fabrication
- The different welding processes
- The different fabrication processes

- Quality control checks and procedures In line with specific codes

The e-learning programmes are divided into the following learning modules:

- Introduction to Welding & Fabrication
- Performing Engineering Operations
- Engineering Materials
- Oxyacetylene Welding
- MMA Welding
- MIG Welding
- TIG Welding
- Metal Fabrication
- Quality Control

The Welding & Fabrication Series

As part of the welding and fabrication series the following e-learning programmes and workbook are available. For more information, please contact the sales team on emea.fesales@cengage.com or visit: www.e-weldingand fabrication.com, www.e-skillszone.com, or www.skills 2learn.com

- E-Welding & Fabrication DVD (Premier Package e-learning programme)
- Performing Engineering Operations DVD (e-learning programme)
- Welding and Fabrication Workbook (supports the full suite of welding and fabrication e-learning programmes)

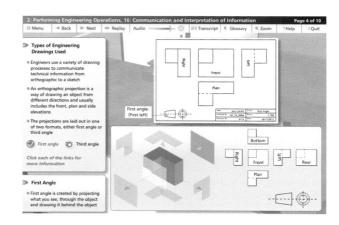

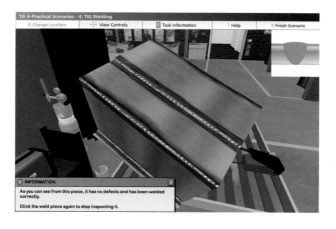

Foreword

The fabrication and welding industry is a dynamic part of the UK economy and a major employer of people. It has a huge impact on the environment and plays a major role in regeneration programmes which have a major impact on our lives. From petro-chemical to transportation, the fabrication and welding industries are so diverse and interact with so much advanced technology to meet global demands, there is a need to educate and re-educate those new to the industry. With environmental issues such as climate change and sustainable sourcing of materials now playing an important part in the design and fabrication of buildings and other structures, there has never been a greater need for education and innovation.

This workbook and supporting e-learning programme have been developed to provide a structured blended learning approach that will enhance the learning experience and stimulate a deeper understanding of the trades and give an awareness of sustainability issues. The content within these learning materials has been aligned to units of the British National Occupational Standards, and can be used as a support tool whilst studying for relevant vocational qualifications.

The uniqueness of this series is that it aims to bridge the gap between classroom-based and practical-based learning. The workbook provides classroom-based activities that can involve learners in discussions and research tasks as well as providing them with understanding and knowledge of the subject. The e-learning programmes take the subject further, with high quality images, animations and audio further enhancing the content and showing information in a different light. In addition, the e-practical side of the e-learning places the learner in a virtual environment where they can move around freely, interact with objects and use the knowledge and skills they have gained from the workbook and e-learning to complete a set of tasks whilst in the comfort of a safe working environment.

The Welding and Fabrication workbook and e-learning programmes are designed to help learners continuously improve their skills and provide confidence and a sound knowledge based before getting their hands dirty in the real world.

Hugh McPhillips
Chairman of the Association for Welding, Fabrication, Training and Education (AWFTE)

Majid Al-Kader
Managing Director of Skills2Learn

National Occupational Standards (NOS)

The National Occupational Standards (NOS) provide a framework of information that outline the skills, knowledge and understanding required to carry out work-based activities within a given vocation. Each standard is divided into units that cover specific activities of that occupation.

Employers, employees, teachers and learners can use the standards as information, support and reference resource that will enable them to understand the skills and criteria required for good practice in the workplace. The standards are used as a basis to develop many vocational qualifications in the United Kingdom for a wide range of occupations.

This workbook and associated e-learning programme are aligned to the following:

Part 1: Performing Engineering Operations

Performing Engineering Operations Suite 2

- Unit 1: Working Safely in an Engineering Environment
- Unit 2: Working Efficiently and Effectively in Engineering
- Unit 3: Using and Communicating Technical Information

Part 2: Welding Processes

- Fabrication and Welding Engineering Suite 2
- Performing Engineering Operations Suite 2

Part 3: Engineering Materials, Metal Fabrication and Quality Control

- Fabrication and Welding Engineering Suite 2
- Performing Engineering Operations Suite 2

Part 1

Performing Engineering Operations

1 Introduction

Welding and fabrication has a long and exciting history and is still a dynamic and evolving craft which impacts upon many aspects of daily life. From construction and transportation to aerospace, it is at the core of both traditional and emerging industries.

Health and Safety

LEARNING OBJECTIVES

By the end of this chapter you will be able to:

● Carry out a risk assessment

● Understand the main requirements of health and safety legislation

● Wear appropriate PPE (Personal Protective Equipment)

● Recognise safety signs

● Work safely in an engineering environment

Different aspects of performing engineering operations

An understanding of health and safety is an essential part of your training. This chapter contains information that is applicable in the workplace, on a work site and at a training provider or college. Wherever you are working, you need to be aware of what is going on around you at all times and have consideration for others. This chapter will give you a good foundation of knowledge that will help you work safely in potentially hazardous environments. You will find more information on safety issues associated with specific processes throughout this book.

Health and Safety at Work Act

The Health and Safety at Work Act, 1974 provides the legal framework to promote, stimulate and encourage high standards of health and safety in the workplace. It protects employees and the public from work activities. It is a good place to start this chapter on health and safety.

Website

Use a search engine to research the Health and Safety at Work Act 1974.

Everyone has a duty to comply with the Act, including employers, employees, trainees, the self-employed, manufacturers and suppliers. Always refer to local laws and regulations when at work.

If negligence can be proved, employers, employees and those who are self-employed can face a heavy fine from a magistrate's court and unlimited fines and imprisonment from a crown court.

Health and Safety at Work Act, 1974 applies to: 1. Employer; 2. Employee; 3. Self-employed

Employers

Employers must provide and maintain safety equipment and safe systems of work. This includes, among other things, ensuring materials are properly stored, handled, used and transported, providing information, training, instruction and supervision and ensuring staff are aware of manufacturers' and suppliers' instructions for equipment. Employers must also look after the health and safety of others, for example the public, and must talk to safety representatives. Employers are forbidden to charge employees for any measures which are required for health and safety, such as helmets or safety gloves.

Employees

Employees must comply with the Act and look after their own health and safety as well as the health and safety of others. They must co-operate with their employers and not interfere with anything provided in the interest of health and safety. All employees must ensure that they have been trained or instructed in the safe use of equipment before they use it.

Self-Employed

Self-employed workers must comply with the Act in the same way as employees. They must adhere to the health and safety guidelines that apply to the employer at all times. They are responsible for their own safety as well as the health and safety of others. They must co-operate with the company they are contracted to and not interfere with anything provided for them in the interest of health and safety.

Activity

An incident has occurred on site which has resulted in a good friend being taken to hospital. You think the accident may have happened because your friend was not wearing the safety equipment he had been issued. The health and safety officer for the site asks if anyone has any information about the incident. Do you:

a. Say you observed the incident and give all the details even if it means your friend could possibly be fired or lose any compensation.

b. Say that you did not see the accident, thereby protecting your friend but possibly putting the rest of your colleagues at risk.

c. Blame a failure in the equipment.

d. Conjure up a false reply in order to save your friend.

e. Tell the truth, thereby preventing any possible prosecution for preventing the course of justice and helping to maintain a safe working environment.

Personal Protective Equipment (PPE)

PPE stands for Personal Protective Equipment and covers a range of different items of clothing or equipment – such as gloves or safety helmets – that you may have to use on a job to avoid harm or injury.

Employers have a legal duty to identify any risks involved with a particular job and thus what items of PPE may be needed. However, you still need to know the basics so you can make sure you get what you need. Employers also have a legal duty to provide full PPE training for any equipment that might be needed and employees have a responsibility to look after and maintain the equipment they are given. If any damage occurs to the equipment, it must be reported immediately. Employees should avoid customising or altering any PPE as this may lead to prosecution. For safety purposes it is good prac-tice to remove all jewellery to prevent it being caught or trapped.

Ideally, risks to health and safety should be eliminated from the workplace before they occur; PPE is a last line of defence. However, if risks remain, then PPE must be provided to you free of charge.

Types of PPE

You need to be familiar with several key items of PPE. You may not need to use them on every job, but you still need to know when they are required and how they should be used.

Some jobs may require specialist items of PPE, for example welding may require a welding mask and leather apron. Always check that you have the appropriate PPE for the job you are about to carry out.

Wear PPE safety sign

E-Learning

Use the e-learning programme for an interactive look at PPE.

Safety Footwear

For many jobs you will need to wear steel-toed boots with intersoles – these are thin pads in the boots or shoes that absorb surface shock – to protect your feet from injury.

If working in wet conditions, rubber boots should be worn which must also have intersoles and steel toecaps.

Overalls

Boiler suits are ideal for many jobs as they provide cover for your entire body. However, you must never wear overalls made from terylene, nylon or similar materials as these catch fire easily.

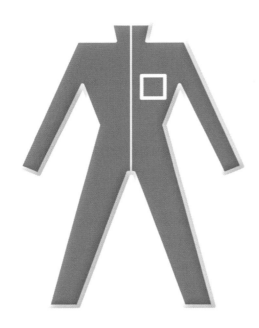

Ear Defenders

If you are exposed to high noise levels, you must protect your hearing with ear defenders or ear plugs.

Ear defenders must always be properly fitted so that the ear is completely covered, otherwise you will not be fully protected.

Ear plugs fit inside the ear, and are often disposable. They offer less protection than ear defenders.

Most employers will need to consider whether they have a noise problem. As a 'rule of thumb', if there are areas in any workshop or factory where people have to shout or have difficulty in being heard clearly by someone about 2 metres away, or find it difficult to talk to each other, there could be a noise problem.

Where the noise level is above 80dB, it is recommended practice that hearing protection should be available.

Some examples of typical minimum noise levels where no steps have been taken to reduce noise are given below:

Operation	dB(A)
Grinding on a pedestal grinder	90 – 95
Discharging metal objects into metal bins	85 – 95
General noise level in fabrication shop	85 – 95
Hammering steel	95 – 100
Guillotining	95 – 100
Multi spindle turning	95 – 105
Circular sawing of metal	95 – 105
Pressing (Blanking)	95 – 110
Punch pressing	110 – 120
Riveting	100 – 110

Respirators

Many different types of respirator are available, but filter masks are the most common. These are rubber face masks that fit over the mouth and nose, containing a filter canister through which the wearer breathes.

Filter masks stop dust but are useless against gases or vapours, so if you are working around these, you must use a canister respirator. Filter canisters must be changed regularly.

Air-purifying respirators have an air-purifying filter, cartridge or canister that removes specific air contaminants by passing the ambient (surrounding) air through the air-purifying element.

Atmosphere-supplying respirators supply breathing air from a source independent of the ambient atmosphere. This type of respirator includes both supplied-air respirators (SARs) and self-contained breathing apparatus (SCBA) units.

Demand respirators are atmosphere-supplying respirators that admit breathing air to the face piece only when a negative pressure is created inside the face piece by inhalation.

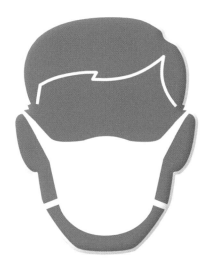

Safety Gloves

Safety gloves protect your hands from injury. Take care to choose the right kind, as different types exist, for example for working with heat or chemicals. Check the glove application data, if it is available.

Do not wear gloves when using machinery such as drills as this is dangerous.

Safety Goggles

You must wear safety goggles when required, for example when welding, when working in dusty conditions or when flying chippings will be produced.

Always check that you have the right type of goggles, as different lenses offer different levels of protection.

If goggles have dirty lenses, clean them before use: never obscure your vision.

Safety Helmets

Hard hats should be worn whenever there is a risk of falling or flying objects. You must always check that your helmet fits properly. Always wear your hat with the peak facing forward, as the peak lip is designed to protect your eyes. When working indoors, a 'bump hat' can be worn instead.

Hard hats sometimes come with an expiry date. It is not advisable to use such hard hats after the expiry date as it may have deteriorated and no longer provides the necessary protection.

If you have long hair you must ensure that your hair is contained within the hard hat to avoid it getting trapped or caught in any way. Hair nets can be used to hold the hair safely within the helmet.

If you carry a hard hat in your car make sure it is out of direct sunlight as some breakdown in the physical properties of the plastic can occur, with potentially drastic consequences.

Never apply any labels or customise a hard hat using paints as this can have a reaction with the base material of the helmet and again reduce its mechanical properties.

Risks and Hazards

Two words are used very frequently in any discussion of health and safety. They are 'risk' and 'hazard'. It is important to understand these terms, as they do not refer to the same thing.

Hazards

A hazard exists if there is something that can potentially damage your health or the health of others. The negative effects of a hazard may be relatively minor, such as making your eyes water, or they may be much more serious, such as suffocation. In some cases, they can even be fatal. Hazards may be difficult to detect and may not affect you immediately, such as the cancers caused by asbestos that may not appear for decades after exposure.

Hazards may be associated with the following:

- machinery;
- electricity;
- slippery or uneven surfaces;
- handling and transporting;
- contaminants and irritants;
- dust and fumes;
- material ejection;
- fire;
- working at height;
- moving parts;
- pressured and stored energy systems (e.g. gas canisters);
- toxic or volatile materials;
- unshielded processes.

Risk

Risk is the chance that a person or persons could be harmed by one or more hazards, together with an indication of how serious the harm could be. Risk assessment is a process which identifies any hazards, evaluates the risk and suggests how to eliminate the hazard or control the hazard. Later in this chapter you will learn how to perform a risk assessment.

Risk is measured on a scale of 1 – 5:

1   Very unlikely to happen, causing harm
2   Unlikely to happen, causing harm
3   Possible to happen, causing harm
4   Likely to happen, causing harm
5   Very likely to happen, causing harm

Linked to this is a scale for severity:

1   Minor injury
2   Major injury
3   Loss of limb
4   Death of an individual
5   Multiple deaths

From the above, a formula can be used to calculate risk:

Risk = Likelihood rating x Severity rating

Safety Signs

Safety signs are used extensively in the workplace to warn of a number of different risks and hazards. To be able to work safely you must understand what the basic safety signs mean.

Prohibition signs – circular with a red diagonal line through them, tell you not to do something.

Mandatory signs – blue circles with white symbols, tell you what you must do.

Warning signs – yellow triangles with a black outline and black symbols, give notice of a particular hazard or danger.

Information signs – green squares with white symbols, are used to communicate safety information.

Specific Safety Signs

You are very likely to come across the following signs in the workplace. You need to be able to recognise their meaning immediately.

 E-Learning

Use the e-learning programme for an interactive look at Safety Signs

No Smoking

This sign tells you that smoking is not permitted within the designated area.

Smoking and Naked Flame Prohibited

When you see this sign neither smoking nor naked flames are permitted within the designated area.

Do not extinguish with water

This sign tells you that fires must not be extinguished with water, as to do so could be dangerous.

Pedestrians prohibited

This sign tells you that pedestrians are not allowed to walk through the workplace.

Wear hand protection

When you see this sign, safety gloves must be worn.

Wear head protection

When you see this sign, safety helmets must be worn by everyone.

Wear eye protection

This sign tells you that safety goggles or glasses must be worn.

Wear hearing protection

If you see this sign, it means that ear defenders must be worn by everyone.

Danger: electricity

When you see this sign, you must pay careful attention, as a source of potential electrical danger is being highlighted.

Risk of fire

This sign gives warning that there is a risk of fire in the immediate vicinity.

General warning

When you see this sign, be alert for possible risks or sources of potential danger.

Fragile roof

This sign gives warning that a workplace roof is not safe, and should be approached with caution.

First-aid point

This sign flags up the location of a first-aid point. Take note of it in case of accidents.

Emergency telephone

This sign indicates the location of an emergency telephone.

Indication of direction

This sign tells you the direction you should be walking or driving in.

Control of Substances Hazardous to Health (COSHH)

There is a legal requirement for employers to prevent or reduce their employees' exposure to hazardous substances. This law is known as the Control of Substances Hazardous to Health or COSHH.

Website

Use a search engine to research COSHH.

Hazardous Substances

Hazardous substances can be divided into four main categories. If you are able to identify these in a practical setting, you will be more alert to possible sources of danger and more able to take appropriate protective action.

Toxic/very toxic substances

Toxic or very toxic substances can cause death or serious damage when inhaled, swallowed or absorbed by the skin. For example, cyanide which is used for surface hardening carbon steel components is a toxic substance which is very dangerous.

Corrosive substances

Corrosive substances, such as sulphuric acid, may destroy parts of your body if they come into direct contact with them.

Harmful substances

Harmful substances such as lead can cause death or serious damage when inhaled, swallowed or absorbed by the skin.

Irritant substances

If irritant substances, such as soft solder flux, come into contact with the skin, eyes, nose or mouth, they can cause inflammation or swelling. Such effects may be felt immediately, or they may come after extended or repeated contact.

Under European law, substances are defined as being officially hazardous to health if they are listed as being 'dangerous to supply'. When they are sold commercially, the packaging for hazardous substances must be clearly marked and labelled.

Hazardous substances are identified by four main warning signs.

Corrosive material

Substances marked as being 'corrosive' could cause permanent damage if they come into direct contact with any part of your body.

Flammable material

Flammable materials must be kept away from naked flames and you should not smoke when near them. Common flammable materials include your own clothes, hair that is worn long, some modern hair products and any oily rags that may have been left lying around.

Explosive material

Explosive materials must be handled and stored with particular care, as they potentially present an extreme hazard.

Toxic material

Some toxic materials, such as gas in a confined area, can harm you even if you do not come into direct contact with them, so ensure you handle them with care. If necessary, seek advice as to whether PPE is required when they are in use.

The Effects of Hazardous Substances

In order to follow safety procedures and use PPE correctly, it is important to understand exactly how harmful substances can affect your body.

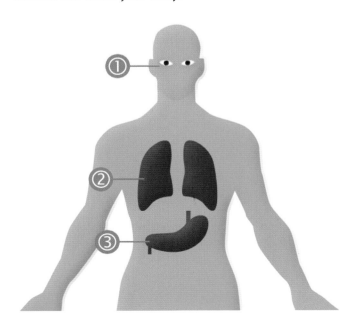

How harmful substances affect: 1. Eyes and skin; 2. Lungs; 3. Stomach.

Skin and eyes

Hazardous substances can cause serious damage if they come into direct contact with your skin or eyes. Harmful substances such as solvents can enter the bloodstream by being absorbed through the skin or through cuts and bruises. Some substances can produce vapours, gases, dust or liquids which cause irritation to the eyes and in severe cases cause serious damage. It's important to always make sure your skin and eyes are protected.

Lungs

Harmful substances can cause damage when inhaled in one of two ways. Either they can cause direct damage to the lungs themselves in the way that asbestos does, or they can enter the bloodstream and so affect other organs.

Stomach

Harmful substances such as lead can reach the stomach in numerous ways if basic hygiene is not observed, or if gloves are not worn. Eating, drinking, smoking and biting your nails can all be responsible for this.

Hazardous substances are anything that can harm your health when you work with them if they are not properly controlled, for example by using adequate ventilation. They can include:

- substances used directly in work activities such as acids, cleaning agents, paints or glues;
- substances generated during work activities such as fumes from welding, brazing or soldering;
- naturally occurring substances such as blood, bacteria, or assorted grain dusts.

For the vast majority of commercial chemicals, the presence (or not) of a warning label will indicate whether COSHH is relevant. For example, washing up liquid does not have a warning label, but bleach does, so COSHH applies to bleach and not to washing up liquid.

There is more than one way that you can know whether a substance is hazardous:

- Manufacturers, importers and suppliers have a 'duty of care' to inform you.
- Look for warning labels on containers.
- Material Safety Data Sheets (MSDS) often known by other names such as Safety Data Sheets and Product Safety Data Sheets, provide information on all hazardous substances.

Website

Use a search engine to research Health and Safety Executive Publication EH40.

There are regulations regarding the transportation of hazardous substances which requires data sheets known as Chemical Hazard Information and Packaging for Supply regulations 2009 (CHIP) and hazard chemical symbols for clear identification. MSDS contain 16 specific sections on all aspects of safety. The EH40 lists substances which have occupational exposure limits assigned to them, based on the concentration of the substance in the air. The entry routes for these substances can be by:

- Inhalation – breathed in;
- Ingestion – swallowed;
- Absorption – entry through the skin.

These substances are controlled by minimum Occupational Exposure Levels (OEL) and Maximum Exposure Levels (MEL) within a working day and maximum PPE to control the hazard.

Dealing with Hazardous Substances

All hazardous substances have their own Material Safety Data Sheet (MSDS). These sheets provide details on the hazardous substance including their composition, how to deal with spillages, any corrosive features and potential fire hazards. All substances should be stored in and disposed of in line with government guidelines.

Storage

The MSDS gives specific information regarding the storage requirements of hazardous substances. Some of the key considerations are the construction of containment vessels, ventilation, the distance from main buildings and disposal arrangements.

Disposal

All COSHH substances are governed by disposal arrangements. The user has a duty of care to ensure the safe disposal of hazardous substances at an approved location.

Failure to comply is a criminal offence and can lead to prosecution.

Sustainability

Concern for the environment and awareness of the need to improve management of 'finite' resources is on the increase. One of the most effective steps a company can take to ensure its commitment to the environment is translated into action is to implement an environmental management system (EMS) such as BS EN ISO 14000 series. Other directives which interact with ISO 14000 are the Clean Air Act and Pollution Prevention and Control Act 1999. All of these regulations place a duty of care on all those involved in the management of waste, be it in collecting, disposing of or treating controlled waste which is subject to licensing. Failure to comply may result in prosecution. Using such as system has a number of reported benefits such as:

- the potential for greater cost savings;
- a competitive advantage when tendering for contracts, especially government contracts;
- minimising the potential for environmental incidents and reducing or eliminating any impacts.

Welding shops generate a lot of waste materials. Much of the waste is scrap metal. All scrap metal, including electrode stubs, can easily be recycled. Recycling metal is good for the environment and can be a source of revenue for the welding shop.

Other forms of waste, such as burned flux, cleaning solvents and dust collected in shop air-filtration systems, may be considered hazardous materials and may come under COSHH regulations. Check with the material manufacturer or an environmental consultant to determine whether any waste material is considered hazardous. Throwing hazardous waste material into the bin, pouring it on the ground or dumping it down the drain is illegal. Protecting our environment from pollution is everyone's responsibility.

Website

Use a search engine to research the Clean Air Act and Pollution Prevention and Control Act 1999.

Working at Height

Ladders

People injure themselves using ladders for four main reasons. They over-reach or slip, or the ladder itself breaks or falls over. These risks can be minimised if you stay aware of how to use ladders properly.

Leaning Ladders

Functional Skills

Before you use a leaning ladder, check that it has clean rungs and undamaged stiles (the side pieces the rungs are attached to). Position the ladder at an angle of 75° from the horizontal e.g. 1m out from the base for every 4m of height.

Make sure that a ladder cannot move about at the top, that it has a strong upper resting point and that its rungs are horizontal. When in use, never stand on the top three rungs, and maintain three points of contact at all times.

Leaning ladder

Here are some general safety and usage rules for ladders:

- Follow all recommended practices for safe use and storage.
- Do not exceed the manufacturer's recommended maximum weight limit for the ladder.

- Before setting up a ladder, make certain that it will be erected on a level, solid surface.
- When using extending ladders, always ensure that the two sections overlap each other by three rungs to ensure rigidity.
- Never use a ladder in a wet or muddy area where water or mud will be tracked up the ladder's steps or rungs. Only climb or descend ladders when you are wearing clean, dry shoes.
- Wear well-fitted shoes or boots.
- Tie the ladder securely in place.
- Climb and descend the ladder cautiously, using both hands at all times.
- Do not carry tools and supplies in your hand as you climb or descend a ladder. Use a rope to raise or lower the items once you are safely in place.
- Never use metal ladders around live electrical wires, fibre glass ladders are available for this type of work.
- Never use a ladder that is too short for the job so you have to reach or stand on the top step.

Step Ladders

Step ladder

Before you get started, check that the stepladder is in good condition, with clean treads and secure locks. It should be fully open, and locked firmly in place.

Do not work sideways on.

Before you start – general principles

General principles before using a ladder

Whatever type of ladder you are using; before you start you should check that it is in good general condition. Are its feet firmly attached? Have you properly secured its fastenings? You must also ensure that it is in a good position. It should not be able to move at the bottom, and should be placed on a firm, level surface that is clear and dry. Finally, you must always be fully fit to work at heights, and never paint wooden ladders as this may conceal damage or cracks.

Using ladders – general principles

General principles when using a ladder 1. Never work on a ladder for longer than 30mins; 2. Stated weight limits must not be exceeded; 3. Always wear non-slip footwear

You should never work on a ladder for longer than 30 minutes, and must not exceed stated weight limits, so only carry light tools and materials.

When working, keep your body centred on the ladder, avoiding over-reaching. You must also keep both feet on the same rung or step. When you climb, always keep a firm grip on the ladder.

Non-slip footwear should always be worn when you are working on a ladder.

Scaffolding

Scaffoldings used in a shipyard

Setting up, using and checking scaffolding must all be done by competent persons, because falls and collapses can cause serious injury or even death. Also, due consideration must be paid to the safety of all personnel.

Using Scaffolding

Scaffolding must always be erected by competent people. It should be put up on firm, level ground away from any power lines. To avoid falls, strong barriers such as guardrails and toe boards must be in place. Heavy or bulky loads should never be carried up or down ladders, which should be strong, secure and in good condition. The top of the ladder should project 1m above the level of the work platform.

The use of domestic ladders should be avoided, as these may collapse. Under no circumstances should components ever be removed from the scaffolding after it has been set up.

Risk to All Personnel

© Joe Gough

Scaffolding should never normally be set up over busy public areas. If a risk exists, limit work to quiet times. Prevent waste materials from falling on people by keeping work platforms clear of debris; if debris is allowed to build up, it could become stacked above the level of the toe boards, from where it could drop on people below.

Checking

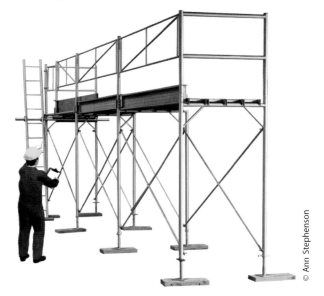

© Ann Stephenson

Check scaffolding regularly

Once it has been set up, scaffolding should be checked on a weekly basis, as well as after any alterations, damage, or extreme weather. These inspections must be done by a competent person. Any problems should be fixed immediately, or the scaffolding must be taken out of use.

Mobile Towers

© Dmitry Vereshchagin

Mobile towers refer to any platform or mobile elevated working platform (MEWP) including scissor lifts or cherry pickers. Before use, you must ensure the mobile tower is braced, has outriggers, and that any wheels are locked. Mobile towers must be kept away from overhead cables, and ladders should never be lent against them. You should never move a tower when people or heavy items of equipment are on board. Finally, as with ladders, you should avoid over-reaching when you are standing on one. To ensure the safety of all personnel in the workplace, the area immediately below the platform should be cordoned off and safety signs displayed. It is also essential to wear a harness and lanyard device when working at height. These will halt the fall of an operator and hold them securely until such time as they can be rescued.

Manual Handling

Lifting

Manual handling includes lifting, carrying, lowering, pushing and pulling. We will consider lifting first, which can be divided into five steps:

Lifting the load

E-Learning

Use the e-learning programme to see an animation of the five steps involved in lifting.

1   Stop and think. Always consider the weight of what you are lifting and carrying and how many times you may need to repeat this process. All packaged goods should have their weight printed on the external packaging and give a guide to the number of people required to lift it. If the load is going to be too heavy to lift then seek assistance or find another method of moving it.

2   Adopt a good posture. Keep your feet apart and angled so the leading leg is forward, which softens the knees in the bend. Fully bend your hips and knees in a squat, so you keep your back naturally straight. Failure to do this can result in a slipped or prolapsed disc, so take care.

3   Take a grip on the load. Make a full assessment of the weight, keep your body, shoulders and eyes forward, keep relaxed, don't tense or twist or over reach. In other words, take a firm grip.

4   Lift the load. Keep the load within the boundary of your legs and elbows, and use the power of your legs to push up. Maintain and control your posture and stand in a smooth upward movement maintaining a naturally straight back. If the load is too heavy do not continue.

5   Finally, keep the load under control. Keep it close to your body and, if there is an uneven distribution of weight, keep the heaviest side closest to you. Be aware that liquids and uneven loads can cause problems.

Carrying the Load

Carrying the load

Here is a summary of a good practice guide to manual handling:

- If it is possible to avoid doing any manual handling by using other ways to move the load, then these alternatives should be investigated. Consider different ways of moving the load such as using lifting equipment. Refer to the Lifting of Loads Equipment Regulations (LOLER).
- If you carry out any manual handling operation, assess the situation and task beforehand and reduce any potential risks.
- Know your limitations and don't try to do too much. Use controlled, steady movements and be vigilant and aware of your surroundings.
- Remember if you are feeling tired or strained – stop, don't overdo it.

E-Learning

Use the e-learning programme to see an animation of carrying the load

Heavier Loads

If a load is too large to be carried by one or two people, then an alternative method of moving it must be found. Options available include trolleys, wheelbarrows and scissor lifts. Mechanised equipment, such as fork lift trucks, require fully trained operatives. First you need to check that the aid you want to use is safe, and check your route for hazards such as slopes and uneven surfaces.

E-Learning

Use the e-learning programme to see an animation of loads that are too large to be carried.

Loading a Trolley

Use your lifting techniques to get the load onto the trolley. (You may need to involve more people or mechanised equipment such as a hoist.) Once you are ready to move

the trolley, take a firm grip on the handles. Taking the weight of the load, lean forward slightly, keeping a natural straight back.

E-Learning

Use the e-learning programme to see an animation of loading a trolley.

Moving the Load

Moving the load

Use the power of your legs to push in an even and controlled way. Aim for a slow walking pace. Once you are moving keep up a steady pace and keep your feet away from the load.

E-Learning

Use the e-learning programme to see an animation of moving the load.

Arriving at the Destination

When you arrive at your destination slow down smoothly to a stop, with no jerking movements. Then unload the trolley in the same way it was loaded.

Stopping the trolley

E-Learning

Use the e-learning programme to see an animation of arriving at the destination.

Returning the Trolley

Finally, return the trolley to its place, to avoid turning it into a hazard in its own right. Also, if the trolley is missing, the next person to need it might be tempted to carry out an unsafe manual handling action.

E-Learning

Use the e-learning programme to see an animation of returning the trolley.

Pushing vs Pulling

Pushing the trolley is safer than pulling

When you have a load on a trolley, or other manual handling aid, you can push or pull it. Pulling is more dangerous than pushing as the load can 'run over' you. If you lose control when pushing the load will move away from you, instead of running towards you. Pulling also puts more strain on the back and makes it less easy to control the load.

Although pushing a load is always preferable, pulling is sometimes unavoidable. The steps you need to follow are very similar to those for pushing a load. Check the equipment is in good working order, assess the route for hazards and safely load the trolley. Then take a firm grip and use the power of your legs to move the load steadily until you reach your destination. Remember to stop gently and then unload the trolley in the same way that you loaded it.

If at any time you feel uncomfortable, stop and reassess the situation.

Manual handling regulations cover the movement and support of any load by physical effort including; lifting, carrying, putting down, pushing and pulling. Typical injuries that can occur as a direct result of improper handling include:

- fractures;
- damage to muscles, ligaments, and tendons;
- spinal disc injuries;
- trapped nerves;
- abrasions and cuts;
- burns;
- hernias.

Lifting Operations and Lifting Equipment Regulations (LOLER)

These regulations were introduced to ensure conformity with regards to any equipment used to lift loads. They cover equipment such as cranes, lifting tackle, chains, straps and manual handling equipment such as motorised fork lifts etc. Under these regulations all equipment must be monitored on a regular frequency, and any repairs recorded in a logbook for inspection by Health and Safety. Inspection is recorded at designated periods. Any equipment that does not pass this inspection must not be used.

Website

Use a search engine to research the Lifting Operations and Lifting Equipment Regulations (LOLER)

Transporting Loads using Lifting Aids

Light loads can be transported with the aid of a variety of hand trucks and trailers largely depending on the shape of the articles.

Hand trucks/sack barrows

These are designed with two wheels having a capacity of around 250kg and can be used to transport sacks, boxes and broad based loads. Special types are available for transporting gas bottles, oil drums and similar items.

Flat trolleys/trailers

These have four wheels, and offer more stability. They are capable of transporting heavier loads of 500 to 800kg, dependent upon design. These trolleys come into their own when uniform shapes such as packages and boxes are to be transported over uneven ground. As a general rule care should be taken NOT to stack so high that you cannot see clearly and that the load is evenly distributed.

Hand pallet trucks

These trucks have two adjustable forks which are pushed under a pallet and a hydraulic lifting system which raises the load off the ground in order to move it easily. They have a loading capacity of up to 3000kg. Make sure that there are no physical obstructions in the proposed route and that the load is only raised clear of the ground so that, if the hydraulic system fails, it has only a short distance to drop.

When you move materials to a new position, be aware of the following guidelines:

Do

- Always wedge cylindrical objects such as bars, tubes and drums to prevent them rolling.
- Keep all heavy objects at floor level.
- Regularly inspect container, racks, pallets, etc. for damage and report any findings.
- Use properly constructed racks secured to the floor or wall.

- All palletised goods should be stacked on a level floor otherwise it is possible for the load to become unstable.
- Packages of a uniform size should be stacked like a brick wall (keyed) in alternative directions so that no tier is independent of another.

Do Not

- Lean heavy objects against structural walls.
- Climb racks to reach upper shelves always use a ladder or steps.
- Exceed the safe working loading of racks, shelves or floors. De-stack by climbing up and throwing down from the top or pulling out from the bottom.
- Allow items to stick out from racks or bins into the gangway.
- Place liquids at height especially if they contain corrosive or toxic chemicals. These items should be stored in controlled environments under COSHH Regulations.

Power Lifting

Where loads are too heavy to be manually lifted, some form of lifting equipment is required. Lifting equipment can be classified according to its power source: manual, hydraulic, pneumatic, electrical, petrol or diesel.

For very frequent lifting and transporting, the use of a fully powered stacker will speed up your operations and reduce the physical effort required, thus preventing strains and injuries. Fully powered stackers offer a cheaper and smaller alternative to forklift trucks. A walk-behind truck reduces the risks of accidents and injury and, although basic training may be necessary, operators are not required to hold a licence which is mandatory with fork lift drivers.

Forklift Trucks

Forklift trucks are used to carry heavy pallets and loads. The lifting mechanism is hydraulically powered and they are normally battery powered for moving around.

Chain blocks

Chain blocks are capable of lifting loads up to around 5000kg. They work on the mechanical advantage obtained through the geared block which reduces the manual effort required in operating the chain. They may be electrically or mechanically powered.

Portable Cranes

Small hydraulically operated portable cranes are available which have an adjustable jib with a lifting capacity anywhere between 350 to 550kg on the smaller models and 1700 to 2500kg on larger models. The lower figure is the load capable of being lifted with the jib in its most extended position. In this case the mechanical advantage is obtained through the hydraulic system which reduces the manual effort. Petrol or diesel is often used to power hoists that are used in site work.

Scissor Lifts

These are so called because of the criss-cross, scissor-like shape of the raising structure, which is normally hydraulically powered. They are often used to raise people to reach high levels of storage or for working off the ground, in which case they include a safe cage. Scissor lifts are the best platform for working on jobs off the ground as they allow a certain degree of free movement.

Wall & Overhead Cranes

Often seen in factories and large store rooms, these are ideal for manoeuvring the lifting tackle and chains into the correct position above the load to be moved.

Precautions when Using Hoists and Cranes

The loads lifted by cranes, hoists and fork lift trucks are quite substantial. If the load slips or falls the injuries that can be incurred can be extremely severe, or even fatal.

When loading:

- Slings should be protected from sharp edged loads by packing pieces of soft wood or other suitable material between the load and the sling.
- Wire ropes must not be bent sharply at any point.
- Wire ropes must never be used in contact with hot metals or acids.
- Wire ropes must never be used singly when hooked by a hand spliced eye. The cable is liable to untwist, allowing the splices to open or slip.

- Ensure that the load is evenly distributed to avoid excessive stresses on one side of the sling.
- Do not use slings that are too short as this creates a wide angle between the legs.
- Do not use slings that are too long as this seriously reduces headroom.
- Do not use ropes that show any signs of corrosion.

Avoid letting the load rest on a wire rope as it may crush strands and render the rope unsafe. Place suitable packing material under the load to prevent the ropes being trapped and to facilitate re-lifting at a later date.

Before Lifting

- Ensure that the load is securely slung.
- Always see that the crane hook is placed centrally over the load to prevent swinging when the load is being raised.
- Take your hands away from chains and ropes before the crane takes the load.
- See that the load is free for lifting.
- Give warnings to people to keep clear of the load.

During Lifting

- Signals must be given by one person responsible for the lift and nobody else.
- Hooks and slings not in use should not be carried on the carrying hook, as they may cause the sling carrying the load to ride on the nose of the hook, from where it could become dislodged.
- The proper pin must be used in all shackles and all end links, rings and shackles must ride freely upon any hook on which they are used.
- Never ride on a crane load, or allow any other person to do so.
- Never allow a load to be carried over the heads of other persons.
- Chains, slings, hooks or loads should never be dragged along the floor.

When Unloading

- Make sure that you have a firm foundation for your stack, and that you can remove slings without disturbing the stack.
- Stack material securely and in a position where there is safe access to remove it in the future.

- Vehicles should be loaded in such a manner that there are NO dangerous projections and the load is safe for transport.
- Do not overload a vehicle.
- Material should not be stacked within three feet of any moving object.

LOLER

LOLER (The Lifting Operations and Lifting Equipment Regulations 1998) requires that a register is kept on all premises where slings and lifting tackle are used. The details recorded in the register include the dates at which various parts of the equipment are inspected.

These regulations are there to ensure that only tested and approved lifting equipment is used. The use of any equipment that does not conform to these requirements is illegal and will constitute a potentially highly hazardous, dangerous practice. Only lifting gear supplied and approved by the organisation should be used. Lifting gear may develop defects between formal inspections and operators should inspect their equipment visually before use, to ensure it is sound and in good condition.

LOLER covers any equipment used at work for lifting or lowering loads. It does not apply to escalators, which are covered by more specific legislation, the Workplace (Health, Safety and Welfare) Regulations 1992. LOLER also does not cover trolleys for gas cylinders as these are specific storing and moving equipment and should never be used for lifting or moving any other items.

Ancillary Equipment for Lifting

Hooks

Hooks are forged from hardened and tempered high-tensile steel and are rated according to their safe working load (SWL). They are tested by being subjected to a load which is twice their SWL.

In certain instances the hook must be provided with an effective device for preventing the displacement of a sling, or be such a shape as to reduce as far as necessary the risk of displacement.

Where there is no safety catch fitted to the hook and there is a danger of the load slipping off the hook, the throat of the hook must be moused (trapped). When a person is to be suspended from a rig a saddle mousing should be applied, even though permanent safety catches are fitted at the throat of the hooks.

Shackles

Shackles come in a range of types and sizes and are selected to suit the particular use to which they will be put. Each is designed to carry a certain SWL and this must be clearly stamped on the shackle, together with an identification mark.

The pin of the shackle is the most important part, because it is subjected to the greatest stress from the load. It is vital that the pin is of the correct type for the shackle.

Eye bolts are used for general lifting and may be permanently attached to loads that need to be moved frequently. They are screwed into location holes provided in loads for the attachment of shackles and slings.

Home-made eye bolts should never be used, and commercial eye bolts should never be modified. Damaged eye bolts should be scrapped and never repaired.

Plate Lifting Clamps

These have a self-tightening action; the heavier the load the tighter the grip. There are many variations of lifting clamps. Some are designed for lifting plates from the horizontal to the vertical position, whilst others are designed for, and must only be used for lifting plates in the horizontal position.

All lifting clamps should be loaded within their marked capacity and the jaws must be as narrow as practicable for the plate being lifted. Only **one** plate at a time should be lifted when lifting plates vertically.

Pipe-lifting Tongs

Lifting tongs, also known as 'grabs', come in a variety of designs relating to the type of load they are intended to lift.

Lifting Beams

Lifting beams are usually designed to enable a particular load to be lifted. A specially designed lifting beam can give a far greater degree of control over the handling of a load than a combination of other lifting gear, especially when the load is long and awkward to lift. When lifting large plates, a spreader bar and plate clamps should be used together.

Slings

Slings are manufactured from a number of materials including man-made fibre, wire rope and chain. Belt slings made from high tenacity polyester webbing are commonly used.

Manufacturers commonly identify the SWL by weaving a colour stripe into the webbing.

Wire rope slings are designated by size, strength and construction, the size being expressed as the diameter across the maximum dimension, usually the average of three measurements along the rope. The strength is dependent on the number and strength of the individual strands and wires from which the rope is constructed.

The construction is designated by the number of strands and the number of wires per strand i.e. 7 x 37 rope has 7 strands, each with 37 individual wires.

Chain slings are used because of the flexibility and superior shock-absorbing properties of chain. They can withstand rough usage and last a long time, high-tensile steel chain is known as grade 40, because its breaking load is 40 times the diameter squared ($40 \times d^2$).

The stresses in the legs of a sling increase as the angle between them increases. Using a human body and two buckets filled with water it is not difficult to demonstrate the effects of lifting a load at narrow and wide angles. The arms represent slings and lift angles. The body and slings are not designed to take unnecessary strains.

The maximum angle any sling can be used at is 120° inclusive.

Risk Assessments

Many accidents in the workplace could have been avoided if a full risk assessment had taken.

There is a legal requirement to carry out regular risk assessments, and, although the law does not expect all risks to be eliminated, people must be protected as far as it is reasonably practicable to do so.

What is Risk Assessment?

Risk assessment means identifying hazards in the workplace then deciding who might be harmed and how. A hazard can be anything that might cause harm, for example, electricity, chemicals, working from ladders or an open drawer. There are five steps in the risk assessment process. Once this process has been completed suitable precautions can be put in place to reduce the risk of harm, or make the harm less serious.

The five steps of risk assessment are:

1   Identifying the hazards
2   Identifying who could be affected
3   Evaluating the risks
4   Record findings and implement them
5   Review risk assessment

Identify the Hazards

The first step is to identify what the hazards are. When you work in a place every day, it is easy to overlook potential hazards, so there are ways to make sure you identify those that matter.

Walking around to look for things that might reasonably be expected to cause harm is a good starting point. It is also useful to talk to the people who work there, as they might be aware of things that are not immediately obvious to you.

Publications and practical guidance are available from a variety of sources, including the Health and Safety Executive (HSE), and relevant trade associations, as well as manufacturers' instructions. These all provide information on where hazards can occur, their harmful effects, and how to control them.

Accident and ill-health records are another source of information which can often help to identify the less obvious hazards. It is also important to remember long-term health hazards, such as those that can occur following prolonged exposure to high levels of noise, or harmful substances.

Consider the hazards in a warehouse working environment:

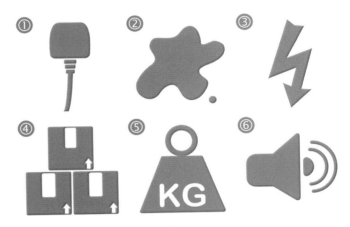

Potential hazards in a warehouse

1   Trailing cables across the floor might cause people to trip.
2   Spillages on the floor might also cause people to slip and/or might be toxic.
3   Faulty or damaged electrical fittings might cause electric shock and possibly fire.
4   Items left lying about may block access or cause people to trip.
5   Lifting heavy loads might cause back injuries.
6   Long term exposure to noise might cause loss of hearing.

Who Might be Harmed?

The second step in risk assessment starts with deciding who might be harmed by each of the identified hazards. Identify groups of people, rather than listing people by name, as this will help later on when it comes to identifying the best ways to manage the risk for each group. It is also necessary to identify how the different groups of people might be harmed, by considering what type of injury, or ill-health might occur.

Here are some people who have different requirements:

Groups of people who might be harmed:

1   Customers or members of the public who are visiting the workplace;
2   Contractors who might not be in the workplace all the time;
3   Maintenance workers visiting the workplace;
4   People with disabilities have their own requirements;
5   Store staff responsible for moving heavy boxes;
6   Pregnant women.

Evaluate the Risks and Decide on Precautions

The next step is to decide what needs to be done to protect people from harm.

The law requires that everything 'reasonably practicable' is done. You should compare what is already being done with what is considered to be good practice.

Compare what is being done with the HSE website

Website

The HSE website is a source of information about good practice.

The first thing to consider is whether or not the hazard can be eliminated. If not, there are certain actions that should be applied, in the order shown here, to control the risk, so that harm is unlikely.

Improving health and safety does not need to cost a lot, and failure to take simple precautions could cost a lot more, if an accident occurs. Before introducing new precautions, always check that these are reasonable, and do not introduce any new hazards.

- Switch to using a less hazardous method.
- Guard the hazard.
- Provide lifting equipment.
- Provide clothing, footwear, goggles etc.
- Provide first aid and washing facilities for removal of contamination.
- Reduce exposure to hazardous substances and hot working processes by using 'permit to work' certification, which controls the amount of time personnel are exposed to the hazard.

Record Findings and Implement

Having spotted the hazards, worked out which groups of people might be affected by them, and how, and decided what needs to be done to protect people from harm, it is important to keep a record of what has been done. In fact, for businesses with five or more employees, the results of the risk assessment must be written down, and actions recorded as they are implemented. Smaller businesses will also find it useful to have a written record of their risk assessment, as it can be reviewed at a later date.

The main thing is to keep the written results of the risk assessment as simple as possible, and to share the document with employees.

A risk assessment document

If several improvements need to be made, it is best not to try and do everything at once. Instead, draw up an action plan to deal with the most important problems first.

A good action plan will often include implementing a few cheap, or easy, improvements which can be done quickly, perhaps as a temporary solution, until more reliable controls can be put in place.

The plan of action might also include long-term solutions for those risks which are most likely to cause accidents, or ill health, or which have the worst potential consequences. It could also contain arrangements which are made for training employees on how the remaining risks will be controlled.

Finally, the action plan should state who has responsibility for the various actions, and when they will complete them, as well as details of regular checks that will be made to make sure that control measures stay in place.

E-Learning
Use the e-learning programme to download a sample risk assessment document.

Review Risk Assessment and Update

The fifth step in the risk assessment process is to review the risk controls, and to update them as necessary.

It is a good idea to do this on an ongoing basis, and by thinking about risk assessment when changes are being planned, and also by conducting a formal, annual review.

Reviewing the risk assessment regularly will mean that controls can be amended each time new hazards are introduced, for example, with the introduction of new equipment, substances, or procedures, when problems are spotted by employees, or when accidents or near misses occur.

By carrying out regular reviews, you can ensure that risk controls are always up to date and do not decline.

Responsibilities

Both employers and employees have responsibilities for health and safety in the work place. Employers are responsible for ensuring risk assessments are carried out on a regular basis. The process does not need to be complicated, nor does it need a health and safety expert to carry it out. Employees have a responsibility to co-operate with their employer's efforts to improve health and safety, by complying with the controls which are in place, and by looking out for each other.

In today's climate, risk assessment has assumed a very high profile; this is due to the increased knowledge of health and safety issues and the increasing use of litigation against companies and individuals following incidents.

As part of any learning programme it is important to use the information given to carry out your own risk assessment. By doing this you get into the mind-set of what risk assessment is all about. This ensures that you have also considered all the potential hazards and risks and have put in place a series of procedures or good working practices to promote a safe working environment for yourself and those around you.

Risks that are associated with the welding environment include the tools, materials and equipment you use, oil or chemical spills, accidental breakages of tools or equipment that are not reported properly and workers not following the correct working practices and procedures.

Activity

You are required to move a heavy load from A to B through a busy workshop, write a risk assessment for this activity; the load exceeds 30kg.

_____

_____

_____

_____

_____

_____

_____

_____

_____

_____

_____

_____

_____

_____

_____

_____

_____

_____

_____

_____

_____

_____

_____

_____

_____

_____

Fire Protection

Fires can be categorised into different classes, depending on the material fuelling the fire. The classes of fire are shown here. Electrical fires are a special case and do not fall into any particular class.

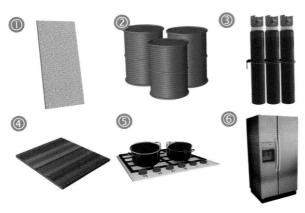

1   Class A - (Solids – e.g. wood, paper, textiles)
2   Class B - (Flammable liquids – e.g. oil, petrol, paint)
3   Class C - (Flammable gases – e.g. acetylene, propane, butane)
4   Class D - (Metals – e.g. magnesium, aluminium, sodium)
5   Class F – (Cooking oils and fats e.g. kitchen fires)
6   Electrical

Types of Fire Extinguisher

All fire extinguishers should be labelled to identify the type of extinguisher and what fires it can be used on. It is vital that the correct extinguisher is used for a particular class of fire, otherwise there could be serious consequences. Different types of extinguishers are shown here.

Water – Class A

Water fire extinguishers are suitable for class A fires.

Foam – Classes A and B

Foam fire extinguishers are suitable for class A fires and class B fires.

Powder – Classes A, B, C and Electrical

Powder fire extinguishers are suitable for class A, class B, class C and electrical fires.

Carbon Dioxide – Classes B and Electrical

Carbon dioxide fire extinguishers are suitable for class B fires and electrical fires.

Wet Chemical

Wet chemical extinguishers are suitable for class A and class F fires.

Metal Powder - Class D fires

Metal powder extinguishers are specialist extinguishers used on class D fires. Class D fires can be very dangerous and you should get advice on them from your local fire authority as they require special extinguishers, depending on the metal involved.

Fire Blankets

Fire blanket

Fire blankets should be available in all locations dealing with sources of heat, to wrap and smother anyone's clothes that may have caught fire.

In the Event of Fire

If a fire breaks out, it is imperative to warn fellow workers by breaking the nearest fire alarm, which may give a ringing tone or klaxon warning, and informing whoever is in charge to contact the fire brigade services. You should remain calm at all times and do not put yourself in any danger. Move as quickly as possible without running to the nearest fire exit. On the way, if it is possible to close windows and doors, this will reduce the oxygen to the fire. At no point should you go back into the building to retrieve personal belongings, as you may well put other people's lives at risk trying to get you out. Remember in a fire only use stairs, as power can be cut to lifts. Always report to the designated assembly point so that your name can be checked off as being safe, and do not enter the building till the fire brigade or fire marshal tells you it is safe to do so.

Procedure on discovery of a fire: 1. Fire alarm; 2. "Fire Exit" sign; 3. "Fire door keep shut" sign; 4. "Fire assembly point" sign

Some of the most common source of fires include discarded matches or cigarettes, un-monitored fires or heaters, multi-adaptors for electrical appliances, and poor storage of chemicals and solvents.

Electrical Safety

All electrical equipment should be looked after, and maintained in a safe condition in compliance with the Electricity at Work Act.

Website

Use a search engine to research the Electricity at Work Act.

Electrical equipment used should be Portable Appliance Tested (PAT) at regular intervals. All work carried out, such as changing a plug on an appliance must be carefully logged.

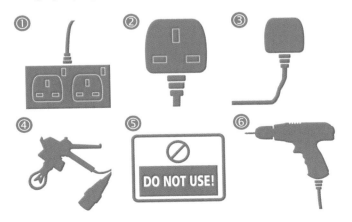

Maintaining Electrical Safety

1   Extension leads that are moved a great deal are particularly prone to being damaged. If the cable, plug or sockets are damaged they should be replaced.

2   The outer sheath of flexible cables must always be firmly clamped to stop the wires (particularly the earth) from pulling out of the terminals.

3   Cables should always be joined with proper connectors or cable couplers not with strip connectors and insulating tape.

4   Lamps and equipment which can easily be damaged must be protected to prevent risk of electric shock.

5   Suspect or faulty electrical equipment must be labelled 'DO NOT USE' and kept secure until it can be examined by a competent person.

6   Equipment unsuited for use in a wet or harsh environment can easily become live and also make the surroundings live.

Visual Inspection

Many faults with electrically operated power tools can be found by visual inspection. By following a simple process before using the equipment, you can minimise most electrical risks.

E-Learning

Use the E-Learning programme to see an animated visual inspection of an electric power tool.

Procedure for carrying out a visual inspection

1   Switch off and unplug.
2   Check plug is correctly wired.
3   Check fuse is correctly rated by checking equipment rating plate or instruction book.
4   Check plug is not damaged, cable is properly secured and no internal wires are visible.
5   Check cable is not damaged and has not been repaired with insulating tape or unsuitable connector.
6   Check outer cover of equipment is not damaged which might give rise to electrical or mechanical hazards.
7   Check equipment for burn marks or staining that might suggest equipment is overheating.

Electrical Site Safety

When it comes to the safe isolation of electrical supplies, and energising electrical installations, it is important to comply with statutory health and safety requirements, as laid down by the Electricity at Work Regulations.

Safe Isolation

In order to avoid fatal accidents, you should follow the recognised procedure:

Procedure for carrying out a safe isolation

1   Identify source of supply.
2   Identify type of supply.
3   Isolate.
4   Secure the isolation.
5   Test the equipment/system is dead.
6   Begin work.

Energising Electrical Installations

A number of deaths and major injuries have occurred when electrical circuits have been energised at the request of building designers, clients, contractors or finishing trades before the electrical installation was complete. It is not considered 'reasonable to work live' solely on the grounds of inconvenience, lost time, or cost.

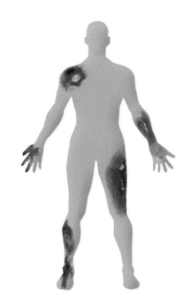

Electrical burns caused by working an electrical installation with 'live' circuit

Electrical contractors are only able to energise circuits when it is 'unreasonable to work dead', and a written request has been made by the main contractor, or his agent. Suitable precautions and testing must also be undertaken before the electrical contractor agrees it is safe to energise the circuit.

Do not touch or switch on circuit sign

Other Aspects of Electrical Site Safety

Here are some more ways in which you can ensure site safety with regard to electricity:

Methods of ensuring electrical safety

Using reduced voltage equipment reduces the risk of injury and the supply voltage should be limited to the lowest needed to get the job done.

1 Battery-operated power tools are the safest.
2 Portable tools designed to run from 110V centre-tapped-to-earth supply are readily available.
3 Using a Residual Current Device (RCD) with equipment of 230V or more can reduce injury.
4 When working near overhead power lines these should be switched off if at all possible.

Workplace Welfare

Workplace welfare involves promoting a healthy and safe environment for working in. Any person employed at the workplace, even if it is for a short amount of time, needs to be given practical information on how to work safely.

Workplaces should display information on health and safety laws outlining what employers and employees must do. If you are new to the job, make sure you familiarise yourself with the rules of the workplace.

Welfare Facilities

Employers must provide basic welfare facilities for all personnel. This includes, working toilets, wash areas, drinking water, seated areas for eating, dedicated areas for changing and storing clothing and a first-aid area with adequate first-aid provisions.

Basic welfare facilities: 1. Wash facilities; 2. Drinking facilities; 3. Eating facilities; 4. Changing facilities; 5. First aid provisions

Washing Facilities

Adequate toilet and washing facilities should always be provided. This means that there should be enough toilets, wash basins, hot and cold running water, a means of drying hands and privacy.

Clean Water

Easy access to a source of clean, drinking water is required by law. Ideally this should come from a public water supply or bottled water dispensers with cups.

Eating Facilities

Workplaces should have a clean and safe seating area that can be used during breaks for eating and resting. The area should include some washing facilities, and a means of heating food or water for hot drinks.

When using a 'break area', make sure you follow good hygiene standards and always ensure that you wash your hands before eating as it is possible to ingest contaminants. Leave the area tidy and dispose of rubbish in the correct bins.

Smaller workplaces require clearly-marked first-aid boxes controlled by a named individual

Work Gear Storage

If you need to wear specialist clothing whilst working then changing rooms need to be provided. Changing rooms should have an area for you to store your clothes, with a separate area for unclean or contaminated clothing. They should also have, or lead directly to, washing facilities.

First Aid

Employers have a legal duty to ensure that first-aid kits are in place, containing sufficient supplies for everyone in the workplace.

For smaller workplaces, clearly-marked first-aid boxes must be placed under the control of a named individual. However, for larger workplaces of over fifty people, there must also be at least one person with dedicated first-aid training.

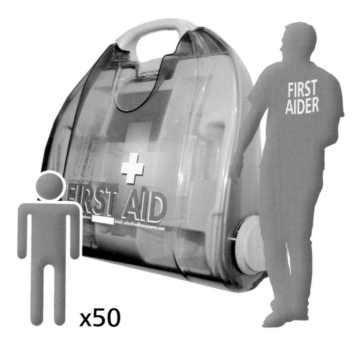

Larger workplaces of over 50 people require at least one person with dedicated first-aid training

As part of an induction programme, all personnel should be made aware of the names and locations of the trained first aiders and the position of the first aid box.

Healthy Working Environment

All workers have the right to work in an environment that considers their personal well-being and the well-being of others. A suitable working environment will take into account all the health and safety issues that concern everyone and deal with them in the appropriate manner.

Heating and Ventilation

Work areas should be well ventilated, have sufficient room and adequate lighting for the work to be done safely. The temperature also needs to be set at an appropriate level.

Maintenance and Cleaning

A workplace can be made safer by regular maintenance and cleaning, this reduces the chances of accidents. All floors and traffic routes should be free from obstruction with fire exits and other safety warnings clearly displayed. If you are using equipment make sure it is in good working order before using it and store it in the right location after use.

Safety Systems and Procedures

As part of a general induction, safe systems of work need to be demonstrated to new personnel to ensure that approved codes of practice are adopted at all times to comply with safe working practices.

Written procedures should be available and followed for any work that is considered high risk.

These codes of practice have been drawn up over a period of time and have been proven to ensure that this is the

safest method of carrying out an activity. Failure to comply with these codes of practice could result in prosecution if someone is injured as a direct result of you not following these procedures.

Written procedures for any work that is considered high risk

Safe Computer Use

Most workplaces in the engineering industry use computers, especially in the manufacture of consumables, components and drawing retrieval. It is important that the operator sits at the computer with their body in the correct position. This is known as ergonomics.

Ergonomic considerations include correctly positioning the height of the table or surface, the sitting position of the operator on the chair, the height of the screen, the location of printing facilities, mouse and any other auxiliaries. There is also guidance regarding the radiation emitted by a screen and the use of anti-glare screens is recommended. The duration which the operator is engaged should be regulated to give breaks at regular intervals.

Correct ergonomics for computer use

By following these ergonomic considerations it is possible to prevent or reduce the risk of injuries such as repetitive strain injury.

Headaches may result from several things that occur with VDU (Visual Display Unit) work such as:

- screen glare;
- poor image quality;
- a need for different spectacles;
- stress from the pace of work;
- anxiety about new technology;
- reading the screen for long periods without a break;
- poor posture; or
- a combination of any of the above.

Reporting Accidents

Any minor injuries that occur at work which do not require hospitalisation should be recorded in a work-place accident book. This provides a formal record of the injury that has occurred, which could be impor-tant if it progresses to something more serious. If you are off work for more than three days as a result of an injury at work, then this should also be reported.

Dangerous occurrences include incidents such as a fire, an explosion or something which stops work for more than twenty four hours. A disease is classified as any illness that is a direct result of a work activity.

If there is an injury at work which requires hospitalisation, a RIDDOR form should be completed and all evidence re-corded by the workplace health and safety representative. RIDDOR stands for the Reporting of Injuries, Diseases, and Dangerous Occurrences Regulations. These forms are used to report accidents such as:

- deaths and major injuries;
- incapacity to work for more than three days;
- specified diseases;
- dangerous occurrences or near misses.

Any of the above must be reported to the Health and Safety Executive (HSE) using the prescribed form. It is essential that accurate records are kept of any incident, including those that involve employers, employees, self-employed persons, trainees and other people, such as visitors, injured on the premises.

Examples of major injuries include:

- any fracture, other than to the fingers, thumbs or toes;
- amputation of any limb;
- dislocation of the shoulder, hip, knee, or spine;
- loss of sight;
- penetrating eye injury.

Examples of serious conditions include:

- certain eye conditions;
- electric shock requiring attention;
- unconsciousness through lack of oxygen;
- poisoning;
- acute illness due to exposure to certain materials.

Examples of reportable disease include:

- certain poisonings;
- some skin diseases, such as occupational dermatitis and skin cancer;
- lung diseases such as occupational asthma, pneumo-coniosis, and asbestosis;
- infections such as hepatitis, tuberculosis, legionellosis and tetanus;
- other conditions such as hand-arm vibration (HAV) system, and repetitive strain injury (RSI).

Examples of reportable occurrences include:

- structural collapses such as buildings or scaffoldings;
- fires and explosions;
- release of gases or other dangerous substances;
- failure of breathing equipment while in use;
- incidents with dangerous substances in transit;
- contact with, or arcing of, overhead cables.

It is also important to remember that in any workshop there should be an accident report book for minor injuries such as a cut to the finger, which should always be cov-ered given the working environment and exposure to sub-stances and bacteria. Even a small cut could possibly develop in to septicaemia, as a direct result of not treating the initial wound. All minor accidents should be recorded as they have the potential to develop into a major incident which will need documented evidence for any claim.

In any establishment provision should be made for first aid, whether this is a designated person within a small workshop or nominated first aiders within a large organisation who have been trained to a minimum standard to deal with predominately minor injuries. Ideally there will be a designated location for first aid with access to clean running water. This location should be suitably supplied with sufficient first aid boxes to cover the number of personnel on site or in an organisation. The first aiders should also have access to an emergency line to call for an ambulance should one be required, all incidents should be recorded in the accident book or on a RIDDOR form.

> ### Website
>
> Use a search engine to research RIDDOR. RIDDOR forms are available from www.riddor.gov.uk

Provision and Use of Work Equipment

All equipment used in manufacturing is governed by the Provision and Use of Work Equipment Regulations (PUWER). You should only ever operate machinery and equipment that you are fully trained to use; this is essential to your safety and that of others.

> ### Website
>
> Use a search engine to research the Provision and Use of Work Equipment Regulations (PUWER).

Any machine or equipment you use should first be assessed to ensure that it is working properly, is free from defects and is properly secured. Any guards or protective devices need to be checked to make sure that they are all working correctly before starting any job. The working area should be kept clean, tidy and free from obstructions at all times.

Safe and working machine guard

If you find any defects you must report them to your supervisor or supplier. If you see a machine with a danger sticker on it, do not use it under any circumstances and do not tamper or remove the sticker from the machine.

Danger do not use sticker

Never distract anyone operating any machinery as this may cause serious injury and always wear the correct personal protective equipment.

Wear PPE safety sign

Machine Guards

When working on a machine with dangerous moving parts there must be sufficient safeguards in place to protect you from injury. If a machine you are using has a guard, make sure it is secured correctly and is not likely to come loose.

Never try to remove a guard, especially whilst the machine is in operation. If you do need to remove a guard in order to carry out an operation, make sure the machine is switched off first. Once you have finished it is imperative that you replace the guard. Under law you are liable for any injuries as a result of removing a guard.

If you do need to go near dangerous parts regularly and fixed guards are not practical, use another method to ensure your safety. Try interlocking the guard, so that the machine cannot start before the guard is closed, and cannot be opened while the machine is still moving.

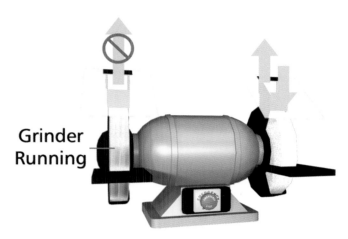

Never remove machine guards when machine is in operation and replace any guard removed after use

Abrasive Wheels

Only certified personnel are allowed to mount abrasive wheels. An abrasive wheel or disc is a wheel that is made up of abrasive particles bonded together. Abrasive wheels are defined by the grit, the bonding agent, the composition of wheel, the range of materials and diameter sizes available. All abrasive wheels come with a recommended revolutions per minute (RPM) and should only be used at these values. Abrasive wheels are available for a range of applications such as off-hand pedestal grinders, angle grinders, flexible rotary grinders and cutting discs.

In the UK only approved personnel can fit or remove abrasive wheels, and anyone found to not being compliant with this ruling, could be prosecuted if an accident where to occur as a direct result of someone fitting a grinding wheel who has not been certified as being competent. Grinding stones have their maximum revolutions per minute (RPM) listed on the paper blotter. They must never be used on a machine with a higher rated RPM. If grinding stones are turned too fast, they can explode.

Each grinding stone is made for grinding specific types of metal. Most stones are for ferrous metals, meaning iron, cast iron, steel, and stainless steel, among others. Some stones are made for non-ferrous metals such as aluminium, copper, and brass. If a ferrous stone is used to grind nonferrous metal, the stone will become glazed (the surface clogs with metal) and may explode as a result of frictional heat building up on the surface. If a nonferrous stone is used to grind ferrous metal, the stone will be quickly worn away.

Angle Grinders

Angle grinder

Angle grinders are available in a range of sizes and means of power such as petrol, electrical or pneumatic. These can be used on steel and masonry and are available as cutting or grinding discs. They consist of fibre glass matting impregnated with a bonding agent and abrasive material. The cutting disc only has a face on the edge of the disc and should never be used for surface grinding; the grinding disc has a full face for grinding and should never be used for cutting.

Pedestal Grinders

Pedestal grinder

Pedestal grinders consist of two mounted wheels which are opposite handed thread and are usually mounted with one soft and one hard abrasive wheel. You can also replace one of the abrasive wheels with a mop head which can be used for polishing. Hard wheels can be used for steels and soft wheels for non-ferrous metals. If a non-ferrous material is used on a hard wheel it will load the wheel by filling the spaces between abrasives and make the wheel virtually useless.

Flexible Rotary Grinders

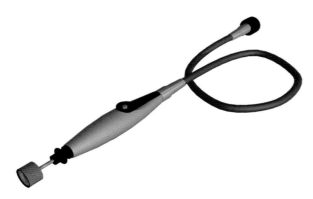

Flexible rotary grinders can be electrical or pneumatic. They are used extensively for grinding or polishing cylindrical components and their composition is similar to the pedestal grinders.

Rotary Cutting Machines

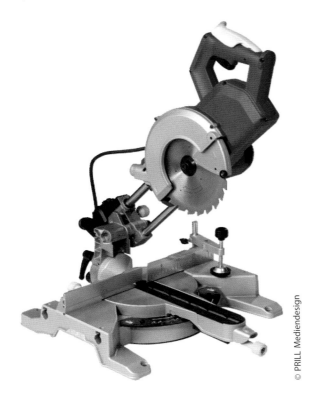

© PRILL Mediendesign

Rotary cutting machines or chop saws are cutting discs used to sever steel sections, box sections or to cut out slots prior to forming operations. They are available in a blade form with tungsten carbide tips or as an abrasive cutting disc to cut steel of a substantial section, and the cutting discs composition is similar to angle grinders.

Material Ejection

Material is ejected from some fabrication processes. This can be in the form of small particles of metal when punching out blanks or nibbling templates or hot sparks when using a hand grinder to prepare metal.

Ensure you follow guidelines and take care when working in these processes as ejected material can be hot and painful. It is always advisable to wear a leather apron when grinding to prevent hot sparks landing on overalls and clothing.

Wear leather aprons when grinding to prevent injury caused by hot material ejection

Vibration

Portable tools which produce vibration can cause damage to your hands, this is known as Vibration White Finger (VWF), and is the most obvious symptom of hand-arm vibration syndrome (HAVS). VWF attacks are painful and can result in the loss of your sense of touch and the ability to grip properly. Vibration can also lead to equipment components becoming loose making them dangerous to use. When using machinery, make sure any fixtures or fittings are secure before and after use.

- Minimise the time individuals use the equipment.
- Design the job so that poor posture (which may cause strain on hands and arms) is avoided.
- Construct jigs to hold materials or tools.

You should always make sure that any tools you use are properly maintained to prevent vibration increasing, check the sharpness of tools, the condition of abrasive wheels, and anti-vibration mounts.

It can also help if workers keep their hands warm and get a good flow of blood into their fingers by wearing gloves, having hot food or drinks, massaging the fingers and not smoking (as this causes narrowing of the blood vessels).

Vibration White Finger (VWF)

There are hundreds of different types of tools and equipment which can expose operators to high levels of hand-arm vibration. Some of the more common ones are:

- chainsaws;
- power hammer drills and chisels;
- hand-held grinders;
- hand-held sanders;
- nut runners;
- riveting hammers and bolsters.

There are many things you can do to reduce the chances of getting VWF:

- Look for alternative ways of working which eliminate the vibrating equipment altogether.

How to reduce the chances of VWF: 1. Keep warm; 2. Eat regularly to maintain blood sugar levels; 3. Change activity period; 4. Correctly maintain tools

CHECK YOUR KNOWLEDGE

1 Imagine you have returned to a job with only a few tasks remaining. You have been wearing overalls and a hard hat, but your gear is in the van. The risks don't seem serious, and the work will only take a few minutes. Do you have to use your PPE?

a. No – the work will only take a few minutes.
b. No – the risks do not seem serious.
c. Yes – the PPE should still be used.

2 You, as the responsible person in the workplace, need to make others aware of a potentially explosive environment. Which four of the options below would you choose to display?

A   B

C   D

E   F

G   H

3 Under the Control of Substances Hazardous to Health Regulations – and European law – who has overall responsibility for controlling exposure to hazardous substances in the workplace?

a. Employer
b. Employee
c. Government Health and Safety Inspectors

4 Number these risk assessment processes in the order they should be done.

☐ a. Decide who might be harmed and how
☐ b. Review risk assessment and update if necessary
☐ c. Record findings and implement them
☐ d. Identify the hazards
☐ e. Evaluate the risks and decide on precautions

5 Which of these fire extinguishers are recommended when dealing with an electrical fire?

a. Carbon Dioxide
b. Foam
c. Metal Powder
d. Powder
e. Water
f. Wet Chemical

6 Which of the following is a minimum requirement for ensuring work place welfare?

a. First-aid areas
b. Clean drinking water
c. Toilets
d. Smoking areas

7 Which of the following grinders is available in blade form?

a. Angle grinder
b. Pedestal grinder
c. Flexible rotary
d. Rotary cutting

End test

1. You are going to be drilling in an extremely dusty environment, and it is likely that a lot of noise will be generated.
   Which of the following items of PPE should you not use?

   ☐ a. Safety goggles

   ☐ b. Safety gloves

   ☐ c. Ear defenders

2. Which of the following is not an item of PPE?

   ☐ a. Safety gloves

   ☐ b. Overalls

   ☐ c. Bump hat

   ☐ d. Padded body warmer

   ☐ e. Safety helmet

3. Which of the following signs indicates the direction you should be walking or driving in?

   ☐ a.

   ☐ b.

   ☐ c.

   ☐ d.

4. Which of the following signs tells you that there is a risk of fire in the immediate vicinity?

   ☐ a.

   ☐ b.

   ☐ c.

   ☐ d.

5. Which of these ladders is correctly positioned?

   ☐ a. <75°

   ☐ b. 75°

   ☐ c. >75°

6. **When working with ladders on scaffolding, how much should the ladder project above the level of the work platform?**

☐ a. Level with the platform

☐ b. 1 metre past the platform

☐ c. 3 metres past the platform

7. **An employer must employ a dedicated trained first aider when the number of employees reaches what amount?**

☐ a. 1

☐ b. 50

☐ c. 100

8. **At what step of the risk assessment procedure do these tasks belong?**

TASK	STEP
Amend controls to take account of accidents or near misses	
Check accident and ill-health records	
Check that new precautions do not introduce new hazards	
Compare what is being done with good practice	
Conduct formal annual review	
Eliminate the hazard if at all possible	
Get good practice information from HSE	
Get practical advice from HSE	
Identify the groups of people who might be harmed	
Identify the hazards	
Identify the injuries or ill-health that might occur	
Record actions when implemented	
Record findings	
Review on an ongoing basis	
Record findings	
Share with employees	
Talk to employees	

9. **Which material belongs to which class of fire? Write your answers in the correct column.**
    Acetylene, Aluminium, Magnesium, Oil, Paint, Petrol, Propane, Textiles, Wood

Class A	Class B	Class C	Class D

10. **Which class of fire can a water fire extinguisher be used on?**

☐   a. Class A – Materials (e.g. wood, paper etc.)

☐   b. Class B – Flammable Liquids (e.g. oil, petrol etc.)

☐   c. Class C – Gases (e.g. acetylene, butane etc.)

☐   d. Class D, Metals (e.g. magnesium, aluminium etc.)

11. **Match the appropriate 'How to maintain' statements on the right to each 'Electrical item' on the left.**

Electrical item	How to maintain
Damaged plug	Must be firmly clamped
No clamp in plug to hold outer sheath of a flexible cable	Must be joined with proper cable connector
Cable joined with strip connector	Must be labelled 'DO NOT USE'
No guard on lamp	Must be replaced
Piece of equipment which should not be used in a wet environment	Must have a guard
Piece of equipment where casing shows signs of burning/overheating	Must not been used in a wet environment

12. An RCD can be used with 230V+ equipment to try and reduce injury. What does RCD stand for?

☐ a. Residual Current Diverter

☐ b. Residual Current Device

☐ c. Re-directed Current Device

☐ d. Re-distribution Current Diverter

13. Here are some statements about site safety with regard to electricity. For each one select whether it is 'True' or 'False'.

Battery-operated power tools are the safest.	True	False
Incomplete circuits can be energised without a written request from main contractor or his agent.	True	False
It is not necessary to identify the type of supply when isolating a supply.	True	False
The supply voltage of electrical equipment should be limited to the lowest needed to get the job done.	True	False
When energising circuits, it is considered reasonable to work 'live' on the grounds of lost time.	True	False
When working near overhead power lines, these should be switched off if at all possible.	True	False

14. Which of the following requirements should a workplace meet in order to be safe?

☐ a. Be approved to ISO9000

☐ b. Have floors and traffic routes free from obstruction

☐ c. Be registered with Investors in People

☐ d. Have adequate lighting

☐ e. Be well maintained

☐ f. Have a fully trained workforce

☐ g. Be approved by a validating body

☐ h. Be well ventilated

15. Which of the following should all major injuries be reported in line with?

☐ a. Reporting of Injuries, Diseases and Serious Occurrences Regulations

☐ b. Reporting of Accidents, Death and Dangerous Occurrences Regulations

☐ c. Reporting of Injuries, Diseases and Dangerous Occurrences Regulations

☐ d. Reporting of Injuries, Death and Dangerous Occurrences Regulations

16. Which of these statements about the different types of equipment that use abrasive wheels are true or false?

a. Angle grinders can be petrol, electrical or pneumatic powered.	True	False
b. Pedestal grinders are usually mounted with two hard abrasive wheels.	True	False
c. Rotary cutting machines are cutting discs used to cut non-ferrous metals.	True	False
d. A cutting disc should never be used for surface grinding.	True	False

17. Which of the following images shows an angle grinder?

☐ a.

☐ b.

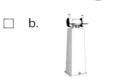

☐ c.

☐ d.

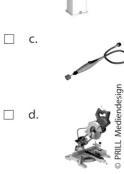

© PRILL Mediendesign

Working and Communicating

LEARNING OBJECTIVES

By the end of this chapter you will be able to:

● Describe what you can do to support your own personal development.

● Maintain good working relationships with other people.

● Outline the principles of team building.

● Identify different sources of information.

● Identify different methods of communication.

● Recognise and interpret various types of engineering drawings.

In this chapter we look at the skills that everyone needs in a working environment. We consider what you can do to support your personal development and how you can maintain good working relationships with your team and the other people you work with. Whatever job you are doing, good communication will help you do it better. This chapter reviews various types of communication that are used at work, including the engineering drawings that you will need to be able to interpret.

Personal Development

Your personal development plays an important part in your working career. You should take an active interest in developing your skill set, and look out for opportunities to improve, as well as taking those given to you.

Success in training or work depends on acquiring knowledge and skills, but it is also about your approach and attitude towards work. Whilst high levels of skill are important, consistency, reliability, loyalty and the ability to work in a team also matter. In this chapter we will take a practical look at the ways in which you can enhance your own development.

Ways to improve personal development: 1. Instructions; 2. Training portfolio; 3. Time keeping; 4. Review; 5. Standard of work

Instructions

Listen carefully to all the instructions you are given, particularly safety instructions. If you have any doubts, or you are unclear about a procedure, ask your instructor for further information.

Training Portfolio

It is essential to keep a log of the operations you are taught in your training portfolio. Practical skills training is assessed on a range of details. Your portfolio should provide a record of the training you have undergone, show details of the exercises you have taken, list how the exercises were performed, indicate the mark you received and give any instructor's comments. In some cases you may be asked to show your portfolio when applying for a job or an apprenticeship.

Time Keeping

Good time keeping is essential in the work environment and in training as it shows commitment and a positive attitude towards your work.

Review

Make sure you review your own development and skills regularly. One way you can do this is by carrying out a skills analysis to identify the skills you have learnt and the skills you think you need. If you have any questions, concerns or doubts about your own development you can discuss these with your instructor. They will be able to offer you advice, support and if necessary, a plan for any additional training needs.

Standard of Work

Always work to as high a standard as possible and show consistency, commitment and dedication in the tasks you carry out. This kind of attitude demonstrates that you have pride in your work, and want to make a positive contribution. The benefit to you is that it builds a reputation for quality, skill and passion in your work. This in turn benefits the workplace by having committed members on the team.

Managing Relationships

Always adopt a positive attitude

When working with other people, you should always try to adopt a positive attitude towards them. Your personal attitudes and your ability to work as a team member are just as important as the quality of your work. Remember to always treat people as you would expect to be treated. Having good interpersonal skills helps you become a valued member of a team and avoid disputes.

● Always make sure you are ready for any tasks that need carrying out. If people think of you as someone who can be relied on, they will be confident in your commitment to the team. No matter how tired you are or how inconvenient, trivial and unnecessary a request may seem to you, always try to be cheerful, helpful and efficient.

● Try to be aware of people's personal beliefs or cultural backgrounds. Think about how your behaviour or the things you say impacts on those around you. What you may think is a joke may be upsetting to someone else.

● Always be respectful of other people's personal property, especially their tools. Never use or take somebody's tools without asking them first, as it will only cause arguments. Imagine how you would feel if somebody borrowed your tools without asking.

● Good communication with your team is essential for establishing successful working relationships. Show respect and consideration for other people, and you are more likely to get what you want. For example, if you think the work you are about to do might impact on others, tell them what you are doing and seek their support.

In an effective team, every person will respect the skills and personality of each member of the team. It is often possible to tell whether a team is successful or not by observing how the team supports even the weakest member.

If you work as part of a team, and use the same workstation, make sure that you keep it clean and well stocked for your colleagues. Remember to pass on any modifications or instructions that may be relevant, and develop good interpersonal skills with people in your team. Get to understand their work and activities and always be appreciative of their support. It costs nothing to say 'thank you', but it is often really appreciated.

Many companies operate a system whereby trainees are moved around the organisation to learn how the company operates and how it functions. This means you will come into contact with a wide range of people, and it may be especially important for you to develop skills of tact and diplomacy.

Avoiding Confrontation

Remain calm and do not lose your temper when in a disagreement

A lot of disagreements arise from breakdowns in communication and arguments and heated discussions can lead to an unhappy working environment.

However, conflict cannot always be avoided. If you do find yourself in a disagreement try to resolve it amicably. Always remain professional and try not to let your personal issues get in the way. Any issues that cannot be resolved should be brought to the attention of your supervisor or instructor.

Activity

You have received a telephone call from a senior line manager to issue instructions to change some of the dimensions on a specific drawing. What action would you take?

a. Assume that because he is a senior manager, automatically implement the changes.

b. Tell a fellow colleague that you have received this information.

c. Ask the senior manager if he could send an email to confirm the dimension changes and not act until that clearance has been obtained.

d. Carry out the instructions and thereby carry favour with the senior manager for being responsive to his demands without any challenges to his authority.

Activity

You have observed one of your colleagues being physiologically bullied by a senior member of staff. What do you do?

a. Keep quiet and not get involved.

b. Log the event for a further case.

c. Report to a senior manager even though you know that the senior member of staff is a friend and there could be reprisals.

d. Seek advice from a body outside the company such as citizen's advice.

e. Report to a union official and surrender any evidence you may have. Be prepared to go before any committee to support a fellow colleague, even if you do not know them well.

If a dispute occurs it is important to remain calm and not lose your temper. Try to be patient and allow the other person to express their views without interrupting. Listen to the other person's views and consider how they might be feeling. Talking through the situation and being open to compromise can often help the situation. Focus on the points you agree on and look at how you can resolve any outstanding issues.

The majority of people realise the importance of good working relationships and will try to get on with others as best they can. However, in any working environment, problems among people sometimes arise. Some of the causes are:

- being inconsiderate: ignoring other people's feelings and needs;
- clash of personalities: difficulties or differences normally related to jealousy;
- unfair treatment: excessive workload or menial tasks;
- lack of trust: arising from a lack of respect for people and property;
- rejection: deliberately excluding people;
- harassment: picking on someone, bullying and continual sarcasm.

If you are aware that a colleague is being bullied, you should never condone it, or be tempted to join in. There may be 'peer pressure' to 'go with the crowd', but these problems must be resolved through sensible and tactful discussion.

Team Building

Team building is an active process by a group of individuals with a common purpose to achieve a specific task or set of outcomes.

Given time, teams form themselves naturally. Individual and shared goals are integrated into team activity as the members of the team get to know each other. Whilst there may be conflict at first, the team eventually aligns itself, has the right people doing the right things and gets on track to achieving its goals. Sometimes, teams are put together to meet an organisational need without having clearly defined goals and in this situation, it may take longer for the team to start delivering.

Team building simply accelerates the natural process of team formation by setting very clear goals right from the start. A team building workshop uses a variety of tools and techniques to accelerate the process further, bringing the team together quickly and effectively.

Today, teams are reorganised increasingly often. There simply is not time in many organisations to allow teams to form naturally. The accelerated process of team building is a cornerstone of organisational change as it allows new teams to harness their initial enthusiasm and convert it into results.

One of the most important aspects of team building is this conversion of ideas and enthusiasm into motivation and delivery. At first, a new team is a collection of individuals. At this stage, all they may have in common is a job title or project. Some of these individuals will have strong ideas as to how the team can best achieve its goals, and these ideas will not always be in tune with each other. A team like this, left to form naturally, will experience some initial discomfort as the direction of the team is established.

Businesses in the 21st century are undergoing some major and far reaching changes in the way that they work. One of the most common is the shift from the old hierarchical organisational structures to a flatter, more responsive one. This usually involves the creation of project teams as organisations become more task focused. Teams are often multi-disciplined, drawing on the skills and experience of individuals from a variety of functional departments around the organisation. Sometimes these teams are not physically located in the same building or town.

Active team building accelerates the process of team formation and quickly creates a team of focused individuals, sharing a common purpose and goal, fully 'bought in' to the direction the team will take to achieve those goals. Enthusiasm and motivation are easily translated into achievements and success without any additional external influence.

Creating the team

The key to building a team is to be very clear about why the team has been formed. Before you start to think about the members of the team, it is important to understand exactly why this team needs to exist. Here are some ideas for questions you need to ask yourself at this stage.

- What task needs to be completed?
- What skills do I need to complete this task effectively?
- What, exactly, do I need this team to do?
- Which people have the necessary skills?
- How long will it take to complete the task?
- How will I know when the task is completed?
- How will I measure ongoing progress?
- How will I recognise and reward team members?
- How will I actively exploit individual ideas and skills?

It is useful to think in this way about teams that are created for a one off project, but permanent teams who have longer term goals, such as sales, need this clarity of purpose just as much. Without clear goals and a reason to exist, the team will lose momentum over time.

For both project teams and long term operational teams, clarity of purpose and alignment of goals is critical to success. Many team building experts say that you should go for quick wins as a way of building motivation. However, if you get the motivation and enthusiasm right before you even start building the team, you can almost guarantee success. Quick wins may look impressive, but they can be quickly forgotten and do not necessarily build into longer term success, which is ultimately how the team will be judged.

Communicating Information

The key to all relationships within a working environment is communication. Not only does good communication improve relationships with others, but it also helps to achieve a better quality of product and a more efficient way of working.

In your working life you will be dealing with people who have a variety of different roles. For example, you may have to take instructions from your employer, communicate information to fellow employees or order goods from suppliers.

The main points to remember when communicating with other people are to be courteous at all times, speak clearly to avoid any misinterpretation, give accurate descriptions and keep the information relevant. You should also listen to people's responses and see things from their point of view. If you are unsure of what is required, ask politely if they could explain the information again.

Communicate clearly and listen to the responses given

Do not be afraid to ask for advice, but try to make sure that it is convenient to the other person to speak to you at that time. It can be distracting if you are constantly being asked questions. Try to strike a balance between asking for advice when you need it, and showing initiative in developing your own skills, although only within the bounds of your training and capabilities.

Sources of Information

Much of the information you will be presented with in an engineering environment is of a technical nature. It is likely to include graphs, exploded views, 3D presentations and workshop manuals.

Manufacturers' Catalogues

Manufacturers' catalogues and technical manuals usually include performance data and instructions for the correct and most efficient use of a product. They are good for keeping up to date with standards and suppliers' product lines.

Production Schedules

Production schedules usually come in the form of charts such as Gantt charts, statistical process control sheets or computer listings. These show an overview of any work that has been scheduled. The plan shows the start and finish dates for jobs, the machines and workforce to be used, and identify any delays or problems in production.

Work Orders

Work orders are issued in a standard form and clearly outline the product specifications. Some of the key specifications given include details of the component to be made, the drawings to be used, the quantity of the product to be made and the material that is to be used. The document also specifies any special jigs, fixtures, tools and cutters that will be required and their location in the stores.

Pocket Books

Pocket books are published for use in manufacturing workshops. These books contain tables of information on dimensions, drill sizes, tapping sizes for thread patterns, and speeds and feeds for materials. Many manufacturers also produce wall charts of the data found in pocket books for easy access to essential information.

Common sources of information used in engineering include data sheets, tables, and graphs. Each has specific applications. For example, data sheets may specify composition, melting ranges or operating ranges with typical applications for use.

Tables are often used to give a reference comparison or operating range, providing information such as drill sizes, speeds and feeds for cutting operations, or tapping and clearance sizes.

Graphs are often used to give a graphical representation of technical data, such as the volt/ampere curve for MIG (Metal Inert Gas) welding required to determine wire feed speed, or temperature gradients for heat treatment.

Methods of Communication

We generally use four methods of communication. These are visual, written, verbal and non-verbal communication.

Methods of communication: 1. Visual; 2. Written; 3. Verbal; 4. Non-Verbal

Visual Communication

Visual communication is a way of sharing information through the use of signs, drawings and diagrams.

Written Communication

Written communication comes in the form of documents, letters and emails. It can be used for both formal and informal modes of communication.

Verbal Communication

Verbal communication involves speaking your ideas and thoughts clearly to a person. It is the way you will communicate most frequently with those around you and it can include conversations, face-to-face meetings, telephone calls and online conferencing. Verbal communication is quick and easy. However, unless there are written records, misunderstandings can occur, especially when you are not face-to-face with the person you are talking to.

Non-Verbal Communication

Non-verbal communication consists of all the ways we project ourselves through our body movements, mannerisms and facial expressions. It includes shaking and nodding your head, making eye contact, waving goodbye and facial expressions that show emotions such as concern, boredom and anger.

When we meet someone for the first time, body language accounts for 55% of the impression we form of them and tone of voice accounts for 38%. Only 7% of our impression is formed by the words someone uses. Pay attention to the body language of people when you speak to them and think about what your own body language is saying. Try to use positive body language at all times.

Discussions at work

As a member of a team, there will be times when you will take part in a discussion about a project. There are a number of considerations to bear in mind.

It is important to involve all parties in the discussion and ensure everyone has the opportunity to contribute. Try not to allow any individual to monopolise the discussion, as this is not conducive to achieving the best outcome.

Note the main points and be aware of people's body language and facial expressions, as these are often used by non-assertive people to make their point of view known. If you are contributing to the discussion, make sure you listen to the views of others. It may be useful to summarise their points in a clear and concise manner. Remember that good decisions are based on getting useful advice from a variety of resources and are not likely to result from a slanging match.

Whenever you talk to a visitor, be aware that you are representing your organisation and yourself. The following points may help you to give a good impression:

- Speak clearly.
- Be polite.
- Insist on safety precautions being taken if required, such as the issue of safety glasses.
- Always present your organisation in a positive light and remember that visitors do not want to get caught up in personal grievances.

Electronic Communication

A large amount of modern communication is by electronic means, especially email. There are some general good practice measures to observe when using email:

- Too much information in one message is a burden on recipients.
- Bear in mind that screens are harder to read than words on paper.
- WRITING IN ALL UPPERCASE LETTERS TENDS TO CONVEY ANGER OR SHOUTING.
- Keep your message readable by breaking up text using short lines and paragraphs.
- Using lists and indentation helps make your points stand out clearly.
- Keep your message focused.
- If you need to introduce a new topic, do it in a separate message with a new subject heading.
- Don't use offensive language.
- Don't be confrontational. You should not say anything in an email that you would not feel comfortable saying to the recipient in person.
- Clear subject headings make everyone's lives easier, helping with prioritising, filing, cataloguing, cross-referencing, and retrieval.
- If you are sending a particularly important message, you might want to organise your thoughts first by drafting it in a word processor.
- Use the automated spell-check.
- Don't say anything in electronic mail that you would not want to be made public or forwarded to others, remember, an email can represent the views of the company you are working for as well as your own.
- Forwarding a chain letter has an impact on system resources and can result in a reprimand.
- Remember that not everyone checks their email regularly. If you are uncertain of a recipient's electronic mail habits or are not getting any response to your messages, a phone call may be quicker and more effective.

Skilful Listening

Good listening skills are essential when working with others. There is an art to being able to discover what another person is trying to communicate, and this can take many years to perfect. However, the following guidelines provide a good starting place.

- Demonstrate clearly that you are listening, using appropriate body language and facial expressions.
- Let people complete the point they are making without interruption.
- Make some reference, however brief, to what they have been saying before you change the subject.
- Listen for the underlying message: what does the person really mean? What do they really want you to hear or to know?
- Check for meaning. Ask questions to check you have heard and understood correctly.
- Clarify the key points by asking for more details. Ask questions to clarify points and to show your interest.
- Don't be afraid to leave silences. This enables other people to enter the dialogue or to work out their own position.

Engineering Drawings

Engineers use a variety of types of drawings to communicate technical information. These drawings can provide very specific and precise information. They may include references to tolerances, dimensions, surface finish and drawing number issues for component parts.

Types of Drawing

The drawings used vary from a standardised orthographic projection to a simple sketch.

Orthographic Projection

An orthographic projection is a way of drawing an object from different directions and usually includes the front elevation, plan and side elevations. The projections are laid out in one of two formats, either first angle or third angle. It is essential that you understand the difference between these two formats.

First angle drawings are indicated by a symbol made up of a tapered rectangle followed by two concentric circles. Third angle drawings are indicated by a symbol made up of two concentric circles followed by a tapered rectangle. You can remember this by first left, third right.

With first angle, the drawing is created by projecting what you see, through the object and drawing it behind the object. The front elevation is centred in the middle of the drawing with the plan view immediately below. The right hand side view is drawn on the left hand side of the front elevation and vice versa for the left hand side view.

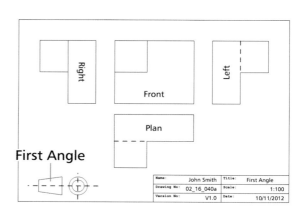

First angle drawing

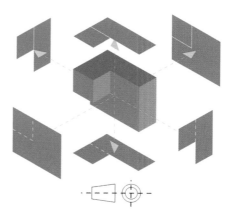

First angle 3D

With third angle, the drawing is created by drawing what you see in front of the object. The front elevation is centred in the middle of the drawing with the plan view immediately above. The right hand side view is drawn on the right hand side of the front elevation and vice versa for the left hand side view.

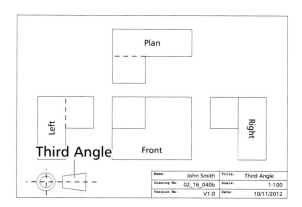

Third angle drawing

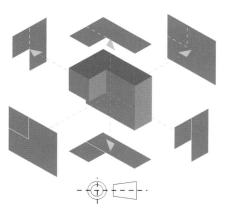

Third angle 3D

Activity

Sketch the standard representation used for first and third angle orthographic projection.

Activity

Identify six features you would expect to find on an orthographic projection drawing for issue into production.

1 _____

2 _____

3 _____

4 _____

5 _____

6 _____

An orthographic projection is used to show views of individual faces. The number of views required depends upon the details of the component. This method is the most commonly used for production engineering, as it is often the only way to give the detailed information required to enable components to be manufactured correctly, direct from the drawings. These drawings may take a long time to prepare and there are times when sufficient information can be given on one drawing. In this situation, we may be able to use isometric or oblique projections, although the main purpose of these two projections is to provide a pictorial drawing of an object, which will convey shape and comparative size, rather than detailed dimensions.

E-Learning

Use the e-learning programme to download examples of each of these types of drawing.

Isometric Drawings

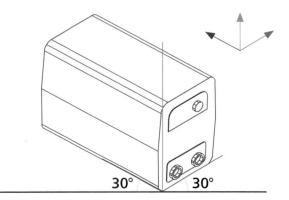

Isometric drawing

An isometric drawing gives a pictorial view of the component and is constructed around three axis. The first is at 90° to a base line and this is connected to two additional lines at 30° either side of first axis. The presentation is built up around these axes. The advantage of this presentation is that you see all three elevations in one drawing.

An isometric projection shows both sides of an object to equal advantage while an oblique projection gives prominence to the side shown at the front. In an isometric projection, all lines represent actual dimensions.

Oblique Drawings

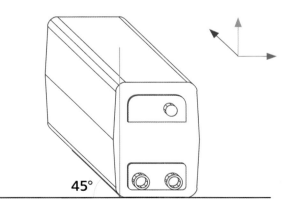

Oblique drawing

Oblique drawings show the front face of the object facing the viewer. They differ from isometric drawings in that only the vertical and horizontal lines show actual dimensions. The third axis is usually drawn at 45° and the dimensions along this axis are foreshortened. They are usually drawn to the ratio 1:2, i.e. a 25mm line represents a 50mm dimension.

Exploded Views

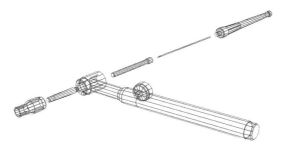

Exploded views

Exploded views are an aid to identifying components, sequence of assembly and dismantling, and are used very effectively in maintenance manuals to assist engineers. They are usually categorised by component numbers and part names.

Sketches

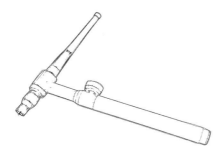

Sketch

Sketches are the simplest form of communicating ideas between engineers and customers. They provide the basis for the more formal drawings and have been used very effectively over the centuries, Leonardo da Vinci being a good example of someone who used this medium.

Assembly Drawings

These drawings show the relative position of all parts and how they fit together. Dimensions of individual parts are not shown but are identified by an item number which may have a separate drawing with dimensions clearly indicated. These drawings are usually accompanied by a parts list giving a description, number and quantity required. As the name implies, these drawings are used by engineers to assemble and dismantle components when doing servicing, repair or replacement of worn parts.

Sectional Views

Where internal detail is complicated and is represented by 'hidden detail' lines in the drawing, the results can be confusing and difficult to interpret correctly. In such cases a cut-away drawing or sectional view is used to convey this information. A 'cutting plane' slices through the component and identifies the interior detail. Where a solid section exists this is often depicted by angular lines at 45° to show the part profile while shafts, holes, and other designated components are left blank to differentiate the parts.

Activity

Give a brief description of the advantages of using the drawings listed here.

Exploded view

_____

_____

_____

_____

_____

_____

Sectional view

_____

_____

_____

_____

_____

_____

_____

Assembly

_____

_____

_____

_____

_____

_____

Component part

_____

_____

_____

_____

_____

_____

_____

Isometric

_____

_____

_____

_____

_____

_____

_____

Sketch

_____

_____

_____

_____

_____

Standardisation

In order for drawing to be effective, it requires some form of standardisation. Standardisation can be adopted within an individual firm, within an industry, or through internationally recognised standards such as British Standards (BS), European Standards (EN), or International Organisation for Standards (ISO).

Adopting such a system gives the following advantages:

- Designs are more efficient.
- Levels of inter-changeability are increased.
- Design and product costs are reduced.
- Mass production techniques can be adopted.
- Quality control can be easily monitored.
- Purchasing and costing are simplified.
- Overheads are often reduced.
- Redundant items and sizes are eliminated.
- Spares can be easily resourced.

Layout of Drawings

All drawings should use the 'A' series of sheet sizes, the dimensions of which are shown on page 64. The drawing area and title block should be contained within a frame border with a drawing reference block and date of issue.

All dimensioning necessary for the manufacture of a part should be shown on the drawing and should only appear once. When you are laying out a drawing, calculate the length and width of a box which will house all the detail within it.

There should also be sufficient distance between the elevation boxes to allow for dimensioning detail to be recorded. Dimensioning should be placed outside the outline of the view wherever possible. Projection lines are drawn from specific points or lines on the view and the dimension line placed between them. There should be a small gap between the outline and the start of the projection lines and the lines should extend for a short distance beyond the dimension line. Dimension lines should not cross other lines and should have a thin arrow head produced by a slight thickening of the line.

Leaders are lines that show where dimensions or notes apply. They are thin continuous lines ending in arrowheads touching the line, or dots within the outline of the component. Wherever possible establish a datum when marking out machining sequences or dimensioning of holes as this gives a 'reference point'.

Activity

Identify the advantages of using standardisation to communicate technical information.

_____

_____

_____

_____

_____

_____

_____

_____

_____

_____

_____

_____

_____

Interpretation of Drawings

In all cases the information presented must be accurate, concise and show the projection symbol. Other details include the scale to reflect the size of component, the drawing number, the issue and date. You should ensure that all drawings comply with designated standards for weld symbols, machining, hidden detail and dimensional tolerances.

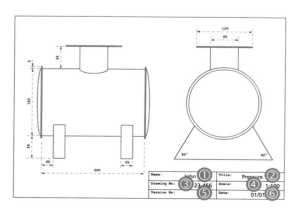

1. Name; 2. Title; 3. Drawing Number; 4. Scale; 5. Version number; 6. Date

1. **Your name:** This allows people to get hold of you if they need to discuss the drawing.
2. **Title:** All drawings should be titled to indicate what is being drawn.
3. **Drawing number:** All drawings should have a drawing number to catalogue the drawing and easily identify it.
4. **Scale:** This lets you calculate your measurements correctly.
5. **Sheet number:** Always add a modified version number to clearly identify any design modifications and ensure that all personnel are working to the same design.
6. **Date:** The date allows you to identify when the drawing was done.

Bill of Materials

As well as the above information given from the drawing it is possible to produce a bill of materials which outlines the cutting sizes and any preparatory machining that needs to be completed prior to welding or joining, such as edge preparation or bevels to allow components to bend to the specified dimension. This gives us the opportunity to order to stock in advance and maintain appropriate levels. Order tooling such as jigs, fixtures, and gauges in advance and allocate work to machines and determine labour costs. All of which will help to determine the selling cost.

Machined Surfaces

Activity

Write in the applications for these different types of line.

Type of line	Description of line	Applications
Detail outline	Thick line continuous	
Construction line	Thin line continuous	
Hidden detail line	Thin short dashes	
Centre line	Thin , chain line with dots between dashes	
Cutting plane line	Chain line with arrow heads	
Sectioning line	Lines at 45° to each other	

Abbreviations, Conventions and Symbols

Standardised abbreviations, conventions and symbols are used in drawings to convey technical details without having to write full descriptions or instructions. This allows for the drawings to be much clearer and easier to read. Some of the common forms of these abbreviations, conventions and symbols are shown in the following images.

These are some of the common abbreviations for written statements and in drawings:

Written Statements Abbreviations

Term	Abbreviation	Term	Abbreviation
Across corners	A/C	Hexagon	HEX
Across flats	A/F	Hexagon head	HEX HD
Assembly	ASSY	Left hand	LH
British Standard	BS	Long	LG
Centres	CRS	Machined	M/CD
Centre line	₵ or CL	Material	MATL
Chamfered	CHAM	Millimetre	MM
Cheese head	CH HD	Not to scale	NTS
Countersunk	CSK	Number	NO.
Countersunk head	CSK HD	Pattern number	PATT NO.
Counterbore	C'BORE	Pitch circle diamter	PCD
Cylinder or cylindrical	CYL	Radius (in a note)	RAD
Diameter (in a note)	DIA	Radius (preceding a dimension)	R
Diameter (preceding a dimension)	Ø	Revolution per minute	RPM
Inside diameter	I/D	Right hand	RH
Outside diameter	O/D	Round head	RD HD
Drawing	DRG	Screwed	SCR
Figure	FIG	Specification	SPEC

Continue >

Written Statements Abbreviations (Continued)

Term	Abbreviation
Spherical diameter	SPHERE Ø
Spherical radius	SPHERE R
Spotface	S'FACE
Square (in a note)	SQ
Square (preceding a dimension)	□
Standard	STD
Standard wire gauge	SWG
Threads per inch	TPI
Undercut	U'CUT

This table shows some of the common abbreviations for written statements and drawings.

These are some of the typical conventions used in drawings:

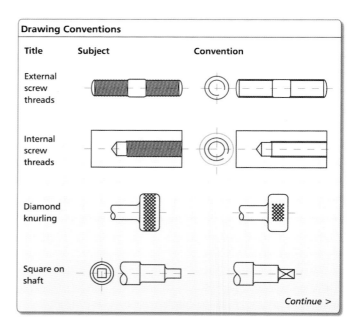

Drawing Conventions

Title	Subject	Convention
External screw threads		
Internal screw threads		
Diamond knurling		
Square on shaft		

Continue >

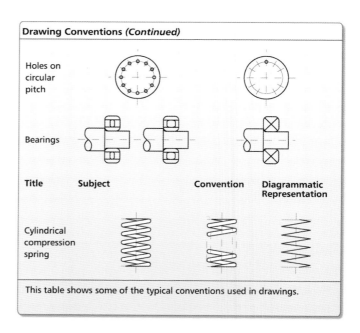

Drawing Conventions (Continued)

Title	Subject	Convention	Diagrammatic Representation
Holes on circular pitch			
Bearings			
Cylindrical compression spring			

This table shows some of the typical conventions used in drawings.

These are some of the weld symbols used in technical drawings:

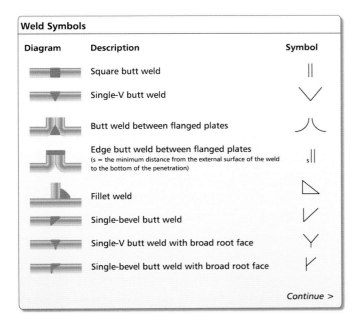

Weld Symbols		
Diagram	**Description**	**Symbol**
	Square butt weld	‖
	Single-V butt weld	∨
	Butt weld between flanged plates	⌣
	Edge butt weld between flanged plates (s = the minimum distance from the external surface of the weld to the bottom of the penetration)	s‖
	Fillet weld	◹
	Single-bevel butt weld	⋁
	Single-V butt weld with broad root face	Y
	Single-bevel butt weld with broad root face	⋎

Continue >

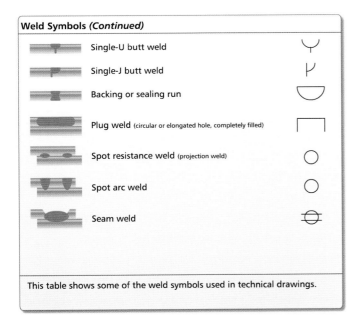

Weld Symbols *(Continued)*		
	Single-U butt weld	⋃
	Single-J butt weld	⊔
	Backing or sealing run	⌣
	Plug weld (circular or elongated hole, completely filled)	⊓
	Spot resistance weld (projection weld)	○
	Spot arc weld	○
	Seam weld	⊖

This table shows some of the weld symbols used in technical drawings.

The use of standardised symbols and abbreviations helps to eliminate mistakes and uncertainty. These standards cover the type of line representation used, and abbreviations for common engineering components in a format that can be easily referenced against ISO standards anywhere in the world.

Storage of Drawings

The use of computers has revolutionised drawing presentation allowing us to produce 3D models for testing, for engineering design and rapid transmission anywhere in the world.

Most drawings these days are stored on computer files rather than as paper hard copies. Storing files in this way allows them to be easily modified, copied, stored, printed or distributed.

The ability to store and retrieve information makes it possible for audits to be carried out effectively and allows the history of a piece of information, such as a drawing, to be traced. A document retrieval system can contain a mixture of computerised spreadsheets, word documents, jpegs such as pictures and scanned drawings, and computer aided design drawings. There may also be a paper (hard copy) system to back up computerised systems and this would include all orders and purchases, design drawings, production schedules and charts, inspection documentation and validation from standards organisations.

Hard copies provide a back up of the computerised system

Summary

You have now finished this chapter on the skills that you need in the workplace. You should now know how to support your own development and understand how to communicate effectively with the people you work with. You should also be able to recognise and interpret various types of technical information.

CHECK YOUR KNOWLEDGE

1   Which of the following will aid your personal development?

  a.   Having an up to date work portfolio
  b.   Being polite and friendly
  c.   Never asking for any help
  d.   Reviewing your skills regularly
  e.   Identifying areas to improve
  f.   Not listening to any other viewpoints

2   Which of the following should you **not** do in a disagreement?

  a.   Apologise if you've caused any offence
  b.   Try to remain calm
  c.   Walk away from the discussion
  d.   Try to reach a compromise
  e.   Keep insisting why you're right

3   What information should drawing references include?

  a.   Tolerances
  b.   Heat-treatment processes
  c.   Dimensions
  d.   Surface finish
  e.   Testing requirements
  f.   Drawing number issue
  g.   Consumables

4   Which of these images best represents an isometric drawing?

  a.

  b.

  c.

  d.

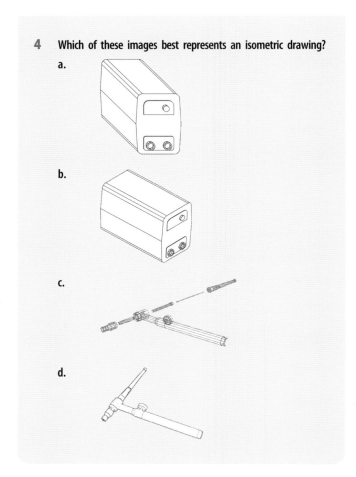

End test

1. **Take a look at each of the statements below and fill in the blank to complete the sentence.**

   ☐ a. Training portfolios provide a _____ of the training you have undergone.

   ☐ b. _____ your own development and skills regularly.

   ☐ c. A training portfolio shows details of the _____ you have carried out.

   ☐ d. Always _____ to a high standard.

2. **Which of the following practices would you adopt when interacting with fellow workers? Circle your answers.**

   ☐ a. Be positive and be determined to get your views across whatever the cost.

   ☐ b. Consider the feelings and views of others.

   ☐ c. Be open to suggestions and consider alternative options.

   ☐ d. Raise your voice to gain superiority and dominate the discussions.

   ☐ e. Be willing to compromise to move the work forward.

   ☐ f. Assume you can automatically use the other person's tools.

3. **Are the following statements about sources of information true or false? Write T or F after each statement.**

   ☐ a. Production schedules usually come in the form of written documents.

   ☐ b. Manufacturing manuals contain a product performance date.

   ☐ c. Works orders outline the product specifications of an item to be made.

   ☐ d. Pocket books contain information on dimensions and drill sizes.

4. **On the third angle drawing shown, label the side view, the plan view and front view.**

5. **Are these statements about engineering drawings true or false? Write T or F after each statement.**

   ☐ a. Abbreviations provide a standardised way of displaying technical detail.

   ☐ b. Modifications to drawings do not have to be given a new version number.

   ☐ c. Orthographic projections involve front, plan and side elevations.

   ☐ d. Isometric drawings are constructed around three axes.

6. **Which of the following methods is the most cost effective and easiest way to store and retrieve engineering drawings? Circle your answer.**

   ☐ a. On paper.

   ☐ b. On microfilm.

   ☐ c. On computers.

   ☐ d. On compact disks.

Torch

The torch is designed to direct the flame and regulate the gases as they pass through the mixer to be burnt at the nozzle. Torches are available in two forms; high pressure and low pressure. High pressure torches are designed for use with high-pressure gases, supplied from cylinders. They come with a 'mixer' designed to accommodate a range of nozzles to weld a wide range of metal thicknesses. The mixer system ensures that the least amount of explosive mixed gases is in the system prior to being burnt.

Nozzle

Torch

Low pressure torches use the 'injector' system where the higher pressure oxygen draws the lower pressure acetylene into the mixing chamber. The injector is usually included as part of the nozzle, so in this respect each nozzle has its own injector. This type of nozzle is far more expensive than those used with the high-pressure system.

Signs of heat damage around the torch valves may indicate that the equipment has suffered internal damage and is leaking, it should be replaced immediately

Nozzle

The nozzle is designed to give the operator a method of applying varying amounts of heat to a weld. The amount of heat is determined by the orifice (hole) at the end of the nozzle and the gas pressures which are directly linked to the job in hand. For example, a number 2 nozzle will use 0.14 of a bar of acetylene in one hour with a steady neutral flame. Nozzles should be regularly checked for damage to the thread patterns or seatings and the orifice cleaned to ensure good welding conditions and to prevent possible damage to the nozzle.

A nozzle with too low a heat value will result in a lack of penetration and fusion. Backfiring may also occur. If you increase the gas pressure, there comes a point where the flame leaves the end of the nozzle. This indicates that the pressure is too high to support the flame and this can be identified by a very noisy flame. If the nozzle is too large, overheating, lack of control of the molten metal and weld pool with excessive penetration can occur. However, if you try to weld with a large sized nozzle and reduced gas pressures, small explosions (backfires) will occur at the nozzle.

Never try to modify a nozzle to suit your welding requirements as this will either reduce the internal bore diameter or cause the nozzle to fracture at the threaded portion of the nozzle.

E-Learning

Use the e-learning programme to download a nozzle selection table that provides more information

The nozzle can become partially blocked and need cleaning. This can happen as a result of poor manipulation of the torch, holding the torch at the wrong angle or holding the torch too close to the weld pool. The nozzle can be cleaned with a set of tip cleaners. File the end of the nozzle smooth and square using the file provided in the tip cleaning set. Next select the size of tip cleaner that fits easily into the orifice and then insert it into the orifice and pull it in and out of the orifice a few times. Be sure the tip cleaner is straight and that it is held in a steady position to prevent the tip cleaner from bending or breaking off inside the tip. Excessive use of tip cleaners will ream the orifice making it too large so only use the tip cleaner as required. Do not use wire brushes or odd bits of wire to clear blockages, as this could lead to 'packing' in the nozzle with possible explosive results and damage to the rest of the welding equipment.

Activity

In the space below, sketch the oxyacetylene welding equipment in your shop and label each part of the equipment.

Set Up Procedure

To set up the oxyacetylene welding equipment, follow the set up procedure from start to finish every time.

1   Ensure the cylinders are in an upright and secured position.

2   Check the labels on the cylinders and ensure the outlets are free from any debris or grease.

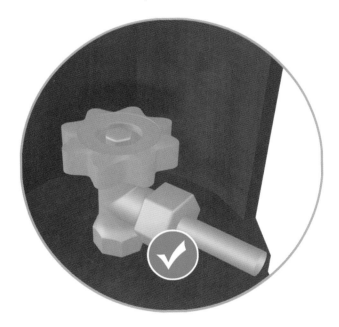

3   Connect the regulators. The acetylene regulator is red with a left hand thread and this is denoted by notches on the connecting nut. The oxygen regulator is blue with a right hand thread. Tighten both regulators with an appropriate spanner to ensure they are tight.

4   Fit flashback arrestors to each of the regulators.

5   Connect the hoses. Again these are colour coded for the appropriate cylinder, red for acetylene and blue for oxygen. Remember to check your local operating standards.

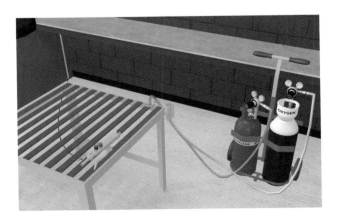

6   Tighten the hoses to prevent leaks and inspect them fully for any signs of damage, wear and tear.

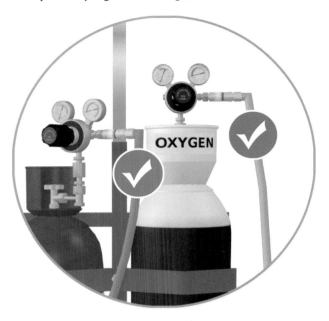

7   Connect the non-return or hose check valve at the end of each hose to the correct connections on the torch.

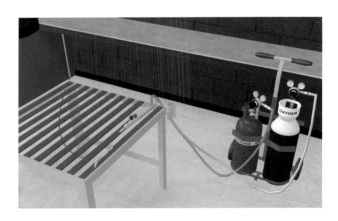

8   Fit the correct sized nozzle to the torch for the job that you need to carry out.

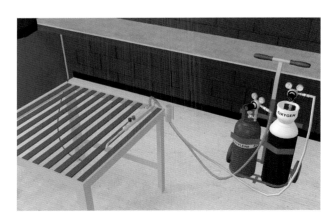

Equipment Checks

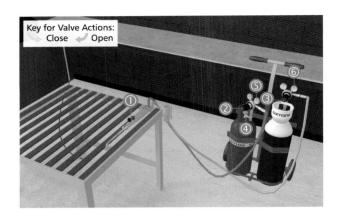

Equipment checks: 1. Torch valves; 2. Acetylene pressure regulator; 3. Oxygen pressure regulator; 4. Cylinder valve; 5. Acetylene pressure gauge; 6. Oxygen pressure gauge

When all the equipment is connected you need to check all the joints for any leaks.

1   Ensure that all valves on the torch and regulators are closed.

2 Slowly open both cylinder valves.

3 Adjust the regulator on the acetylene cylinder until it reaches 0.14 bar then do the same for the oxygen cylinder. You now have a positive pressure of 0.14 bar from the regulator to the torch.

4 Use an oil-free leak detection solution to check all joints from each of the cylinders to the torch valve.

5 Tighten any loose joints but do not attempt any repairs.

6 Open the oxygen valve on the torch to apply a positive pressure and again check for leaks using the oil-free solution.

7   Close the oxygen valve on the torch.

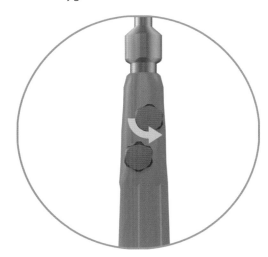

8   Close both cylinder valves.

9   Open both torch valves to release the pressure from the equipment.

10   When all the gas has been released, close both regulators and the valves on the torch.

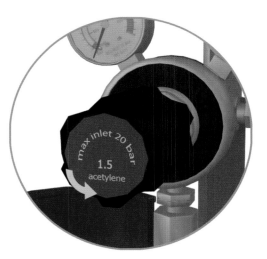

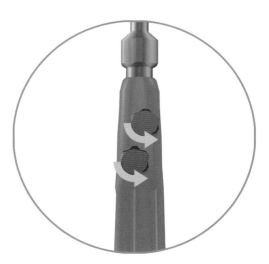

11 Dry all the leak tested joints with a lint free cloth.

12 Hang the torch on a bracket ready for use.

Purging the System

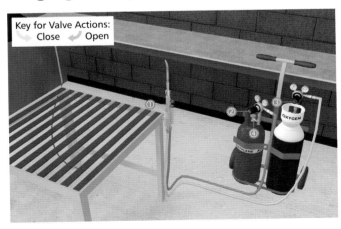

Purging the system: 1. Torch valves; 2. Acetylene pressure regulator; 3. Oxygen pressure regulator; 4. Cylinder valve

Before using the equipment you must purge any gas that may be in the system. This must be carried out every time before use.

1 Ensure the cylinder, regulator and torch valves are all closed.

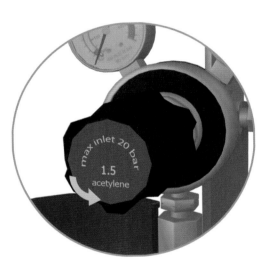

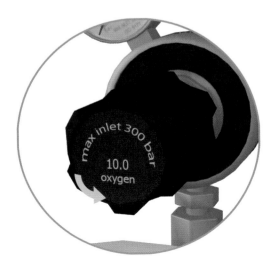

2   To purge, slowly open the cylinder valves and adjust the regulators until the correct operating pressure is reached for the size of nozzle being used.

3   Open the acetylene valve on the torch and allow the gas to flow to purge any existing gas out of the acetylene equipment and hose, then close the acetylene valve on the torch.

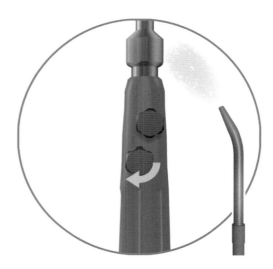

4   Ensure the oxygen regulator is at the correct pressure and then repeat the procedure, this time with the oxygen valves. Open the oxygen valve on the torch and allow any existing gas to be purged from the system, then close the oxygen valve on the torch.

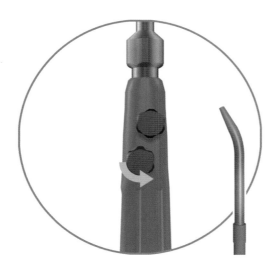

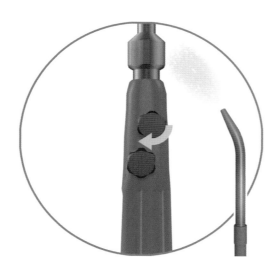

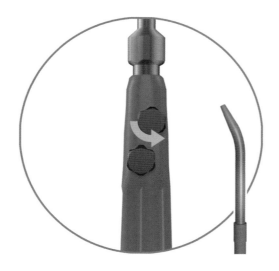

Lighting Up Procedure

Oxyacetylene welding can be very dangerous so make sure you are using the required PPE and adopt safe working practices within the environmental conditions.

1   Once the system has been purged, the torch can be lit. Open the acetylene valve and use a spark lighter in a safe position next to the torch nozzle to ignite the gas. Do not use a butane lighter as this is a potential explosion hazard.

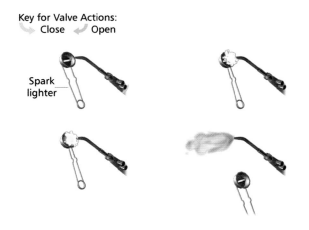

Open the acetylene valve and ignite gas using a spark lighter

2   Increase the amount of acetylene until the black soot just disappears and the flame is no longer smoking.

Increase acetylene until black soot disappears

3   Open the oxygen valve and increase the amount of oxygen until the required flame is achieved.

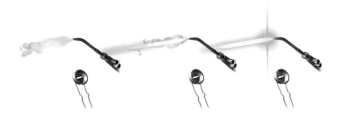

Open the oxygen valve and increase until the flame is achieved

Closing Down Procedure

Closing down Procedure: 1. Torch valves; 2. Acetylene pressure regulator; 3. Oxygen pressure regulator; 4. Cylinder valve

To close down the system:

1   Close the acetylene valve on the torch followed by the oxygen valve.

2   Close both the acetylene and oxygen cylinder valves.

3   Re-open both torch valves to remove unused gas from the regulators and hoses.

4   When all gas has been removed, close the regulators and the torch valves.

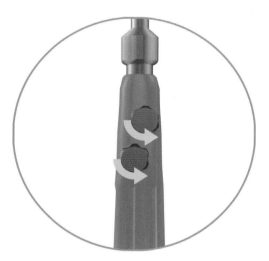

5   Hang the torch in the bracket and make sure all equipment is left in a safe position.

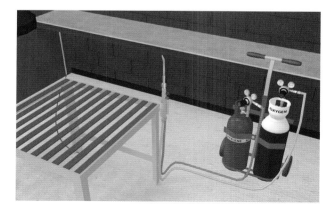

If the equipment is to be left for any period of time, close the cylinders and drain the equipment as a safety measure.

Consumables

Filler wire used in oxyacetylene welding

Oxyacetylene welding uses a filler wire or rod to add filler material to the weld. Filler wires can be made from a number of different materials and come in a range of diameter sizes.

The type of filler wire needed depends on conditions such as its compatibility with the materials to be welded, any need for additional mechanical properties and to add any de-oxidising elements to the weld pool.

Filler wires should be stored in clean and dry conditions and packages should be clearly labelled. You should not mix different types of filler wires.

Always handle with care and make sure they are free from contamination such as moisture, oil, grease and rust before use.

E-Learning

Use the e-learning programme to download some information about oxyacetylene consumables.

Welding Parameters

Welding parameters are settings that an operator can change to suit a particular work situation.

Some of the parameters in oxyacetylene welding that the operator can change are: the nozzle size, gas pressures, selection of appropriate filler wire or the flame settings.

The settings for these parameters can change depending on the conditions of the job, such as the weld position, the thickness and type of material and any need for additional alloying elements.

The Welding Process

The oxyacetylene process is made up of two elements which are carried out simultaneously. The first is penetration of heat via the torch and the second is the deposition of filler metal via the filler rod. This joins the base materials together.

When the oxyacetylene flame impacts upon the base materials, localised heating occurs and a molten weld pool is created. A filler material is added to the weld pool via a filler rod to complete the weld. As the process moves along the joint the deposited material cools and solidifies leaving a weld bead. This process can also fuse the parent metal together without the need for filler wire, this is known as an autogenous weld.

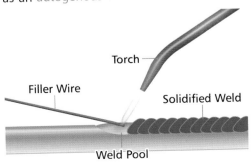

Welding process diagram

Preparing to Weld

Before commencing welding, there are a number of checks you need to make to ensure safe working practices.

Preparation of Work Area

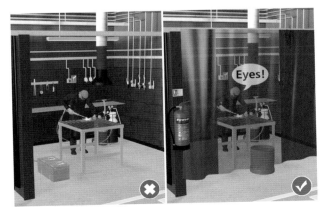

Correct and incorrect ways of preparing the work area

Before carrying out any welding or fabrication operation you should carry out a risk assessment. This can include:

● checking for hazards, for example slips, trips, obstructions and flammable materials;

● checking the existing safety procedures and equipment, for example fire extinguishers, water buckets, containment vessels and screening provision;

● making people in the vicinity aware of what work is being carried out, giving a verbal warning of when you are about to light up the flame and restricting access to the work area.

Material Preparation

You should familiarise yourself with the manufacturers' safety data sheets (MSDS) before using any equipment, materials, solvents or chemicals.

It is good practice to de-burr and degrease the material to be welded to prevent contamination of the weld and remove any flammable substances.

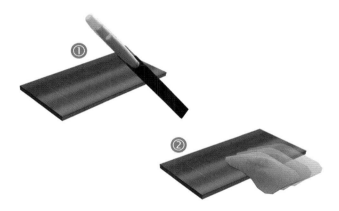

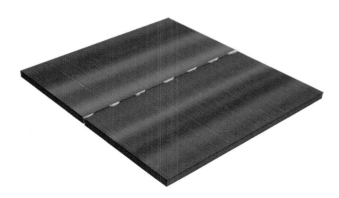

Material preparation: 1. De-burring; 2. De-greasing

Prior to any weld deposition, it is recommended that the joint is tacked to aid alignment and distortion control.

Tacking the joint

Position of Welder

Before welding, you should get into a comfortable and balanced position that can be maintained throughout the period of welding. You will need to be in a position where you are able to see the weld develop and that you can weld along the joint in one continuous movement. Fatigue and discomfort can cause poor quality welds.

Flame Settings

The flame produced from an oxyacetylene torch can reach temperatures up to 3200°C so it is essential that the correct PPE is worn and all safety checks have been made.

There are three main types of flame which are created from different amounts of acetylene and oxygen being burnt. In each type of flame, the area between the end of the inner cone and the tip of the outer flame is called the 'reducing zone', in which any rust or surface oxide will be burnt off or reduced so that it does not impact on the weld deposit.

Neutral Flame

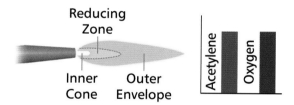

Neutral flame (Acetylene = Oxygen)

When both gases are roughly equal, the flame produced will be neutral. This flame has a rounded inner cone approximately twice as long as it is wide with a blue outer envelope. A neutral flame is used for welding steel and some non-ferrous metals.

Carburising flame

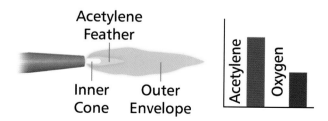

Carburising flame (Acetylene > Oxygen)

When more acetylene than oxygen is being burnt, the resulting flame is a carburising flame. It has a bright, luminous, 'feathered' inner cone with a ragged blue outer envelope.

A carburising flame is used for surface deposition when hard surfacing or adding wear resistant coating to a material.

Oxidising Flame

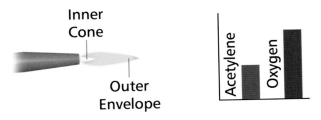

Oxidising flame (Acetylene < Oxygen)

When more oxygen than acetylene is being burnt, an oxidising flame is produced. The inner cone is sharp and pointed and a distinctive hissing noise can be heard. The blue outer envelope is much smaller and narrower than a neutral or carburising flame with tinges of red towards the tip.

An oxidising flame can be used for brazing and braze welding.

Techniques

Each welding process uses specific techniques which require the understanding of the tilt angle and slope angle.

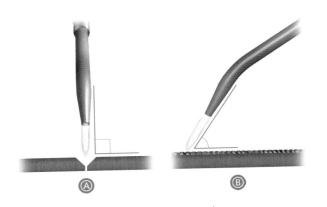

Techniques: A. Tilt angle; B. Slope angle

The tilt angle is the angle the welding torch is held at between the two pieces of material to be welded.

The slope angle is the angle the welding torch is held at between the joint to be welded and a 90° angle from the joint.

Oxyacetylene welding uses two main techniques as well as specific techniques for starting and stopping a weld.

Leftward Technique

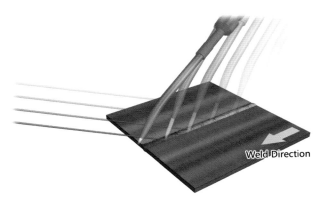

Leftward technique

Using the leftward technique, the filler wire is held in front of the molten pool at a slope angle of 20–30°. It is fed into the centre of the molten pool. The torch is held at a slope angle of 60–70° to the material being welded. This is followed by the solidifying weld metal.

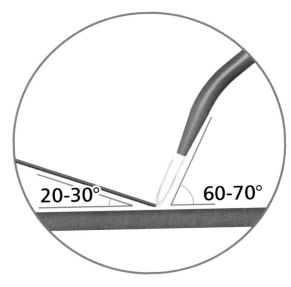

Leftward technique slope angles

The flame should be moved in a side to side motion and the cone of the flame should not leave the weld pool as it advances.

Do not hold the filler wire continuously in the molten pool, as this could prevent the heat of the flame and the molten pool from reaching the lower parts of the joint, resulting in possible lack of fusion. The correct technique is to dip the filler wire in and out of the pool at regular intervals as the weld proceeds. The frequency of this action will be determined by the size of the weld being deposited. At the end of the weld the flame should be lowered and manipulated on the metal and the use of the filler wire increased to correctly terminate the weld and prevent crater cracking.

Rightward Technique

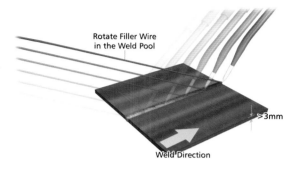

Rotate Filler Wire in the Weld Pool

>3mm

Weld Direction

Rightward technique

The rightward technique is used on materials in excess of 3mm thick. In this instance, the torch is held in front of the molten pool at a slope angle of 40–50°, followed by the filler wire at a slope angle of 30–40°, to the material being welded. The filler wire is fed into the centre of the molten pool. This is followed by the solidifying weld metal. The flame moves in a straight line while the filler wire is rotated in the weld pool. Time should be taken to allow for the keyhole to appear to ensure that adequate penetration of the thicker material has been achieved.

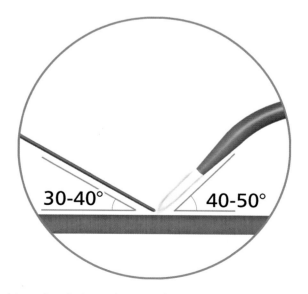

30-40°   40-50°

Rightward technique slope angles

Because the torch is pointing backwards towards the part that has been welded, there is no likelihood of the molten metal being pushed forward over any unheated surface, giving poor fusion or cold lapping. The advantages of rightward on thicker plate are:

- lower cost per metre run due to less filler wire being used and increased speed;
- less expansion and contraction;
- annealing action of the flame on the weld metal;
- better view of the molten pool, giving better control of the weld.

Start Stop Technique

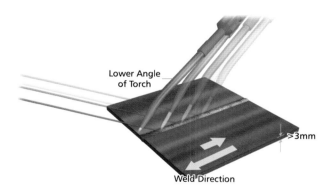

Lower Angle of Torch

>3mm

Weld Direction

Start stop technique

When you want to recommence a weld, you need to re-heat the weld back approximately 12mm from the point at which you stopped. When the molten pool has been established, move forward and apply the filler material as and when required.

As you work towards an open end, you need to lower the angle of the torch and gently manipulate the flame before stopping, so as not to burn through the edges.

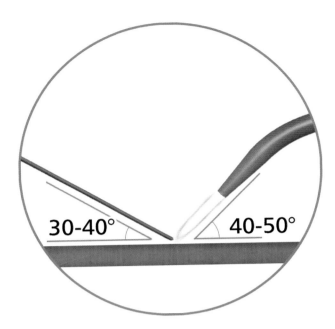

30-40°   40-50°

Start stop technique slope angles

E-Learning
Use the e-learning programme to see an animated version of starting and stopping a weld.

Fusion Runs

Fusion runs are the combination of penetration into the base metal and additional filler wire to produce a weld deposit. They are predominantly used to determine heat input, speed of travel and rate of filler addition in order to produce a satisfactory weld deposit.

The flame should be adjusted to a neutral flame and the steel sheet placed on firebricks on the welding bench to allow air to circulate underneath. Using the leftward technique, hold the torch at 60°–70° to the work surface with the inner cone, about 3-5mm from the metal's surface. The metal is brought up to its melting point, which is indicated by 'sweating' followed by the formation of the molten pool. Once the pool is formed, using a rotational movement of the torch, encourage the molten pool to move along the metal at a steady rate to ensure 'fusion' into the plate. This is indicated by a regular continuous bead on the underside and a gouging or groove effect on the top side of the plate. The sparks that occur as the weld progresses are due to components of the metal that are being burned out of the weldment. Silicon oxides make up most of the sparks and extra silicon can be added with the filler metal so that the weldment retains its desired qualities. A change in the sparks given off by the weld as it progresses, indicates a change in weld temperature. An increase in sparks on clean metal means an increase in weld temperature. Often there is a large increase in the amount of sparks in the air just before 'burnthrough' takes place, when this occurs the torch should be pulled back to allow the metal to cool and prevent burnthrough.

When this has been mastered, further practice should involve the use of filler wire to fill the groove made previously. The deposit should be within 3mm reinforcement (excess weld metal).

Potential Welding Failures

Potential weld failures in oxyacetylene welding can occur for a number of reasons, for example insufficient gas flow rates and incorrect pressures; the selection of the wrong sized nozzle; incorrect diameter or composition of filler wire; poor operator technique in depositing the weld bead; insufficient gap on butt joints and failure to align plates correctly.

One example of a welding failure is known as a 'blowback'. This occurs when the nozzle is too close to the metal and molten metal attaches itself to the nozzle. Pressure then builds up in the nozzle which can lead to a small explosion. To prevent blowback, or to fix it if it occurs, ensure that the gas pressures are set to the appropriate levels for the nozzle being used and that the nozzle is clean.

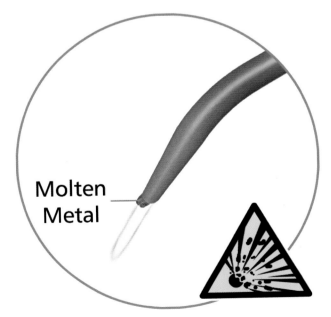

Molten Metal

Blowback can be dangerous

A second, and potentially more dangerous occurrence, is a 'flashback'. This is where the flame travels back inside the torch and hoses and can be identified by a high pitched noise (similar to a squealing pig) with sparks and black smoke being emitted from the end of the nozzle. If this happens, immediately turn off the gas bottles and check the wall of the cylinders for signs of heat, if any heat is detected spray with water and notify the fire service.

Cleaning the Weld

After the weld is complete, oxyacetylene welds can be cleaned with a wire brush.

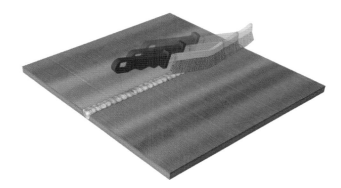

Clean welds using a wire brush

Reinstate the Work Area

When you have finished welding, ensure all equipment is closed down correctly and turned off. Make sure the equipment is stored away safely and does not create any hazards.

Sustainability

Cool all scrap metal and place it in the appropriate container to be recycled.

Return all tools that have been used and tidy up the work area.

Joints

There are four main types of joint in welding. Any weld on any joint should be equal to the thickness of the plate and have a smooth transition from the weld to the plate surface.

The slope and tilt angles will change with the position in which the weld is carried out. In this instance, the tilt and slope angles mentioned are for the flat and horizontal vertical positions using the leftward technique only.

Outside Corner Joint

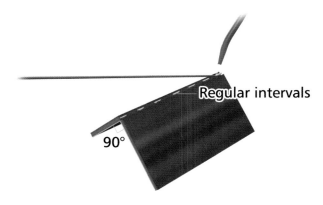

Outside corner joint

An outside corner joint is formed by two work pieces positioned with their edges next to each other at an angle of 90°. The weld is placed on the outside of this corner. The pieces should be tacked at each end and at regular intervals along the joint.

The oxyacetylene torch is positioned so it is halfway between (bisects) the two work pieces and has a slope angle of 60–70°. The filler wire is positioned so it is halfway between the two work pieces and has a slope angle of 20–30°. Penetration should not exceed 3mm and the finished weld should display a rounded profile with an even weld ripple.

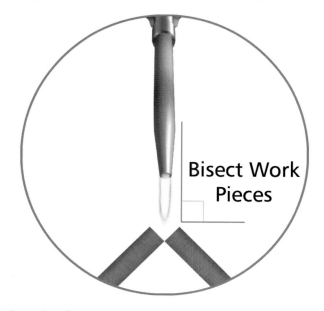

Tilt angle of torch

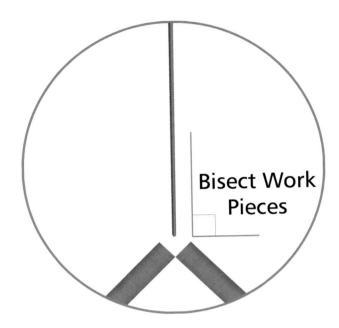

Tilt angle of filler wire

A lap joint is formed by two work pieces overlapping each other. The weld is placed where the two pieces meet. The pieces should be tacked at each end and at regular intervals along the joint.

The oxyacetylene torch should be at 45° to the two work pieces and have a slope angle of 60–70°. The filler wire should be at 45° to the two work pieces and have a slope angle of 20–30°. The angle will ensure that most of the heat goes into the bottom plate and both plates reach melting point at the same time. The filler wire should be fed at regular intervals to the top edge to prevent under-cut on the vertical plate edge, whilst maintaining a fusion at the interface where the plates meet.

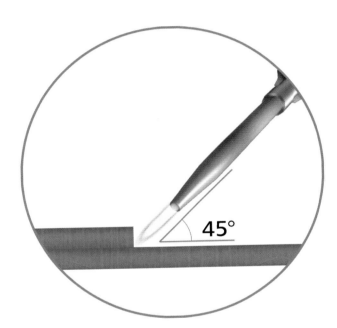

Tilt angle of torch

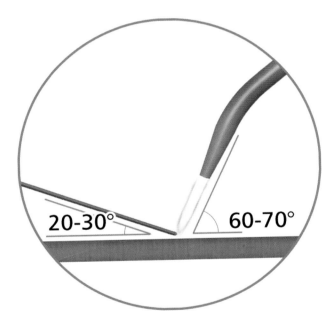

Slope angles of torch and filler wire

Lap Joint

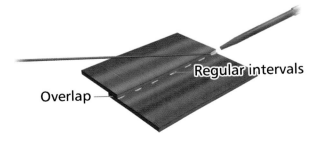

Lap joint

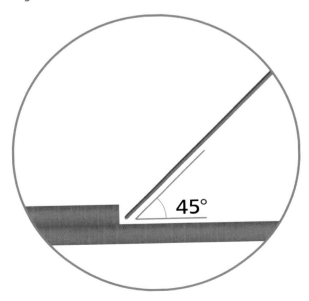

Tilt angle of filler wire

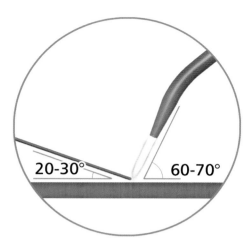

Slope angles of torch and filler wire

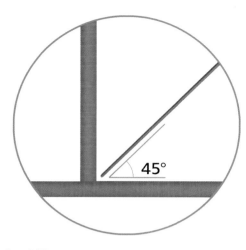

Tilt angle of filler wire

Tee Joint

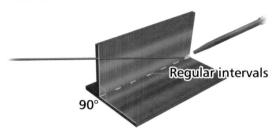

Tee joint

A Tee joint is formed when one work piece is positioned at 90° to another work piece. The weld is placed where the two pieces meet. The pieces should be tacked at each end and at regular intervals along the joint.

The oxyacetylene torch should be at 45° to the two work pieces and have a slope angle of 60–70°. The filler wire should be at 45° to the two work pieces and have a slope angle of 20–30°. The technique used for filler deposition is the same as that previously described for the lap fillet. The weld deposit should exhibit a slightly convex profile with smooth blending of the toes and a consistent leg length.

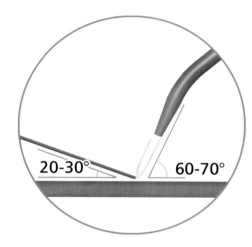

Slope angles of torch and filler wire

Butt Joint

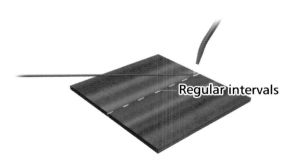

Butt joint

A butt joint is formed when the two work pieces are positioned side by side with a gap between them to ensure penetration. The weld is then placed between the two pieces.

The space between the plates is called the gap, also commonly called the root gap, and this can vary from 0–3mm dependent upon the thickness of metal. If the gap is too

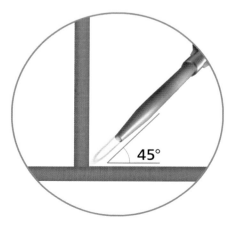

Tilt angle of torch

large or too small it can result in defects in the welded joint. When welding thick plate, an edge preparation is put on the plates to ensure penetration and a sound weld deposit. The pieces should be tacked at each end and at regular intervals along the joint using a taper spacing technique, in which the gap is tapered to take into account the expansion and contraction stresses that are associated with this joint configuration.

The oxyacetylene torch should be at 90° to the surface of the work pieces and have a slope angle of 60–70°. The filler wire should be at 90° to the two work pieces and have a slope angle of 20–30°. The weld should exhibit a smooth, slightly raised profile with a maximum root penetration of 3mm and smooth blending of the toes.

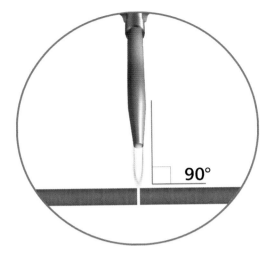

Tilt angle of torch

Activity

In the space below, sketch an outside corner joint.

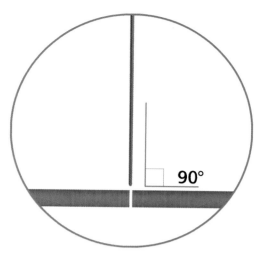

Tilt angle of filler wire

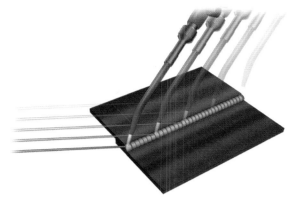

Brazing

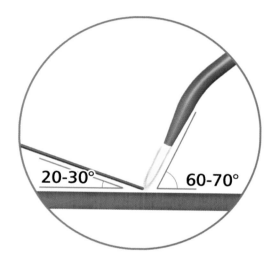

Slope angles of torch and filler wire

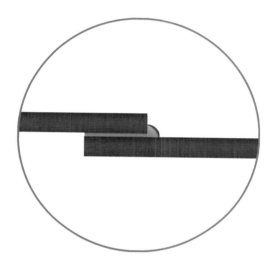

Brazing – close up of the joint

Braze Welding

Braze welding is the surface deposition of the filler material which forms an intermetallic bond to produce a fillet deposit, similar to a conventional weld deposit. It is used extensively for the repair of cast iron and other heat sensitive materials.

Non-Fusion Welding

Non-fusion welding is a process in which a filler material forms a chemical bond with the parent material but does not fully fuse into that material. In these processes the filler metal is of a relatively low melting point and is drawn into the joint by capillary attraction or surface deposition. Brazing, braze welding and soldering are three types of non-fusion welding.

Brazing

In brazing, filler material is drawn through closely fitting surfaces by capillary attraction. It forms an intermetallic bond with the base material and has the ability to flex, which makes it ideal for joints subjected to shock loading, for example bicycles on roads and footpaths.

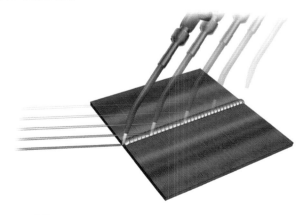

Braze welding

Braze welding – close up of the joint

Hard Soldering

Hard soldering is similar to brazing as it relies on capillary attraction but the composition of the filler material can be based on silver, as in silver soldering, or copper phosphorous, as in copper flow. Typical uses include jewellery making and repair as well as refrigeration pipe work. The composition of the filler wire can be adapted to produce an alloy that matches the base material in colour.

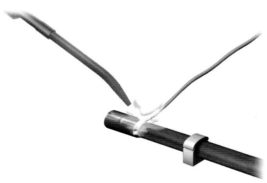

Hard soldering

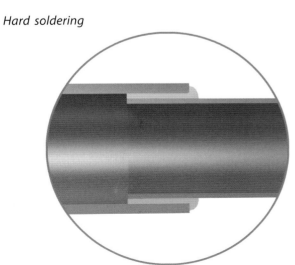

Hard soldering – close up of the joint

Advantages of Soldering and Braze Welding

Soldering and brazing have several advantages over other methods of joining, including:

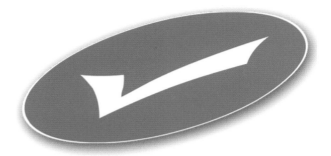

- Low temperature – since the base metal does not have to melt, a lower temperature heat source can be used.

- May be permanently or temporarily joined – since the base metal is not damaged parts may be dismantled at a later time by simply reapplying heat and the parts then can be reused. However, the joint is solid enough to be permanent.

- Dissimilar materials can be joined – it is easy to join dissimilar metals, such as copper to steel, aluminium to brass and cast iron to stainless steel.

- Speed of joining – Parts can be pre-assembled and dipped, furnace soldered or brazed in large quantities.

- Slow rate of heating and cooling – because it is not necessary to heat a small area to its melting temperature and then allow it to cool quickly to a solid, the internal stresses caused by rapid temperature changes can be reduced.

- Parts of varying thicknesses can be joined – very thin parts, or a thin part and a thick part, can be joined without burning or overheating them.

- Easy realignment – parts can easily be realigned by reheating the joint and then repositioning the part.

Quality Control

Terminology

When visually inspecting welds certain terminology is used to describe the joint configurations including:

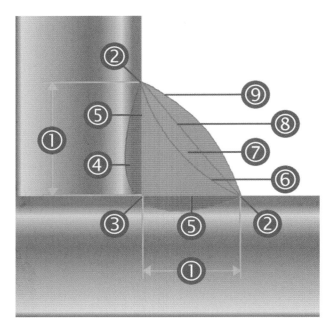

Quality control terminology: 1. Leg length; 2. Toe; 3. Root; 4. Fusion penetration; 5. Fusion face; 6. Concave; 7. Throat thickness; 8. Flat; 9. Weld face convex

- root: the furthermost point of fusion in a welded joint;
- root face: a section of the weld edge preparation which is filed or machined to a square edge to control penetration and act as a heat sink;
- root gap: the space between abutting plates designed to ensure penetration of the metal;
- leg length: the distance out from the intersection of fusion faces and the toes of a fillet weld measured across the fusion face;
- toes of a weld: the junction between the face of a weld and the parent metal;
- throat thickness: the shortest distance from the root to the outside of a fillet weld, or the smallest thickness of a butt weld;
- Weld face: total width across the face of the completed weld deposit;
- fusion face: place where the fusion zone joins with the parent metal.

Weld Defects

In all welding techniques there are a number of weld defects and discontinuities that can be identified once a weld is complete.

Discontinuities are irregularities that are within acceptable limits and do not bring about failure of the component.

A defect is a discontinuity which exceeds acceptance levels and renders the component subject to failure.

Porosity

Porosity is created when gas becomes trapped in the weld deposit as the metal cools.

Causes: Use of incorrect filler rod and weld technique, surface contamination, unclean filler, atmospheric contamination.

Remedies: Keep plate surfaces clean and use correct flame setting to avoid gas entrapment.

⬭ Gas Pockets

Porosity

Inclusions

Inclusions are created when foreign matter such as oil, grease or mill scale becomes trapped within the solidifying weld deposit as irregular pores.

Causes: Unclean parent or filler metal, accidental contact of nozzle with weld pool.

Remedies: Keep plate surfaces and filler rod clean, use correct weld technique to avoid contact of nozzle with weld pool.

Non-metallic Materials

Inclusions

Lack of Root Penetration

This is the failure of the weld metal to extend into the root of a joint.

Causes: Incorrect joint preparation and set up, with too small a gap, moving too quickly with not enough heat applied.

Remedies: Ensure correct preparation and set up, a large enough gap, use the correct nozzle size and adjust the speed.

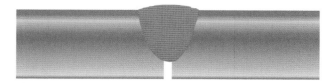

Lack of root penetration

Lack of Side Wall Fusion

This is a lack of fusion between weld metal and the parent metal at the side of the weld and on the inter-run deposition.

Causes: Incorrect alignment of joint edges, not enough heat applied, moving too quickly.

Remedies: Set up joint edges and maintain correct alignment or torch and filler rod, increase the heat applied and adjust the speed.

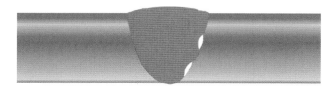

Lack of side wall fusion

Undercut

This is created when metal is removed from a joint without being replaced by weld material. It is commonly found at the toe of a run or in previously deposited weld metal.

Causes: Using too large a nozzle size, poor torch manipulation, excessive movement of the torch, incorrect distance of the torch from the plate.

Remedies: Use the correct nozzle size, adjust the distance of the torch from the plate and manipulate the torch and filler rod with a sideways movement.

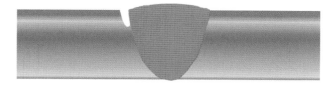

Undercut

Underfill

Underfill is created when the weld metal is insufficient to produce the required deposit as stated in the specification.

Causes: Using too large a nozzle and/or too much torch manipulation while moving too quickly, insufficient filler rod diameter.

Remedies: Use the correct nozzle size, adjust the speed and sideways torch movement and use correct diameter filler rod.

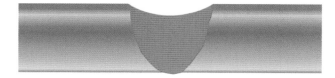

Underfill

Excessive Weld Reinforcement

Excessive weld reinforcement is created when the weld metal deposited leaves the weld and protrudes on the surface of the weld.

Causes: Insufficient heat from the torch, using too small a nozzle, using too large a filler rod, moving too slowly.

Remedies: Adjust the speed to produce sufficient heat and select the correct size nozzle and filler rod.

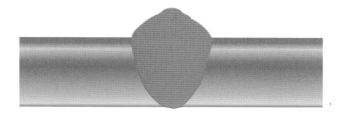

Excessive weld reinforcement

Excessive Root Penetration

This is produced by excessive weld metal protruding through the root of a fusion weld.

Causes: Using incorrect size of nozzle and filler rod, moving too slowly, the slope angle of the torch is too great.

Remedies: Select the correct nozzle size and filler rod, adjust the speed and reduce the slope angle of the torch.

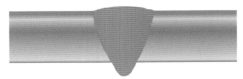

Excessive root penetration

Misalignment of Plates

This is created by failing to align the plates after tacking and prior to welding, giving a stepped appearance.

Causes: Failure to tack weld prior to welding.

Remedies: Tacking at regular intervals and dressing the plates prior to welding.

Misalignment of plates

Poor Weld Profile / Dimension

This is caused by failure to maintain design specifications.

Causes: Not using the appropriately sized nozzle for the job, incorrect gas pressures, unsuitable filler wire, poor manipulation of torch.

Remedies: Ensure that the appropriate nozzle, filler wire and gas pressures are selected for the job and that the operator's technique is correct.

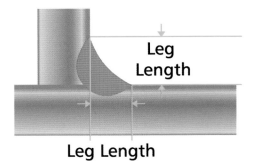

Leg Length

Leg Length

Poor weld profile/dimension

CHECK YOUR KNOWLEDGE

1 Which of the following applications can oxyacetylene welding be used for? Circle the correct answer.
   a. Cutting
   b. Flame cleaning
   c. Hard soldering
   d. Welding 10 mm plate
   e. Welding modern automobiles
   f. Soft soldering
   g. Pre-heating

2 What colour and thread pattern is the acetylene regulator?
   a. Red, left hand thread
   b. Red, right hand thread
   c. Blue, left hand thread
   d. Blue, right hand thread

3 Match the description to the flame. Write a, b or c beside each diagram.
   a. Neutral
   b. Carburising
   c. Oxidising

4   Can you identify these weld defects? Write a, b or c next to the appropriate diagram.

   a.   Lack of Root Penetration
   b.   Lack of Side Wall Fusion
   c.   Undercut

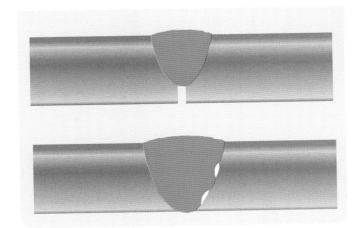

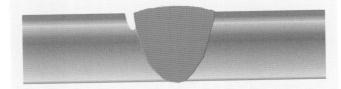

Summary

This concludes this chapter on oxyacetylene welding. You should now be able to explain the principles of oxyacetylene welding, list the specific health and safety requirements, list the equipment used and how to set it up, explain how to carry out the oxyacetylene welding process and list the weld defects that can occur.

End test

1. **Which of the following welders is wearing the appropriate PPE for oxyacetylene welding? Circle the correct answer.**

   ☐ a.

   ☐ b.

   ☐ c.

2. **Identify the components of the oxyacetylene equipment shown.**

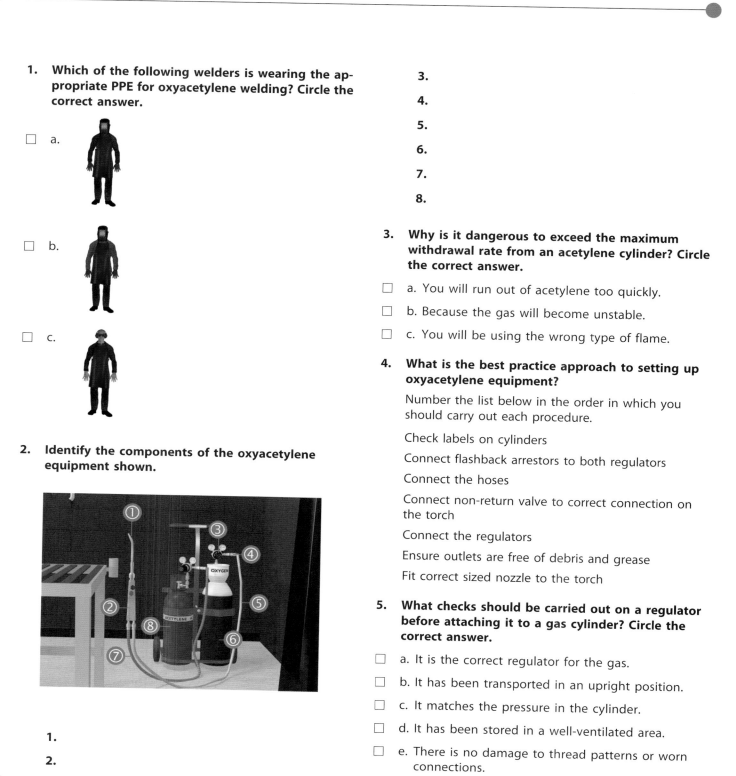

   1.
   2.
   3.
   4.
   5.
   6.
   7.
   8.

3. **Why is it dangerous to exceed the maximum withdrawal rate from an acetylene cylinder? Circle the correct answer.**

   ☐ a. You will run out of acetylene too quickly.

   ☐ b. Because the gas will become unstable.

   ☐ c. You will be using the wrong type of flame.

4. **What is the best practice approach to setting up oxyacetylene equipment?**

   Number the list below in the order in which you should carry out each procedure.

   Check labels on cylinders

   Connect flashback arrestors to both regulators

   Connect the hoses

   Connect non-return valve to correct connection on the torch

   Connect the regulators

   Ensure outlets are free of debris and grease

   Fit correct sized nozzle to the torch

5. **What checks should be carried out on a regulator before attaching it to a gas cylinder? Circle the correct answer.**

   ☐ a. It is the correct regulator for the gas.

   ☐ b. It has been transported in an upright position.

   ☐ c. It matches the pressure in the cylinder.

   ☐ d. It has been stored in a well-ventilated area.

   ☐ e. There is no damage to thread patterns or worn connections.

6. **If the level of acetylene is set to 50%, what level of oxygen is required to achieve a carburising flame?**

   _____

7. **What would each of these types of flames be used for? Write a, b or c next to the appropriate diagram.**

   ☐ a. Hard Surfacing

   ☐ b. Braze Welding

   ☐ c. Welding Steel

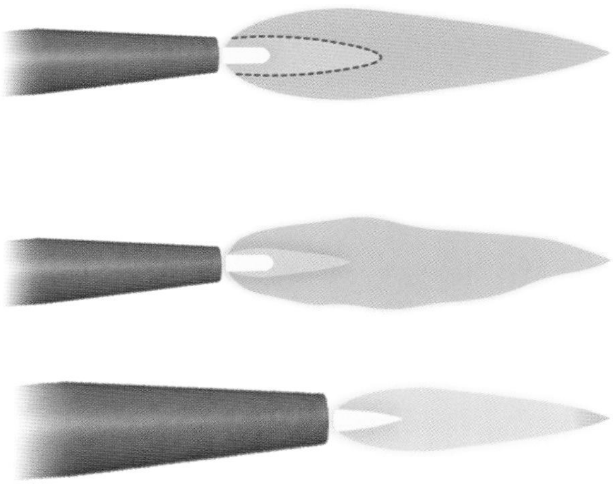

8. **Which of these statements describes the best practice approach when oxyacetylene welding using the leftward technique? Circle the correct answer.**

   ☐ a. Filler wire is in front of the molten pool at an angle of 20–30° and the torch is at a slope angle of 60–70° to the material being welded.

   ☐ b. Filler wire is in front of the molten pool at an angle of 60–70° and the torch is at a slope angle of 20–30° to the material being welded.

   ☐ c. The torch is in front of the molten pool at an angle of 40–50° and the filler wire is at a slope angle of 30–40° to the material being welded.

   ☐ d. The torch is in front of the molten pool at an angle of 30–40° and the filler wire is at a slope angle of 40–50° to the material being welded.

9. **Identify these four types of joint. Write a, b, c or d next to the appropriate diagram.**

   ☐ a. Butt joint

   ☐ b. Lap joint

   ☐ c. Outside corner joint

   ☐ d. Tee joint

10. **What are these weld defects called and what causes them? Write a, b or c next to the appropriate diagram.**

    ☐ a. Inclusions

    ☐ b. Porosity

    ☐ c. Underfill

Write d, e or f next to the appropriate diagram.

☐   d. Created when the weld metal deposited is
        insufficient to produce a weld deposit in excess
        the parent metal surface

☐   e. Created when non-metallic materials such as oil,
        grease or mill scale become trapped within the
        solidifying weld deposit

☐   f. Created when gas in the weld pool becomes
        trapped in the weld deposit as the metal cools

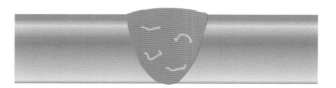

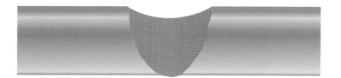

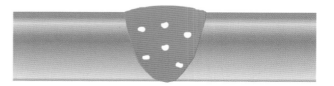

Manual Metal Arc (MMA) Welding

5

LEARNING OBJECTIVES

By the end of this chapter you will be able to:

● Explain the principles of MMA welding.

● List the specific health and safety requirements.

● List the equipment and explain how it should be set up.

● Explain how to carry out the MMA welding process.

● List the weld defects that can occur.

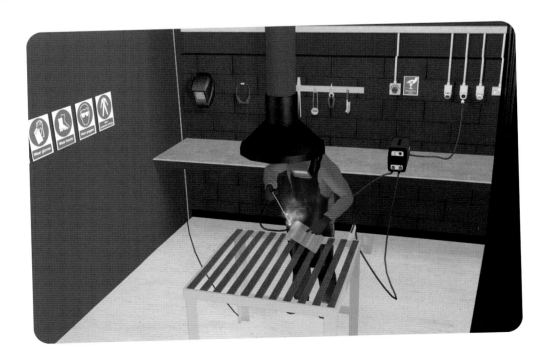

Introduction

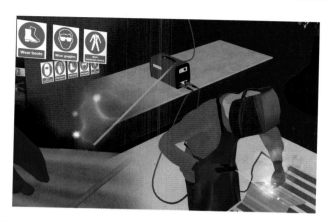

The many aspects of MMA welding

Manual Metal Arc (MMA) welding is a process that uses electricity to form an electric arc heat source between the tip of a consumable electrode and the work piece. The heat from the arc energy melts the base material as well as the electrode, which is consumed to form the filler metal for the weld. The molten metal is transferred across the arc by electromagnetic forces at the same time as the arc is enveloped in a gas shield provided by the disintegration of some of the ingredients of the electrode coating. Approximately 60–70% of the conventional electrode is deposited as weld metal with a small percentage evaporating off within the arc and the final percentage remaining as a stub end in the electrode holder. Caution should be observed at all times and full personal protective equipment (PPE) is recommended.

MMA welding has a number of advantages and disadvantages.

Advantages

- Mobile equipment is available
- Can be used on a widge range of materials
- Is suitable for use on site
- Does not require the use of compressed gas cylinders
- Is less susceptible to the negative effects of draughts
- Relatively cheap to purchase especially the new inverters

Advantages of MMA welding

Disadvantages

- Limited deposition rates due to length of electrode.
- Wasteful of consumables.
- Electrodes are hygroscopic (absorb moisture) and require careful storage to avoid porosity in the weld deposit.

Disadvantages of MMA welding

Activity

Use the internet to make a list of up to six jobs that are currently being advertised that may require MMA welding skills.

_____

_____

_____

_____

_____

_____

Applications

MMA welding is used for a wide range of applications, including:

- steel structures;
- fabricating mild steel, e.g. ship building, storage tanks, bridges;
- in processing plants, e.g. refineries, nuclear plants;
- pipe welding;
- repair and refurbishment of plant and mechanical components, e.g. skips, JCBs.

Activity

Identify four applications to which MMA welding is particularly suited.

_____

_____

_____

_____

Health and Safety for MMA Welding

Health and Safety

Before entering a workshop environment always make sure that you are wearing the appropriate personal protective equipment (PPE) for the job. Standard PPE includes fully protective, flame-retardant overalls, safety boots, ear defenders and clear safety goggles. It may also be necessary to wear an additional respirator in certain circumstances.

For MMA welding you should also be wearing leather gauntlet-style gloves, a welding cap, a welding mask, a flame-retardant jacket done up to the neck and a welding apron. If extra manual dexterity is required, soft leather gloves may be worn. Always check to make sure the welding mask is set to the correct filter level.

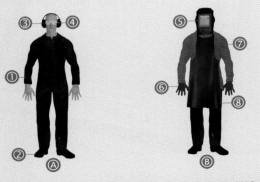

Personal Protective Equipment (PPE): A. Workshop PPE; B. Additional PPE when MMA welding. 1. Flame-retardant overalls; 2. Safety boots; 3. Ear defenders; 4. Clear safety goggles; 5. Welding mask (welding cap); 6. Leather gauntlet-style gloves; 7. Flame-retardant jacket; 8. Welding apron

E-Learning

Use the e-learning programme to download a filter lens guide that provides more information.

You should already be aware of some of the health and safety requirements described below. Some apply to any form of welding and some are specific to the MMA process.

Working in Confined Spaces

Working in confined space safety sign

You should not work in a confined space until the area has been checked to confirm that oxygen levels are suitable and no poisonous gases are present.

An oxygen level of below 16% can lead to dizziness and a shortness of breath, which can be fatal if not noticed in time for the operator to get to a source of fresh air. Operators should be observed at all times when in confined spaces. The use of a lifeline (a rope around the welder) is recommended. This allows the observer to remove the welder from the area without putting themselves at risk. The use of low-voltage lighting and battery-powered tools is also recommended.

The arc welding processes produce a number of potentially harmful fumes such as Ozone (O_3), Carbon Monoxide (CO) and Carbon Dioxide (CO_2). It is recommended that good extraction, close to the source of fumes, be used at all times. If this is not possible due to site access then the welding operator should be equipped with a self-contained air supply welding shield.

Due to the high humidity that may be experienced in confined spaces and the potential for shock, use of a low-voltage safety device is recommended. This drops the normal open-circuit voltage (present in non-welding periods) down to 25–30 volts, thereby reducing the effects of a shock. Full open-circuit voltage is restored on striking the arc.

Electric shock risk safety sign

Personal Safety

Wear PPE safety sign

Always make sure you are wearing the appropriate PPE when welding and that you are working in accordance with safe working practices. Harmful fumes and gases are produced in all welding processes so appropriate fume extraction should always be in place.

The heat from the MMA welding process, sparks, hot slag and hot metal can cause severe burns. The electric arc from the process also gives off a form of radiation which can cause burns similar to sunburn on the skin and the light from the arc can also cause burning to the eyes. This is known as arc eye and is a painful condition that can cause watering of the eyes, headaches and a temporary loss of vision. All arc processes give off the full spectrum of light from visible light, through infra-red and up to ultra-violet light radiation.

Materials Safety Data Sheet

Materials Safety Data Sheet (MSDS)

Always consult the Material Data Sheets before any welding is undertaken. These data sheets contain important information on items such as gases, filler wires, electrodes and degreasing solvents. They are available from the manufacturers of the products. You need to understand the properties of all the items you use, the hazards associated with them and what to do in an emergency. As stated in the previous chapter, there are sixteen sections to these data sheets. It is important that you understand the potential consequences of using these products for your own well-being and that of those around you.

Electrical Safety

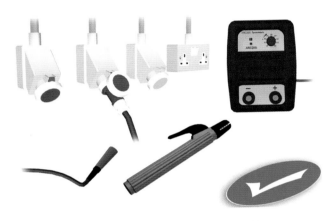

Always check that electrical equipment is safe to use

Before switching on the equipment and carrying out any welding, check that the equipment is not damaged and is set up correctly and earthed appropriately. Also be aware that electric arc processes present a danger to people with pacemakers.

Damaged cable insulation, incorrectly sized fuses, faulty connections and lack of a suitable earth can all cause electric shock, fire and burn hazards. Appliance testing and repairs should only be carried out by competent personnel.

Conditions where water or moisture is present can be hazardous to the welder. You should erect a shelter for protection and ensure the work piece is properly insulated. The use of a low-voltage safety device is recommended.

Fumes, Gases and Ventilation

Fume extraction should be approximately 250mm from the weld zone

In addition to general ventilation of the welding area, fume extraction should also be provided. Fumes can be produced by fluxes, surface coatings, base materials, solvents used to degrease the material and shielding gases. Fumes can cause breathing difficulties and even asphyxiation.

Fumes need to be drawn off by a localised extraction ventilation system. This should be placed close to the weld and in a position which ensures that the fumes are not drawn past the face of the welder. It should also be set to an appropriate extraction rate so it removes the fumes but not the gas shield where applicable.

Working at Height

You may be required to work at height. Scaffolding must be competently erected with earth bonding, along with a static safety harness. The weld area should be screened to protect fellow workers from the effects of radiation and the area should be cordoned off with clear signage. Where ladders are used to access the scaffold, they must project past the landing stage by 1m and be secured at the top and bottom of the ladder. All tools are to be raised to the landing stage by a rope and containment vessel. With the development of mobile elevated working platforms (MEWPS), it is possible to get relatively easy access to most locations by the use of scissor lifts and cherry pickers (often used to harvest fruit). However you need a licence to operate these platforms and the use of harnesses and lanyards is mandatory. Safety must come first.

Activity

What health and safety precautions should you take when carrying out MMA welding?

_____

_____

_____

_____

_____

_____

_____

_____

_____

_____

_____

_____

Activity

List three potentially hazardous fumes associated with MMA welding.

1 _____

2 _____

3 _____

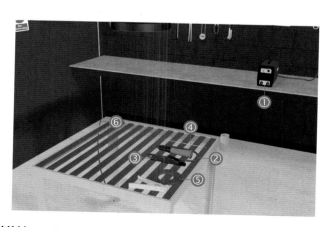

MMA equipment setup: 1. Power source; 2. Welding lead; 3. Electrode holder; 4. Electrode; 5. Welding return lead and clamp; 6. Earth connection

MMA equipment consists of a power source linked to an electrode by the welding lead which passes a current via the arc at the tip of the electrode. This current passes through the work piece and returns to the power source via the welding return clamp and welding return lead to form a continuous circuit.

Always check your equipment before use to make sure it is in good working order.

Power Source

MMA welding can use an alternating current (AC) power supply, a direct current (DC) power supply or a combination of AC and DC.

Power sources for MMA welding include generators and rectifiers which provide a DC supply, transformers which provide an AC supply and inverters which can be AC, DC or both.

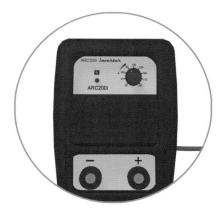

1. Power source

There are two methods of producing a welding current. One method generates the current by providing power to a generator or alternator rotated by an electric motor or a petrol / diesel engine. The second method uses one of several types of step-down transformer, in which the output side of the transformer has a reduced number of windings which means that the voltage is reduced but the output amperage is increased. Transformer-rectifiers can produce the same smooth DC welding current output as motor generators, but are less expensive to operate, quieter in operation, more energy efficient and require less maintenance.

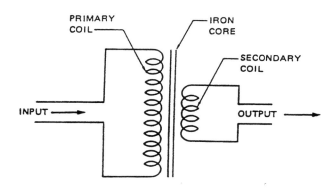

Primary coil

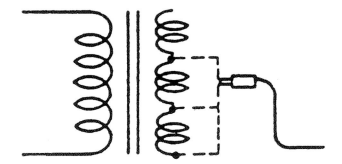

Tap type

Welding machines can be classified by the method by which they control or adjust the welding current. The multiple coil machine or tap-type allows the selection of higher current settings by tapping into the secondary coil at higher turn values. The greater the number of turns, the higher the amperage that is induced in the turns.

Movable coil or core machines are adjusted by turning a handwheel that moves the internal parts closer together or further apart. These machines may have a high and low range, but they do not have a fine adjusting knob. The closer the primary and secondary coils are, the greater the induced current. The greater the distance between the coils, the smaller the induced current. Moving the core in concentrates more of the magnetic force on the secondary coil, thus increasing the current. Moving the core out allows the field to disperse and the current is reduced.

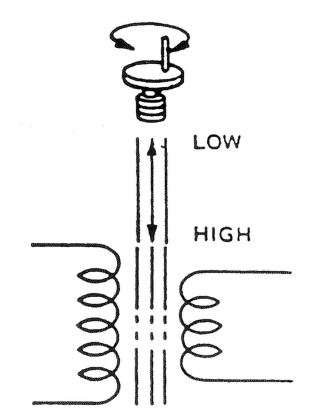

Movable core

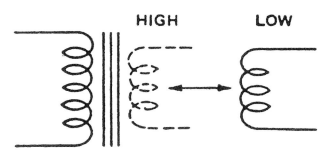

Movable coil

Welding Lead

The welding lead connects the power source to the electrode holder. The construction is primarily copper with a PVC insulation of suitable thickness. The cross-sectional area of the conductor is most important as it will dictate the amount of current that can be distributed. The higher the amperage is, the greater the cross-sectional area of the cable.

2. Welding lead

Electrode Holder

The electrode holder provides the insulation between the electrode and the operator. Before use, you should check that there are no signs of physical damage to the electrode holder or the insulation.

The operator can manoeuvre the holder so that the arc length, the tilt angle and the slope angle of the electrode can be controlled.

3. Electrode holder

The electrode is clamped between copper jaws which are usually spring loaded, and a simple movement of the side lever enables the electrode to be changed easily and quickly. In another type of holder, the electrode fits into a socket in the electrode holder head and is held by twisting the handle until the electrode is held tightly. Electrode holders are designed for specific current-carrying capacities, for example 200–400 amperes. The maximum current MUST NOT be exceeded.

Electrode

The electrode is made up of a suitable wire core, coated with a flux material. These melt at the same time with the wire core providing the filler material for the weld and the flux providing a gas shield and slag coating.

4. Electrode

E-Learning

Use the e-learning programme to download a table of electrodes.

Welding Return Lead and Clamp

The welding return lead completes the circuit by connecting the power source to the work piece via the clamp. The clamp could be bolted, swivelled or an alligator type depending on the type of job being carried out.

5. Welding return lead and clamp

Earth Connection

The work piece should be connected to a suitable earth via a clamp and earth lead. The clamp could be bolted, swivelled or an alligator type depending on the type of job being carried out.

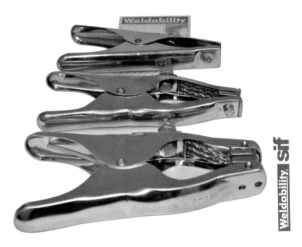

Earth clamps

The work clamp must be of the correct size for the current being used and it must clamp tightly to the material or component. Heat can build up in the work clamp, reducing welding efficiency. It is easy to overlook these power losses and you should touch the clamp occasionally to find out if it is getting hot. In addition to power losses due to poor work-lead clamping, a loose clamp may cause arcing that can damage a part. On circular work it may be necessary to weld a tab so that the work lead can be clamped to the tab. Where the work needs to be moved during welding, a swivel-type clamp may be needed.

Here are some possible effects of incorrect selection and poor connections:

- If the welding lead / return cable has insufficient cross-sectional area then it is liable to overheat with the possible risk of fire and electric shock.
- Excessive voltage drops occur in overlong lengths of cable and in loose or poorly fitted connections. This leads to a waste of power and reduced output for welding.
- Breakdown of insulation and loose connections result in increased shock hazard, cable damage and the development of excess heat.

Low-voltage Safety Device

When working in conditions that increase the risk of shock, a low-voltage safety device is recommended. This reduces the open-circuit voltage to less than thirty volts during non-welding periods, which safeguards the operator. When the arc is struck, full open-circuit voltage is available and this reduces to the operating range when the arc has been established.

Comparison of AC/DC Welding Equipment

With the many different welding sets available, the choice comes down to which will perform best under the operational conditions. In order to make this judgement, it helps to have a knowledge of the advantages and disadvantages of AC and DC.

The advantages of AC are:

- The capital (purchase) cost is comparatively low.
- There is higher operational efficiency because power is only used during welding.
- It is not susceptible to arc blow, which is commonly associated with DC supply.
- Multi-operator sets can be used from a single transformer. This gives better use of space and reduces cost.
- A static transformer (no moving parts) requires little maintenance.
- Transformers are relatively quiet in operation.
- The mains supply is readily available in the workshop.

AC also has some disadvantages:

- Due to the requirement for a high Open Circuit Voltage (OCV) in order to strike the arc, only certain electrodes can be used with AC.
- Although AC generators are available, the majority of the sets require mains supply.
- A potentially greater shock hazard exists due to the higher OCV voltages (80–100 volts) with a peak voltage 1.41 times this voltage available on the positive half-cycle.
- It can cause muscular contraction and make it difficult for the welder to release their grip on the source of electricity.
- There is no polarity therefore little control over heat input.
- It is less efficient than DC for the welding of thin plate.

Here are the advantages of DC:

- Engine-driven generators give mobility and can be used for site work.
- It has better all-round application and can be used for ferrous and non-ferrous metals.
- It has a lower OCV range (60–80 volts) with no peak voltage, giving a reduced shock hazard. It is therefore recommended for site applications.
- The choice of polarity means that heat can be directed where it is required with the greatest heat input at the

positive pole. This can be directed into the work piece by connecting the return lead to the positive terminal on the welding set or to the electrode, thereby controlling heat input on thinner metals.

- It can provide additional auxiliary power for lighting, drilling, etc.
- It produces smoother arc conditions and hence control of the weld profile.

These are the disadvantages of DC:

- The capital cost is higher.
- It incurs greater maintenance costs since there are more moving parts.
- It tends to be noisier in operation.
- It is prone to arc blow in corners and when using large electrodes with amperages in excess of 200 amperes.
- It uses power even when no welding is taking place.
- There is the added hazard of storage for petrol and diesel.

Setup Procedure

Setup Using Alternating Current (AC)

When using an AC supply, the electrical flow reverses direction around 100 times per second; this is a speed of 50Hz per second. This means the electrode has no specific polarity and the heat that is produced in the electrode and the heat produced in the work piece are equal.

Activity

In the space below, sketch the MMA welding equipment in your shop and label each part of the equipment and identify specific areas for inspection.

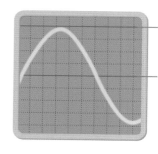

Peak Voltage
(1.41 x Mean Voltage)

Mean Voltage

Alternating Current (AC)

When setting up MMA welding equipment using an AC power supply, carry out the following steps:

AC setup procedure

1   Ensure you have a safe work environment and that the power supply is off.

2   Connect one end of the welding return lead to the power source.

3   Connect the other end of the welding return lead to the work piece using the welding return clamp.

4   Next, connect the welding lead to the power source.

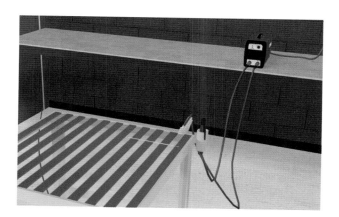

5   Ensure that the work piece is independently earthed.

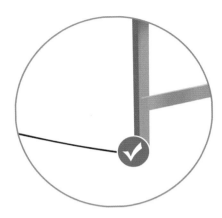

6   Insert an electrode into the electrode holder then hang the holder up in a safe position. If the electrode is touching the work piece or table when the power is switched on it could result in an arc being created.

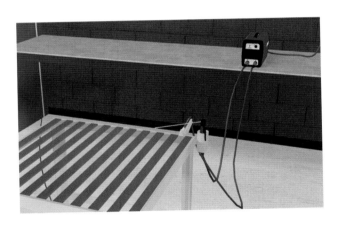

7   Turn the power on.

8   Set the current to an appropriate setting for the job.

Setup Using Direct Current (DC)

When using a DC supply, the electrical flow is in one direction meaning the electrode is either positive or negative.

Direct Current (DC)

In most cases you would work with electrode negative which means approximately two thirds of the heat produced will be located in the work piece and one third in the electrode.

When using electrode positive, approximately two thirds of the heat produced will be located in the electrode and one third in the work piece. You would use an electrode positive to suit particular requirements.

The type of flux coating on an electrode can have an effect on the heat input, so always check with manufacturer's instructions before use.

When setting up MMA equipment using a DC supply, electrode negative, carry out the following steps:

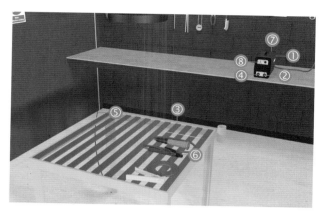

DC setup procedure

3   Connect the other end of the welding return lead to the work piece using the welding return clamp.

1   Ensure you have a safe work environment and that the power supply is off.

4   Connect the welding lead to the negative terminal of the power source.

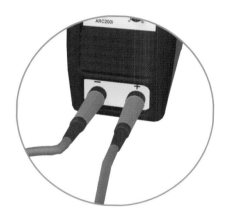

2   Connect one end of the welding return lead to the positive terminal of the power source.

5   Ensure that the work piece is independently earthed.

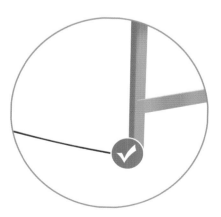

6   Insert an electrode into the electrode holder then hang the holder up in a safe position. If the electrode is touching the work piece or table when the power is switched on it could result in an arc being created.

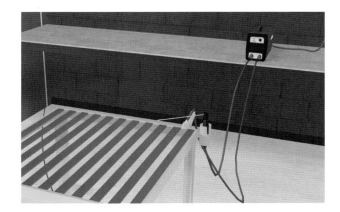

7   Turn the power on.

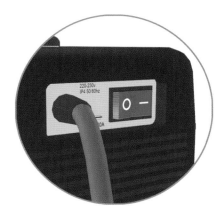

8   Set the current to an appropriate setting for the job.

Duty Cycle

The duty cycle is the percentage of time that a welding machine can be used continuously. A 60% duty cycle means that out of every ten minutes the machine can be used on maximum amperage for six minutes with the remaining four minutes being used for cooling. Welding machines produce internal heat at the same time that they produce the welding current and, except for automatic welding machines, they are rarely used every minute. The welder must take time to change electrodes, change position or change component parts. The duty cycle percentage increases as the amperage is lowered. Most welding machines weld at a 60% duty cycle or less, therefore most manufacturers list the amperage rating for a 60% duty cycle on the nameplate that is attached to the machine. The duty cycle should not be exceeded because a build-up of internal temperature can cause the transformer insulation to break down with the added risk of fire, electric shock and the destruction of the welder due to burnt out windings.

Equipment Checks

Before commencing MMA welding, you should carry out a visual inspection of all the equipment being used, for example making sure that the insulation is intact and that there are no frayed cables or poor connections especially on the return clamp.

Check that the cables are of the correct diameter for the amperage being used. Cables should be protected from damage by placing ramps on either side of the cable or clipping the cables overhead when using in busy thoroughfares.

Check that the appropriate electrode is being used and that it is in good condition. Check for lack of coating and any indication of dampness.

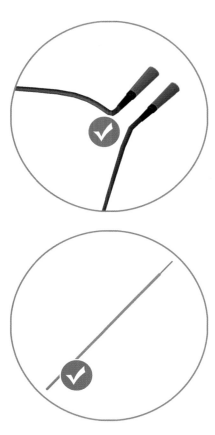

Check return clamp, cables and electrodes

Closing Down Procedure

When you have finished MMA welding, the equipment should be closed down properly. Turn off the power and disconnect the cables. Check the equipment for any damage including insulation, fraying and condition of the electrode holder and return clamp. Tidy up the cables and make sure the equipment is left in a safe position and that the electrode holder is secure to prevent damage.

Consumables

Electrodes used in MMA welding

MMA welding uses an electrode. Electrodes can be made from a number of different materials and come in a range of diameter sizes.

The electrode is made up of a metal wire core and is coated with a flux material. When melted, the metal wire provides the filler material for the weld and the flux coating carries out a number of functions. These include creating a gas shield which protects the molten metal from atmospheric contamination; creating a solidified slag over the top of the weld bead for protection and also to help ensure the arc is stable.

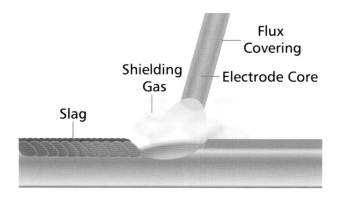

Parts of an electrode

The type of electrode needed depends on its compatibility with the materials to be welded and any need for additional mechanical properties or the addition of any de-oxidising elements to the weld pool.

The diameter of the electrode depends on the material thickness and joint configuration. Deposition width should be no more than three times the core wire diameter for carbon steel, two times the core wire diameter for stainless steel and stringer bead width for cast iron. If using low-hydrogen electrodes then they must be kept in either vacuum packs or in a heated quiver (box with internal heating coil) at 70°C to prevent any moisture being transferred to the weld deposit which could cause hydrogen cracking.

Damaged electrode

Excessive coating dampness from a welder's viewpoint is indicated by one or more of the following signs:

● During welding the arc is unusually 'fiery' with distinctive coarse crackling or explosive sounds; there may also be white vapour emitted.

- Excessive weld spatter is produced.
- When welding is interrupted before the entire electrode is consumed, longitudinal cracking of the coating occurs, starting at the tip and with subsequent spalling of the flux.
- Formation of porosity and piping (wormholes) occurs in the deposited weld metal.
- The flux coating may have a slight discolouration with a white fur.

You need to learn to recognise damp or wet electrodes. Select an electrode from a batch and, holding it horizontally by both ends between thumb and forefinger on each hand, bow it. If the coating is damp or wet, flux will crack longitudinally and transversely and flake off. If it is dry or contains a small amount of moisture, it will crack but tend to be more brittle and spring off the core of the wire. If doubts exist whether or not the electrodes are damp or wet they should be dried accordingly.

Electrodes should be stored in clean, dry and well-ventilated conditions and packages should be clearly labelled. You should not mix different types of electrodes.

Always handle electrodes with care and make sure they are free from contamination such as moisture, oil, grease and rust before use.

Clearly label electrode packages and store in the correct conditions

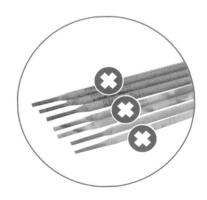

Contaminated electrodes

Functions of the Flux Coating

The flux coating has a considerable effect on the quality, deposition rate and shape of the resulting weld profile:

- It provides a gas shield to prevent atmospheric gases such as hydrogen, oxygen and nitrogen affecting the weld deposit.
- It cleans the surface of the metal and provides a silicate coating (slag) which retards the cooling rate and helps to improve the mechanical properties of the weld deposit.
- It acts as a mould when welding in position by fast freezing to hold the weld metal in position.
- It can add extra alloying elements to the weld deposit to increase certain mechanical properties for service environments.
- It can increase the deposition rate as is the case with iron powder electrodes.
- It can help to shape the final weld profile to be either convex or concave.

E-Learning

Use the e-learning programme to download some information about MMA consumables.

Welding Parameters

Some of the settings that an operator can change in MMA welding are the open-circuit voltage available on the machine, the current range and the selection of the most appropriate electrode. The settings for these parameters can change depending on the conditions of the job, which could include the weld position, joint configuration, the thermal conductivity, thickness and type of material and any need for additional alloying elements.

You need to be aware of the effects of these parameters.

Current too Low

If the current is too low the resulting weld has poor penetration, due to the lack of heating to create complete fusion. The weld filler metal tends to heap up on the surface of the plate without fusing to it and the arc has an unsteady spluttering sound.

Current too High

When the current value is too high the electrode becomes red hot and a large amount of spatter takes place. This can result in blowholes being formed in the plate, excessive penetration resulting in weld metal beads on the underside of the plate, undercut along the edge of the weld and excessive oxidation and slag which is hard to remove. The arc has a fierce crackling sound.

Correct Current

With the correct current the arc has a steady crackling sound. The weld formed has good penetration and is easily controlled.

Arc Voltage too High

The welding voltage primarily affects the weld cross-section and the general appearance of the weld. Increasing the welding voltage produces a wider and flatter weld bead and increases the susceptibility to arc blow. When the arc length is too long, which makes the welding voltage too high, the weld bead can look irregular with poor penetration and spatter. Also the weld metal may not be properly shielded by the gas shield from the decomposition of the electrode coating and much of the heat may be lost to the atmosphere.

Arc Voltage too Low

If the arc voltage is reduced as a result of reducing the arc length, it becomes difficult to maintain the arc, due to the increase in welding current that takes place. It can result in the electrode sticking to the base metal.

Speed of Travel too Fast

A fast rate of travel results in a thin deposit of the filler metal and can result in insufficient fusion of the filler metal with the base metal. The surface has elongated ripples and a porous crater.

Speed of Travel too Slow

Too slow a rate of travel gives a wide, thick deposit of the filler metal and it can allow the slag to flood the weld pool making it difficult to deposit the filler metal. The surface of the weld appears as coarse ripples and has a flat crater.

The Welding Process

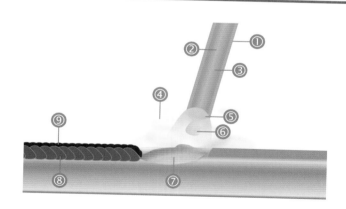

Welding process diagram: 1. Flux covering; 2. Consumable electrode; 3. Electrode core; 4. Shielding gas; 5. Electric arc; 6. Molten droplets; 7. Weld pool; 8. Solidified weld; 9. Slag

MMA welding uses an electric current to generate an electric arc between the tip of an electrode and the work piece. An electric arc happens when electricity jumps across a gap between two conductors. This gap is known as the arc length. The arc can create a heat in excess of 4000°C.

The arc causes instant heating of the parent material and a molten weld pool is formed, into which additional material is added in the form of the filler wire contained within the electrode to complete the weld. The metal is transferred from the tip of the electrode across the arc into the weld pool in the form of droplets by electromagnetic forces.

As the process moves along the joint, the deposited material cools and solidifies leaving a weld bead. The weld zone is protected from atmospheric contamination by a gas shield created by the flux coating. The flux coating also provides a slag which protects the weld bead. When the MMA electrode is being operated correctly it makes a quiet crackling sound.

Preparing to Weld

Before commencing welding, there are a number of checks you need to make to ensure safe working practices.

Preparation of Work Area

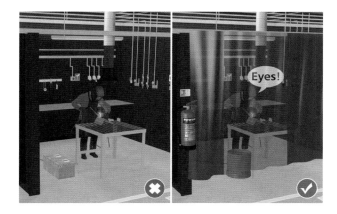

Correct and incorrect ways of preparing the work area

Health and Safety

Before carrying out any welding or fabrication operation you should carry out a risk assessment. This should include checking for hazards, checking safety procedures and equipment, making people in the vicinity aware of what work is being carried out, restricting access to the work area and giving a verbal warning when you are about to strike up an arc.

Material Preparation

Remember to familiarise yourself with the manufacturer's safety data sheets (MSDS) before using any equipment, materials, solvents or chemicals.

It is good practice to de-burr and degrease the material to prevent contamination of the weld and remove any flammable substances.

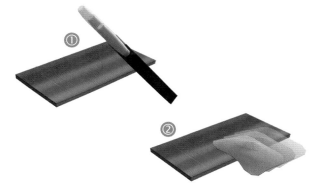

Material preparation: 1. De-burring; 2. De-greasing

When welding plate in excess of 3mm some form of edge preparation may be required in order to ensure fusion into the root of the weld. This can be in the form of a V, U or J preparation and with or without a backing strip.

Prior to any weld deposition, it is recommended that the joint is tacked to aid alignment and distortion control.

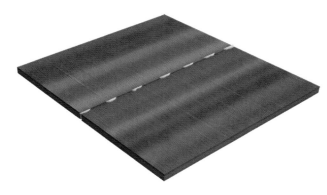

Tacking the joint

Position of Welder

Find a comfortable and balanced position that you can maintain while you are welding. You need to be able to see the weld develop and be able to weld along the joint in one continuous movement. Remember that fatigue and discomfort can cause poor-quality welds.

Striking the Arc

Before welding can begin, you need to 'strike the arc'. This means briefly touching the electrode to the work piece before drawing it away to the correct distance or arc length to start welding.

This can be difficult to achieve at first as the electrode may stick to the work piece if it is held in one position too long. If this occurs then you must follow the appropriate procedure to free the electrode from the work piece.

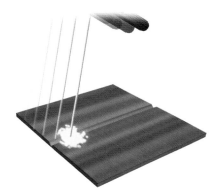

Motion for striking the arc

The position of the strike is also important as a strike outside the weld joint may produce a weld defect.

Once the arc has been struck and the arc length established, it must be maintained as the electrode is consumed. The standard arc length is 1.5 x core wire diameter and should be maintained to ensure even weld deposition. Too much current leads to undercutting and spatter, whereas too small a current will result in insufficient penetration, unstable arc conditions and too small a weld deposit.

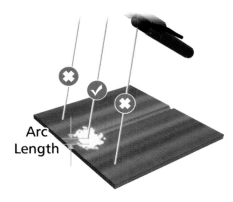

Arc length and strike position

Techniques

Each welding process has specific techniques which require understanding of the tilt angle and slope angle.

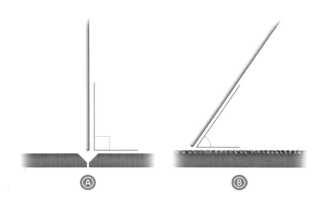

Techniques: A. Tilt angle; B. Slope angle

The tilt angle is the angle the electrode is held at between the two pieces of material to be welded.

The slope angle is the angle the electrode is held at between the joint to be welded and a 90° angle from the joint.

MMA welding has two main techniques, as well as a specific technique for starting and stopping a weld.

Drag Technique

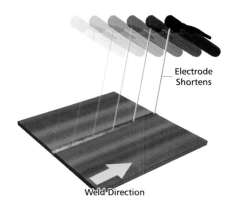

Drag technique

The drag technique is when the electrode is held at a slope angle between 70° and 80° to the work piece and is pointed in the opposite direction to the direction of travel. It should be moved at a consistent speed whilst maintaining a constant arc length.

Be aware that the length of the electrode gets smaller the longer you weld.

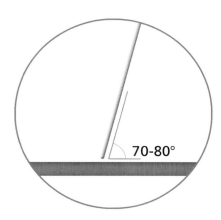

Drag technique slope

E-Learning

Use the e-learning programme to see an animated version of the drag technique.

Push Technique

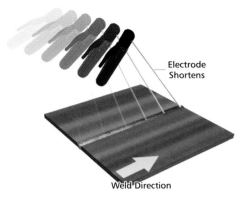

Push technique

The push technique is generally used in positional welding to try to control the weld pool. The electrode is pointed in the direction of travel to ensure deposition on the front edge and solidification of the molten weld pool on the back edge of the weld. The slope angle of the electrode will vary in relation to the position of the joint.

Again, the length of the electrode gets smaller the longer you weld.

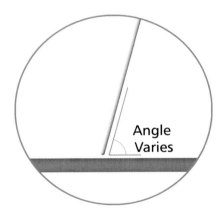

Push technique slope

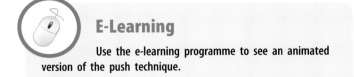

E-Learning

Use the e-learning programme to see an animated version of the push technique.

Start Stop Technique

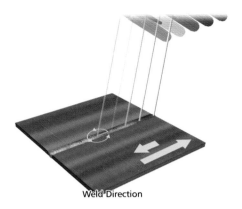

Start stop technique

When you want to recommence a weld, you need to strike the arc within the weld zone in front of the last deposition. Then move back towards the previous weld deposit and loop around the top edge of the deposit to ensure fusion before continuing to move forward along the joint.

E-Learning

Use the e-learning programme to see an animated version of starting and stopping a weld.

Weaving Techniques

Weaving refers to the side-to-side movements of the electrode required to manipulate the molten metal across the joint width or, in the case of positional welding, to control heat input and weld profile. The maximum recommended width for a given electrode size is; three times the core wire diameter for carbon and carbon-manganese steels, two times the core wire diameter for stainless and heat-resisting steels and equal to the core diameter for cast iron (stringer bead technique). Slight pauses at the sides of the weave will also help ensure fusion and prevent undercut or underfill. However if the pause is excessive the metal may sag and overlap (cold lapping) the edges of the joint. Try to keep weaving to a minimum.

One tip when welding is to weave so that the electrode overlaps the parent metal by 50%–splitting the electrode. In many cases, especially with structural steels, the recommended practice is to use the stringer bead technique, which entails dragging the electrode down the weld joint with no weaving to prevent heat build-up. Heat build-up can affect the resultant structure and induce defects which will result in weld failure.

The weave patterns shown above would also be applicable for Metal Inert Gas (MIG) welding as the process has similar techniques.

Potential Welding Failures

Potential failures in MMA welding can occur for a number of reasons. For example, if the slope angle of the electrode is too high, the depth of penetration is increased; if the slope angle of the electrode is too low, a turbulent weld pool can be created. Both of these can result in defects in the weld.

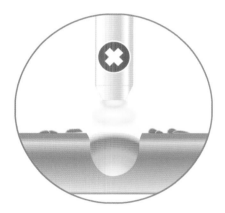

Electrode angle too high

Electrode angle too low

Cleaning the Weld

After the weld is complete, MMA welds can be cleaned by chipping off the slag and wire brushing.

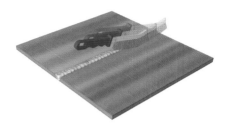

Clean welds using a wire brush

Reinstate the Work Area

When you have finished welding, ensure all equipment is closed down correctly and turned off. Make sure the equipment is stored away safely and doesn't cause any hazards.

 Sustainability

Cool all scrap metal and place it in the appropriate container.

Return any tools that have been used to their appropriate storage area and tidy up the work area.

Joints

There are four main types of joint in welding. Any weld on any joint should be equal to the thickness of the plate and have a smooth transition from the weld to the plate surface.

The slope and tilt angles will change with the position in which the weld is carried out. In this instance the tilt and slope angles mentioned are for the flat and horizontal vertical position only.

Outside Corner Joint

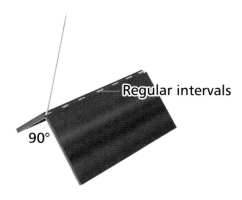

Outside corner joint

An outside corner joint is formed by two work pieces positioned with their edges next to each other at an angle of 90°. The weld is placed on the outside of this corner. The pieces should be tacked at each end and at regular intervals along the joint.

The electrode should be tilted so it bisects the two work pieces and has a slope angle of 70–80°. Root penetration should not exceed 3mm and the weld profile should blend smoothly at both toes of the weld.

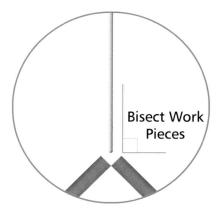

Tilt angle of electrode

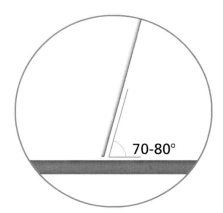

Slope angle of electrode

Lap Joint

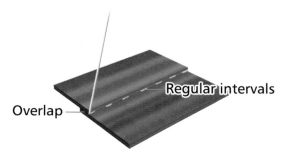

Lap joint

A lap joint is formed by two work pieces overlapping each other. The weld is placed where the two pieces meet. The pieces should be tacked at each end and at regular intervals along the joint.

The electrode should be tilted at 45° between the two work pieces and have a slope angle of 70–80°. The tilt will ensure that most of the heat goes into the bottom plate and both plates reach melting point at the same time. There should be a smooth transition between the plates making up the joint.

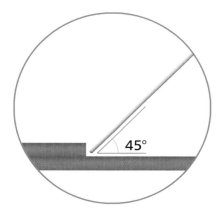

Tilt angle of electrode

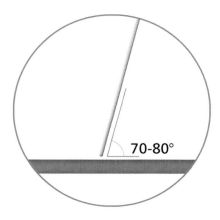

Slope angle of electrode

Activity

In the space below, sketch a lap joint and indicate the position of the electrode on the capping run.

Tee Joint

The electrode should be tilted at 45° and have a slope angle of 70–80°. The electrode should be manipulated to ensure sufficient dwell on the vertical plate to prevent undercutting.

Tee joint

A Tee joint is formed when one work piece is positioned at 90° to another work piece. The weld is placed where the two pieces meet. The pieces should be tacked at each end and at regular intervals along the joint.

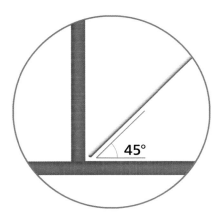

Tilt angle of electrode

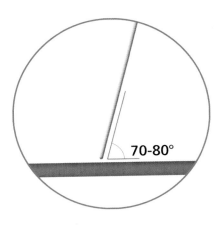

Slope angle of electrode

Butt Joint

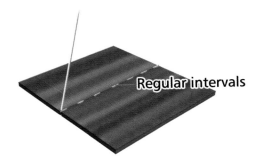

Butt joint

A butt joint is formed when the two work pieces are positioned side by side with a gap between them to ensure penetration. The weld is then placed between the two pieces.

The space between the plates is called the gap, or root gap, and this can vary from 0–3mm. If the gap is too large or too small it can result in defects in the welded joint.

When welding thick plate, an edge preparation is put on the plates to ensure penetration and a sound weld

deposit. The pieces should be tacked at each end and at regular intervals along the joint.

When working with certain electrodes the root gap may be reduced. The electrode should be tilted so it is at 90° to the surface of the work pieces and have a slope angle of 70–80°. The finished weld profile should have a slightly raised weld deposit and root penetration that does not exceed 3mm. There should be a smooth transition between the plates.

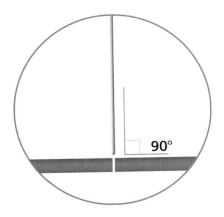

Tilt angle of electrode

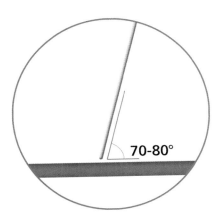

Slope angle of electrode

Activity

Use your preferred method (paper and pencil, calculator, online converter, mobile phone app) to calculate the number of electrodes required to make a T-fillet weld 150mm long with a 10mm leg length which will require a root run and two capping runs. The total length of weld metal from a 2.5mm electrode is 75mm and from a 3.25mm electrode 100mm.

_____

_____

_____

_____

Quality Control

Weld Defects

In all welding techniques there are a number of weld defects and discontinuities that can be identified once a weld is complete. The following section describes some problems that can arise with MMA welding and how they can be remedied.

Porosity

Porosity is created when gas becomes trapped in the weld deposit as the metal cools.

Causes: Damp electrodes or surface contamination

Remedies: Correct storage facilities for all electrodes with particular attention being paid to low-hydrogen electrodes to ensure weld integrity. Surface cleaning of all parent materials prior to welding

◯ Gas Pockets

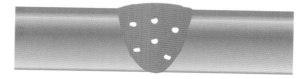

Porosity

Inclusions

Inclusions develop when foreign matter such as oil, grease or mill scale becomes trapped within the solidifying weld deposit as irregular pores.

Causes: When weld is not cleaned between runs and poor technique

Remedies: Ensure meticulous cleaning of the previous deposit to ensure the integrity of the weld deposit

〜 Non-metallic Materials

Inclusions

Poor Weld Profile / Dimension

These result when there is a failure to maintain design specifications.

Causes: When using incorrect current settings, poor manipulation of electrode or an incorrect speed of travel

Remedies: Selection of current settings to match material specification and thickness, correct manipulation of the electrode and monitor speed of travel to ensure weld integrity

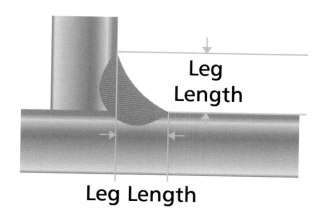

Poor weld profile/dimension

Lack of Side-wall Fusion

This is a lack of fusion between weld metal and parent metal at the side of the weld and on the interrun deposition.

Causes: Using too low a current setting or when the arc is placed outside the weld joint or insufficient time spent on side wall to ensure fusion

Remedies: Ensure correct manipulation of electrode with due regard to fusion on the side walls

Lack of side-wall fusion

Undercut

An undercut is created when metal is removed from a joint without being replaced by weld material. This is commonly found at the toe of a run or in previously deposited weld metal.

Causes: Excessive current, insufficient weld deposition, excessive speed of travel and poor manipulation of the electrode

Remedies: Careful control of current, matching the electrode diameter to the weld specification, control of travel speed and manipulation of electrode

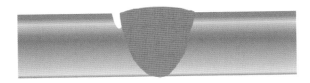

Undercut

Spatter

Spatter is created by a surface deposition adjacent to the weld which is not fully fused into the surface of the material.

Causes: Using too high a current setting, an excessive arc length or failure to manipulate the electrode correctly

Remedies: Correct use of amperage setting, correct arc length and correct manipulation of the electrode

Spatter

Excessive Root Penetration

This is produced by excessive weld metal protruding through the root of a fusion weld.

Causes: Using a poor technique, incorrect edge preparation or too high a current setting

Remedies: Close control of edge preparations, especially root face dimensions and root gaps, correct selection of current settings to parent material and electrode diameters

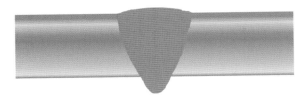

Excessive root penetration

Stray Arcing

This arises when an arc is struck outside of the weld zone and may produce a hardened zone which may bring about ultimate failure of the weld.

Causes: Striking the arc outside the weld zone

Remedies: Always ensure that all strikes are within the weld zone to establish the arc

Stray arcing

Excessive Weld Reinforcement

This is created when the weld metal deposited is excessive and leaves the weld protruding on the surface.

Causes: Inappropriate type of electrode, the speed of travel is too slow

Remedies: Ensure that the appropriate electrode for the material is used and that the operator's technique is correct

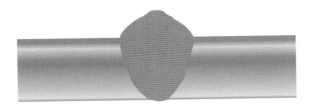

Excessive weld

Underfill

This is created when the weld metal is insufficient to produce the required deposit as stated in the specification.

Causes: Speed of travel is too fast, using the wrong diameter electrode, failure to pause on the side of the weld

Remedies: Ensure that the appropriate electrode for the material is used and that the operator's technique is correct

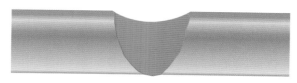

Underfill

Lack of Root Penetration

This is a failure of the weld metal to extend into the root of a joint.

Causes: Incorrect joint preparation and setup, with too small a gap, moving too quickly with not enough heat applied

Remedies: Ensure correct preparation and setup, with a large enough gap; use the correct settings and adjust speed

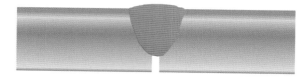

Lack of root penetration

Misalignment of Plates

This is created by failing to align the plates after tacking and prior to welding, giving a stepped appearance.

Causes: Failure to tack weld prior to welding

Remedies: Tacking at regular intervals and dressing the plates prior to welding

Misalignment of plates

CHECK YOUR KNOWLEDGE

1 Which of the following applications can the MMA welding process be used for? Circle the correct answer.

a. Pre-heating materials
b. Mechanical components
c. Hard soldering
d. Fabricating mild steel
e. Pipe welding
f. Soft soldering
g. Brazing

2 When using a DC electrode negative setup for MMA, approximately how much heat is produced in the electrode and how much in the work piece? Circle the correct answer.

a. 2/3 in the electrode, 1/3 in the work piece
b. 1/3 in the electrode, 2/3 in the work piece
c. 1/2 in the electrode, 1/2 in the work piece

3 Which of these are functions of an electrode flux coating when MMA welding? Circle the correct answer.

a. To provide a polished finish
b. To protect the welder from radiation
c. To protect the molten metal from the atmospheric contamination
d. To form a viscous slag to protect the weld as it cools

4 Can you identify these weld defects? Write a, b or c next to the appropriate diagram.

a. Spatter
b. Stray arcing
c. Misalignment of plates

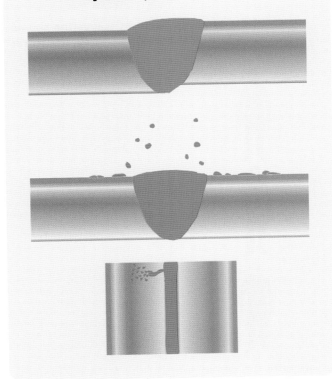

Summary

This concludes this chapter on manual metal arc welding or MMA welding. You should now be able to explain the principles of MMA welding, list the specific health and safety requirements, list the equipment and explain how it should be set up, explain how to carry out the MMA welding process and list the weld defects that can occur.

End test

1. Which of the following welders is wearing the appropriate PPE for MMA welding? Circle the correct answer.

☐ a.

☐ b.

☐ c.

2. Identify the components of the MMA equipment shown.

1.
2.
3.
4.
5.
6.
7.

3. What does AC stand for? Circle the correct answer.

☐ a. Assisted Current

☐ b. Alternating Current

☐ c. Alternative Current

☐ d. Artificial Current

4. What is the best-practice approach to setting up MMA equipment? Number the list below in the order in which you should carry out each procedure.

☐ Insert electrode into holder and hang up holder

☐ Turn power on

☐ Connect welding lead to the negative terminal of the power source

☐ Ensure work piece is independently earthed

☐ Set current to an appropriate setting for the job

☐ Connect welding return lead to the positive terminal of the power source

☐ Ensure power supply is off

☐ Connect welding return lead to work piece using the welding return clamp

☐ Check electrode is not touching work table

5. Identify the different parts of the MMA welding process shown.

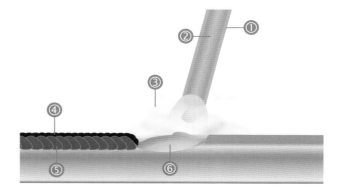

1.
2.
3.
4.
5.
6.

6. How do you 'strike the arc' when MMA welding? Circle the correct answer.

☐ a. Attach the earth connection to the work piece

☐ b. Turn the power on and adjust settings

☐ c. Touch the electrode to the work piece

7. In MMA welding, what is the space between the tip of the electrode and the work piece known as?

☐ a. Arc gap

☐ b. Arc length

☐ c. Weld length

☐ d. Electrode gap

8. Which of these statements describes the appropriate angle when MMA welding using the drag technique? Circle the correct answer.

☐ a. Electrode held at a slope angle of 10–20° to the work piece

☐ b. Electrode held at a slope angle of 30–40° to the work piece

☐ c. Electrode held at a slope angle of 50–60° to the work piece

☐ d. Electrode held at a slope angle of 70–80° to the work piece

9. Match these four types of joint to their descriptions. Write a, b, c or d next to these joints.

Butt joint

Lap joint

Outside corner joint

Tee joint

☐ a. Joint formed by two work pieces overlaid on each other

☐ b. Joint formed when the two work pieces are positioned side by side

☐ c. Joint formed when one work piece is positioned at 90° to another work piece.

☐ d. Joint formed by two work pieces positioned with their edges next to each other at an angle of 90°

10. Which of these defects are caused by using too high a current setting? Circle the correct answer.

☐ a. Excessive penetration

☐ b. Slag inclusions

☐ c. Spatter

☐ d. Undercut

6

Metal Inert Gas (MIG) Welding

LEARNING OBJECTIVES

By the end of this chapter you will be able to:

- Explain the principles of MIG welding.

- List the specific health and safety requirements.

- List the equipment and explain how it should be set up.

- Explain how to carry out the MIG welding process.

- List the weld defects that can occur.

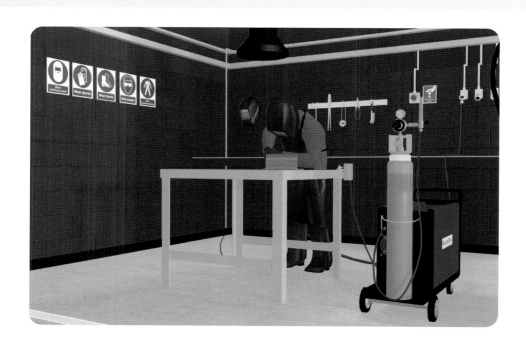

Introduction

Metal inert gas welding and metal active gas welding are also known as MIG and MAG welding, although it is most commonly referred to as MIG welding.

The many aspects of MIG Welding

MIG welding is a process that uses electricity to form an electric arc heat source between the tip of a consumable filler wire and the work piece. The heat from the arc energy melts the base material as well as the filler wire, which is consumed to form the filler material for the weld.

MIG welding is a semi-automatic process. This means that when the welding machine senses a voltage drop it automatically increases or decreases the wire feed to match the burn-off rate. This is known a self-adjusting arc.

The shielding gas protects the molten weld pool and affects the electric arc and weld deposit.

The total radiant energy produced by the MIG and TIG processes can be higher than that produced by manual metal arc welding because of the significantly lower welding fume and the more exposed arc. Generally the highest ultraviolet radiant energy intensities are produced when using an argon shielding gas on aluminium.

Caution should be observed at all times and full personal protective equipment or PPE is recommended.

Advantages and Disadvantages

MIG welding has a number of advantages and disadvantages.

Advantages

- Relatively easy to learn
- Produces a consistently high weld rate
- Current can be adjusted to weld thick and thin materials
- Produces less distortion due to narrower Heat Affected Zone
- Easier to control the weld pool
- Can be used in a range of weld positions
- Easier to start in an accurate position
- Efficient deposition of weld material
- Low hydrogen process produces fewer defects
- Lower voltage range

Advantages of MIG Welding

Activity

Use the internet to make a list of up to 6 jobs that are currently being advertised and may require MIG welding skills.

_____

_____

_____

_____

_____

_____

Disadvantages

- Welds can appear more sound than they actually are
- Cold lapping can occur
- Can be affected by draughts
- Power supply required
- Risk of asphyxiation

Disadvantages of MIG Welding

Applications

MIG welding is used for a wide range of applications, including:

- rebuilding equipment;
- automotive repair;
- overlay of wear resistant coatings;
- robotics;
- wind farms;
- modern manufacturing processes;
- structural steel work.

Activity

List four applications of MIG welding and state what makes them so suitable for these applications.

_____

_____

_____

_____

Health and Safety for MIG Welding

Health and Safety

Before entering a workshop environment always make sure that you are wearing the appropriate PPE for the job. Standard PPE includes fully protective, flame retardant overalls, safety boots, ear defenders and clear, safety goggles. It may also be necessary to wear an additional respirator in certain circumstances.

Personal Protective Equipment (PPE): A. Workshop PPE; B. Additional PPE when MIG welding; 1. Flame retardant overalls; 2. Safety boots; 3. Ear defenders; 4. Clear safety goggles; 5. Leather gauntlet style gloves; 6. Welding mask (Welding cap); 7. Spats; 8. Flame retardant jacket; 9. Welding apron

For MIG welding you should also be wearing leather gauntlet style gloves, a welding cap, a welding mask, spats over your safety boots, a flame retardant jacket done up to the neck and a welding apron. Always check to make sure the welding mask is set to the correct filter level.

E-Learning

Use the e-learning programme to download a filter lens guide for an operation table that provides more information.

You should already be familiar with the health and safety requirements that apply to all forms of welding. There are some specific health and safety issues associated with MIG welding.

Working in Confined spaces

Warning
Confined spaces

Working in confined space safety sign

You should not work in a confined space until the area has been checked to confirm that oxygen levels are suitable and no poisonous gases are present.

If the oxygen in the confined space falls below 16%, then it can lead to dizziness and a shortness of breath. This can be fatal if signs are not noticed in time for the operator to get to a source of fresh air, so they should be observed at all times when in confined spaces.

The arc welding processes produce a number of potentially harmful fumes such as Ozone (O_3), Carbon Monoxide (CO) and Carbon Dioxide (CO_2).

Due to the asphyxiant nature of the shielding gases and the fact that argon cannot be detected by sense of smell, it is essential that good ventilation and extraction are used around MIG and TIG welding processes. Argon is heavier than air gas and will settle at low levels, building up until it replaces the welder's breathing zone with potentially fatal results. Do not be caught out; ensure that the correct procedures are in place to deal with the threat. It is recommended that good extraction, close to the source of fumes be used at all times. If this is not possible due to site access then the welding operator should be equipped with a self-contained air supply welding shield.

Personal Safety

Wear personal protective equipment

Wear PPE safety sign

When welding you should always make sure you are wearing the correct PPE and are working in accordance with safe working practices. Harmful fumes and gases are produced in all welding processes so appropriate fume extraction should always be in place.

The heat from the welding process, sparks and hot metal can cause severe burns. The electric arc from the process also gives off a form of radiation which can cause burns similar to sunburn on the skin. The light from the arc can also cause 'arc eye', a painful condition that can cause watering of the eyes, headaches and a temporary loss of vision.

Materials Safety Data Sheet

Materials Safety Data Sheet (MSDS)

Material Safety Data Sheets should always be consulted before any welding is undertaken. These contain important information on items such as gases, filler wires, electrodes and degreasing solvents. They are available from the manufacturers of the products. You need to understand the properties of all the items you use, the hazards associated with them and what to do in an emergency.

Gas Cylinders

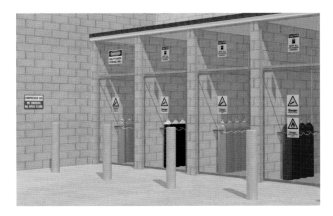

Appropriate storage of gas cylinders

Before welding, always make sure you are using the correct gas or gases and that the cylinders containing the gas are not damaged. If the cylinders are damaged, do not use them and report any damage to the suppliers.

Cylinders should be stored upright in a cool, well-ventilated area, well away from any sources of ignition. The correct fire extinguishers should be provided. Signage should show which cylinders are being stored there and access to the area should be restricted to appropriately trained operators.

Appropriate fire extinguishers located nearby

Cylinders should always be transported upright and secured with chains at all times. If transporting cylinders in a vehicle then it should be an open backed vehicle. If this is not possible then open the windows to ensure there is sufficient ventilation.

Electrical Safety

Always check that electrical equipment is safe to use

Before switching on the equipment and carrying out any welding, check that the equipment is not damaged, is set up correctly and is earthed appropriately. Remember that electric arc processes present a danger to people with pacemakers.

Remember that damaged cable insulation, incorrectly sized fuses, faulty connections and lack of a suitable earth can all cause electric shock, fire and burn hazards. Appliance testing and repairs should only be carried out by competent personnel.

Be aware that it can be hazardous to weld in conditions where water or moisture is present. You should erect a shelter for protection and ensure the work piece is properly insulated.

Where water-cooled guns are used, additional checks should be made to ensure that there is no damage to the torch or lines, this would be indicated by a stain or a pool of water prior to operation. If there is damage, do not use and report it to your supervisor.

Fumes, Gases and Ventilation

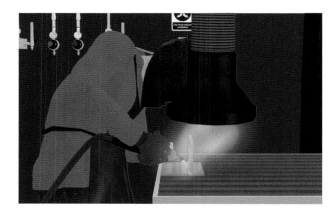

Fume extraction should be approximately 250mm from the weld zone

In addition to general ventilation of the welding area, fume extraction should also be provided. Fumes can be produced by fluxes, surface coatings, base materials, solvents used to degrease the material and shielding gases, all of which can cause breathing difficulties and in severe cases asphyxiation.

These fumes need to be drawn off by a localised extraction ventilation system. The extraction system should be placed close to the weld and in a position which ensures that fumes are not drawn past the face of the welder. It should also be set to an appropriate extraction rate so it removes the fumes but not the gas shield, where applicable.

The arc welding processes produce a number of potentially harmful fumes such as Ozone, Carbon Monoxide, Carbon Dioxide and Phosgene.

Ozone : the ultraviolet light emitted by the MIG arc acts on the oxygen in the surrounding atmosphere to produce ozone. The amount of ozone produced will depend upon the intensity and wave length of the ultraviolet energy, the humidity, the amount of screening afforded by any welding fumes and other factors. The ozone concentration will be increased with a rise in the welding current, where argon is the shielding gas and when welding highly reflective metals such as stainless steel and aluminium.

Carbon Monoxide: carbon dioxide shielding used with the MIG process will be separated by the heat of the arc to form carbon monoxide. Only a small amount of carbon monoxide is created by the welding process, although relatively high concentrations are formed temporarily in the plume of fumes. The concentrations of carbon monoxide become insignificant at a distance of 76-100mm away from the welding plume, so care needs to be exercised in confined spaces.

Phosgene – phosgene gas could also be present as a result of thermal or ultraviolet decomposition of chlorinated hydrocarbon cleaning agents located in the vicinity of welding operations. Degreasing operations should be located so that vapours from these operations cannot be reached by radiation from the welding arc.

Working at Height

Welders are often required to work at height. Competently erected scaffolding with earth bonding, along with a static safety harness should be used. Screening of the welding area should be erected to protect fellow workers from the effects of radiation and the area should be cordoned off with signage clearly displayed.

Activity

What health and safety precautions should you take when MIG welding, and what additional hazards does working with this process hold?

_____

_____

_____

_____

_____

_____

_____

_____

_____

_____

_____

_____

_____

List 3 ways to avoid potentially hazardous fumes when MIG welding.

1

2

3

Equipment and Set Up

Equipment

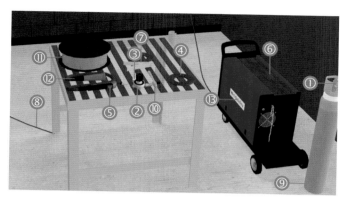

MIG welding equipment set up: 1. Cylinder valve; 2. Pressure regulator; 3. Pressure gauge; 4. Flexible hose; 5. Welding gun; 6. Power source; 7. Welding return lead and clamp; 8. Earth connection; 9. Shielding gas cylinder; 10. Flow meter; 11. Wire feed; 12. Welding cable assembly; 13. Cooling system

MIG welding equipment consists of a power source which feeds gas from a cylinder, filler wire from a wire feed unit and a direct current through a welding cable assembly to the welding gun.

An electric arc is struck between the filler wire and the work piece which generates heat and creates the weld pool.

The current passes through the work piece and returns to the power source via the welding clamp and welding return lead, completing the circuit.

All pressure regulating equipment including regulators, and hoses are governed by a designated working life from the manufacturers. These should be regularly inspected and changed if any damage is noted.

Always check your equipment before use to make sure it is in good working order.

Cylinder Valve

The cylinder valve allows the flow of gas from the cylinder into the regulator to be controlled so the regulator is not damaged. The cylinder valve should always be closed when not in use. If the gas cylinder valve is too tight or shows signs of damage, return the cylinder to the supplier.

1. Cylinder valve

Pressure Regulator

The regulator reduces the pressure from the cylinder to a constant safe working pressure which can be maintained during different flow rates and volumes. The pressure in supplied gas cylinders has been increased over the years so it is essential that you use a regulator capable of withstanding the pressure of the cylinder you are using.

2. Pressure regulator

Pressure Gauge

In MIG welding, the regulator has two pressure gauges. The first shows the pressure from the cylinder, the second shows the pressure from the regulator to the gun. Pressure readings may be shown in bars and pounds per square inch.

3. Pressure gauge

Flexible Hose

The hose from the cylinders consist of two layers of rubber with a reinforced canvas layer, preventing them from ballooning under pressure. The canvas layer also acts as a safety indicator; if you can see the canvas layer then the hoses must be replaced and NOT repaired. The hoses should be long enough to reach your power source, but not so long as to cause a trip hazard.

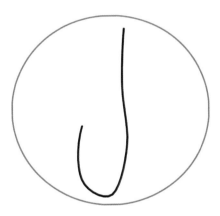

4. Flexible hose

Welding Gun

A MIG welding gun consists of the gun body, gun trigger, gas diffuser, contact tip holder, contact tip and outer sleeve.

When the trigger is pressed, it activates the electric current, the shielding gas and the wire feed. The electric arc is struck when the trigger is first pressed so it makes it very easy to begin welding in the correct position.

The contact tip provides an electrical path to the filler wire as it passes through the contact tip to the work piece. The contact tip is made of a copper alloy and has an orifice designed to fit the filler wire being used.

The outer sleeve should be sprayed with a spatter release compound to ensure good gas shielding conditions. This should be constantly monitored, especially when positional welding.

5. Welding gun

Power Source

There are many MIG power sources available, but the most widely used is the transformer-rectifier which uses a direct current or DC output. The power source will have a series of controls, usually located on the front of the machine, to power on and off and to control the voltage, gas flow, the wire feed speed and inductance while welding.

The MIG welding process may be operated on both constant voltage and constant current power sources. Any welding power source can be classified by its volt-ampere characteristic as either constant voltage (sometimes referred to as constant potential) or constant current (sometimes referred to as variable voltage) type. Constant voltage machines are the preferred power source for MIG welding applications. In the constant voltage arc system,

Activity

Use your preferred method (paper and pencil, calculator, online converter, mobile phone app) to convert 4 bar into pounds per square inch or Cubic feet per minute the voltage delivered to the arc is maintained at a relatively constant level which gives a 'flat' or nearly flat volt-ampere curve. In this system, the arc length is controlled by setting the voltage level on the power source and the welding current is controlled by setting the wire feed speed. A slight change in arc length or voltage will produce a large change in the welding current – 2V/100A.

Most machines have a fixed slope that is built in for a certain type of MIG machine. However, some machines are equipped with a slope control which is used to change the slope of the volt-ampere curve. This has the effect of limiting the amount of short-circuiting current that the power source can deliver. The short-circuit current determines the amount of 'pinch force' that is available on the electrode. The pinch force causes the molten electrode tip to neck down so that the droplet will separate from the solid electrode. The flatter the slope of the volt-ampere curve, the higher the short-circuit current and pinch force.

6. Power source

Welding Return Lead and Clamp

The welding return lead completes the circuit by connecting the power source to the work piece via the clamp. The clamp could be bolted, swivelled or an alligator type depending on the type of job being carried out.

7. Welding return lead and clamp

Earth Connection

The work piece should be connected to a suitable earth via a clamp and earth lead. The clamp could be bolted, swivelled or an alligator type depending on the type of job being carried out.

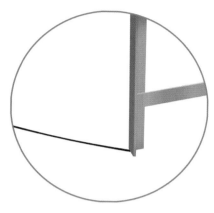

8. Earth connection

Shielding Gas Cylinder

If you are using a cylinder to provide the shielding gas for the welding process then the cylinder should contain the appropriate gas for the job, and have been transported and stored correctly.

In some cases, the gas may be supplied via a manifold from cylinders stored outside the welding area. Always check you are connecting to the correct gases.

9. Shielding gas cylinder

Flow Meter

The flow meter controls the flow of gas from the regulator to the welding gun. A ball in the flow meter indicates the gas flow rate and can be read with the top, centre or bottom of the ball, lining up with the measurements on the meter. This provides a more accurate reading.

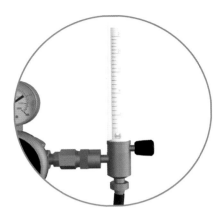

10. Flow meter

Wire Feed

The wire feed assembly consists of a wire on a reel that is fed between rollers. The power source drives the rollers to feed the filler wire to the welding gun. The feed can be set to a constant speed before welding begins or can be a voltage sensing circuit that increases or decreases the wire feed speed in-line with changes in the arc length.

It is essential that the wire feed rollers are the correct size for the wire being used. For example, if the rollers are too large, they will not grip the wire so the feed speed will be intermittent or stop completely. Yet, if the rollers are too small, they will crush the wire as it is fed causing it to distort.

11. Wire feed

Systems may have two or four feed rollers and, in the four roller system, the lower two rolls drive the wire and have a circumferential "V" groove in them, depending on the type and size of wire being fed. The remaining two rolls ensure that the wire does not slip out of the groove. Wire feed systems may be push, pull or push-pull, depending on the type and size of electrode wire and the distance of the welding gun and coil or spool of electrode wire. The

push type is commonly used for steels. Here, the wire is pulled from the wire feeder by the drive rolls and then pushed into the flexible conduit (liner) through the gun. The length of the liner can be up to 3.7m for steel wire and 1.8m for aluminium. A helical coiled wire liner is used for hard materials; steels, stainless steel, etc. and this may be Teflon coated. For soft metals such as aluminium, magnesium, etc., the liner is plastic or Teflon based to avoid contamination and all liners should be clearly marked for specific applications.

Spool on gun

Pull type wire feeders have the drive rolls attached to the welding gun, and this system works best for feeding wires up to 1.2mm diameter with a hand held welding gun. The push-pull system is particularly well suited for use with low strength wires such as aluminium and when driving long distances from the power source. It uses the standard feeder as the drive motor (push) and the gun as a slave motor (pull).

Welding Cable Assembly

The welding cable assembly connects the filler wire and liner, the shielding gas hose and the current conductor to the welding gun. The liner supports and protects the filler wire and ensures good electrical contact as it is fed to the welding gun.

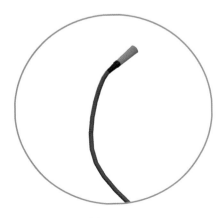

12. Welding cable assembly

Cooling System

MIG welding guns used for high amperage work are water-cooled and for low amperage work are air-cooled. Both systems have advantages and disadvantages. Air-cooled torches are safer, lighter and easier to manipulate but water-cooled guns can operate continuously without overheating. These factors make the air-cooled system more practical for small workshops whereas water-cooled systems are more efficient for production welding.

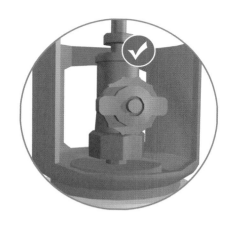

Set Up Procedure

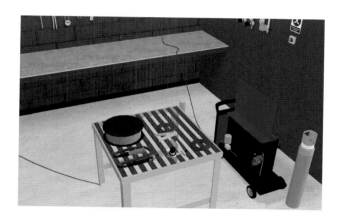

To set up the MIG welding equipment, first ensure that the cylinder is secured in an upright position.

1   Check the thread patterns on the cylinder for damage or debris then attach the regulator with flow meter and attach the gas feed hose to the power source.

2   Check the condition of the wire spool prior to fitting for any signs of contamination on the wire and damage to the carrier or spool. Then enter the wire through the correct groove and into the guide tubes until it exits the front of the machine. Apply the pressure roller and a slight tension.

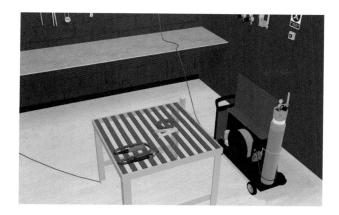

3   Attach the gun assembly with an appropriate liner for the wire being used. Then check the condition of the contact points to operate the gas flow and wire feed mechanisms before coupling the mechanism to the power source. Remove the outer sleeve contact tip ready for the filler wire.

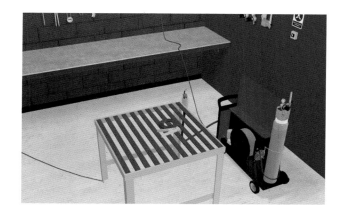

4   Turn on the power to the machine and increase wire feed speed to inch the filler wire through the gun until it emerges through the end. Ensure that the welding return lead is not connected to the work table when turning the power on so as to prevent stray arcing.

5   Match the contact tip to the diameter of the filler wire being used and the material being welded. Hold the end of the wire and operate the trigger to check the wire tension; it should give a positive forward movement of the wire. If not, increase the pressure on the drive wheel slightly until this is achieved.

6   Open the cylinder and set the gas flow to an appropriate level on the flow meter, then purge the lines to ensure adequate gas coverage.

Key for Valve Actions:
Close   Open

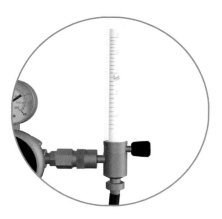

7   Attach the welding return lead and clamp to the work piece.

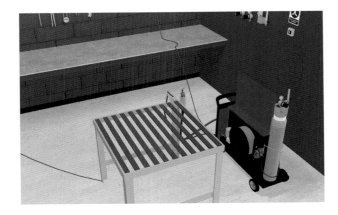

8   When you have adjusted the machine parameters to appropriate settings for the materials you are welding, then you're ready to begin.

Equipment Checks

Before commencing MIG welding, you should carry out a visual inspection of all the equipment being used. This can include inspection of the welding gun, checking for damage to insulation or leakage of the cooling fluid hose and gas hose, plus a functional check on the regulators and flow meters. You should also ensure the equipment has been purged.

Check that the cables being used are of the correct diameter for the amperage being used.

Also check that the appropriate filler wire is being used and that it is in good condition. Look for any signs of damage to copper coating or possible electrolytic corrosion as a result of condensation.

Closing Down Procedure

When you have finished MIG welding, the equipment should be closed down properly. Turn off the power, gas and water or air supply where applicable. Check the equipment for any damage and ensure you roll up and store all hoses and leads that have been used during the process. Make sure the equipment is left in a safe position and that the torch is secure to prevent damage. Cool down any hot metal in a water bucket and collect up all off-cuts of wire from the floor to put in appropriate containers.

Turn off all equipment and check for damage then leave equipment in a safe position

Key for Valve Actions:
Close   Open

Consumables

Filler wire used in MIG welding

MIG welding uses a filler wire to add filler material to the weld. Filler wires can be made from a number of different materials and come in a range of diameter sizes.

The type of filler wire needed depends on conditions such as its compatibility with the materials to be welded, any need for additional mechanical properties and to add any de-oxidising elements to the weld pool.

The electrode must also meet the demands of the process regarding arc stability, metal transfer and solidification characteristics. Deoxidisers or other scavenging agents are added to compensate for base metal reactions with oxygen, nitrogen and hydrogen from the surrounding atmosphere or the base metal. The deoxidizers most frequently used in steel are silicon, aluminium and manganese. Nickel alloys generally use titanium and silicon while copper alloys use titanium, silicon or phosphorous.

Filler wires should be stored in clean, dry conditions with an absorbent such as silica gel crystals. Packages should be clearly labelled. If the wire is not to be used for any period of time it should be placed back in its packaging with the absorbent to prevent contamination by condensation. You should not mix different types of filler wires.

Always handle with care and make sure they are free from contaminative agents such as moisture, oil, grease and rust before use.

E-Learning
Use the e-learning programme to download some information about MIG consumables.

Shielding Gases

The function of the shielding gas is to protect the weld zone from atmospheric gases which can cause defects.

An inert gas is one which will not readily combine with other gases, for which MIG welding uses an inert gas shield. The inert gas produces a bell-like shape coverage of the weld areas and prevents atmospheric gases, e.g. oxygen, hydrogen and nitrogen from reaching the hot weld metal.

MAG welding uses an active gas shield. An active gas is a gas that will readily combine with other gases. These are used in addition to the inert shielding gas to improve certain characteristics of the welded material. For example, the addition of oxygen to argon for stainless steel improves the surface penetration characteristics.

Gas selection is dependent upon the material being used and any additional requirements.

Welding Parameters

Some of the settings that an operator can change in MIG welding are: the voltage used, the wire feed speed or amperage, the shielding gas flow and the composition of the filler wire.

The settings for these parameters can change depending on the conditions of the job. For example: the weld position, joint configuration, the thermal conductivity, thickness and type of material, plus any need for additional alloying elements.

After selecting the basic process variables, the operating conditions to be met are as follows:

- deposition rate – travel speed;
- wire feed speed – welding current;
- welding voltage – penetration characteristic;
- electrode extension – stick out;
- inductance – amount of spatter produced.

Deposition Rate

This defined as the amount of weld metal deposited in a unit of time kgs/hour. It is particularly important in semi-automatic welding when weld quality depends upon the physical movement capability of the welder.

Wire Feed Speed

This is determined in conjunction with the required stick out and related welding current, which achieves the deposition rate. In a practical application, the deposition rate is more accurately set, maintained and reproduced by measurement of the wire feed speed. To calculate wire speed feed rate, a length of electrode wire is measured after a ten second period with the trigger on the gun depressed. This length is then multiplied by six to get a length for one minute.

	Shielding Gas	Chemical Behaviour	Typical Applications	Information
1	Argon (pure)	Inert	Virtually all metals except steels	Initiates arc easily Limited heat input (combined with Helium to increase temperature)
2	Helium (pure)	Inert	Aluminium, magnesium and copper alloys	Inputs more heat input to weld deposit Minimises porosity High flow rate due to Helium being a light gas (2 x the flow rate for argon) Doesn't initiate the arc easily
3	Argon + (25-80%) Helium	Inert	Aluminium, magnesium and copper alloys	Initiates arc easily (Argon) Good heat input (Helium) Minimises porosity (better arc action than 100% Helium) Added cost of adding Helium
6	Argon + (1-2%) Oxygen	Active (Slightly oxidising)	Stainless and alloy steels; some deoxidised copper alloys	Improves 'wetting' or surface deposition and arc conditions
7	Argon + (3-5%) Oxygen	Active (Oxidising)	Carbon and some low alloy steels	Increases surface deposition rates
8	Carbon Dioxide	Active (Oxidising)	Carbon and some low alloy steels	Low cost Unstable deposition rates
9	Argon + (20-50%) Carbon Dioxide	Active (Oxidising)	Various steels, chiefly short-circuiting mode	Improves arc stability and deposition characteristic. Not suitable for high strength low alloy steels.
10	Argon + (10%) Carbon Dioxide + (5%) Oxygen	Active (Oxidising)	Various steels (Europe)	Extends the range of steels that can be welded using this mixture
11	(90%) Helium + (7.5%) Argon + (2.5%) Carbon Dioxide	Active (Slightly oxidising)	Stainless steels	Good surface deposition characteristics Good corrosion resistance Short circuiting mode

Activity

In the space below, sketch the MIG welding equipment in your shop. Label each part of the equipment and indicate the correct procedure for dealing with a burnback.

Welding Voltage

This is linked to arc length and is established to maintain arc stability at selected wire feed speed and to minimise spatter.

Electrode Extension (Stick Out)

This variation in electrode stick out, results in a change in the electrical characteristics of the balanced system, as determined by the resistivity of the electrode length between the contact tip and the arc. In essence, as the contact tip to work distance increases, the welding current reduces. This produces cooler welding conditions which are especially useful if you burn a hole. Conversely the closer the contact tip to work distance the greater the

heat input and the possibility of a **'burnback'** occurring. This is why it is essential to maintain a constant contact tip distance for all weld configurations.

Inductance

This is a method of controlling any surges in heat input into the weld deposit and helps reduce spatter deposits. High inductance allows maximum heat input into the weld deposit, while low inductance gives a cooler heat input into the weld deposit.

It should be noted that when using water cooled guns, you are operating at higher amperages which will have an effect on heat input.

The Welding Process

MIG welding uses an electric current to generate an electric arc between the tip of a filler wire and the work piece. An electric arc is when electricity jumps across a gap between two conductors. This gap is known as the arc length. The arc can create a heat in excess of 4000° centigrade.

The arc causes instant heating of the parent material and a molten weld pool is formed, into which additional material is added in the form of the filler wire to complete the weld.

As the process moves along the joint, the deposited material cools and solidifies leaving a weld bead. The weld zone is protected from atmospheric contamination by a gas shield.

This gives a rapid deposition rate which can be achieved in some cases in a single pass with minimal or no distortion.

When the MIG gun is being operated correctly it makes a loud crackling sound.

Welding process diagram

Preparing to Weld

Before commencing welding, there are a number of checks you need to make.

Preparation of Work Area

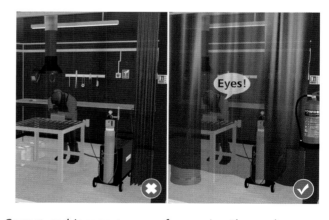

Correct and incorrect ways of preparing the work area

Health and Safety

Before carrying out any welding or fabrication operation you should carry out a risk assessment. This can include:

- Checking for hazards, for example slips, trips, obstructions and flammable materials.

- Checking the existing safety procedures and equipment, for example fire extinguishers, water buckets (for cooling hot metal only), containment vessels and screening provision.
- Making people in the vicinity aware of what work is being carried out, restricting access to the work area and giving a verbal warning of when you are about to strike up an arc.

Material Preparation

You should familiarise yourself with the manufacturers' safety data sheets, MSDSs, before using any equipment, materials, solvents or chemicals.

It is good practice to de-burr and degrease the material to prevent contamination of the weld and remove any flammable substances.

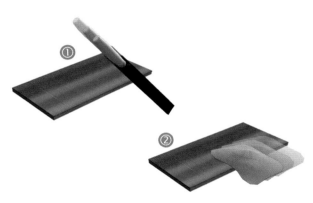

Material preparation: 1. De-burring; 2. De-greasing

As the plate thickness increases, it may be necessary to put some form of edge preparation on the plates in order to ensure fusion into the root of the joint.

Prior to any weld deposition, it is recommended that the joint is tacked to aid alignment and distortion control.

Tacking the joint

Position of Welder

Before welding, you should get into a comfortable and balanced position that you can maintain throughout the period of welding. You will need to be in a position where you are able to see the weld develop and that you can weld along the joint in one continuous movement. If you become uncomfortable or fatigued the quality of your welds may suffer.

Striking the Arc

When setting up ready to strike the arc in MIG welding, align your gun in the weld zone and initiate the arc by pressing the trigger on the gun. This will activate the current, the shielding gas, the wire feed and the cooling system to commence the weld.

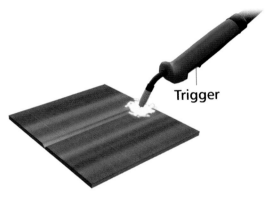

Trigger

Strike the arc by pressing the trigger at the correct arc length and position

The position of the strike is important as a strike outside the weld joint may produce a weld defect.

Once the arc has been struck and the arc length established, it must be maintained.

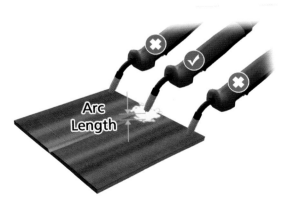

Arc Length

Correct and incorrect strike position and arc length

Techniques

Each welding process has specific techniques which require the understanding of the tilt angle and slope angle.

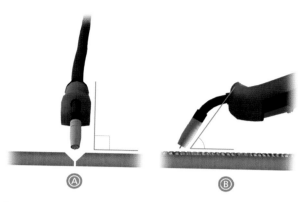

Techniques: A. Tilt angle; B. Slope angle

The tilt angle is the angle the welding gun is held at between the two pieces of material to be welded.

The slope angle is the angle the nozzle of the welding gun is held at, between the joint to be welded and a 90° angle from the joint.

MIG welding has two main techniques as well as a specific technique for starting and stopping a weld.

Drag Technique

Drag technique

The drag technique is used in situations where the push technique is not practical, for example on thin material or the inside curvature of a panel.

The welding gun is held at a slope angle of 45° and the filler wire is used to control the molten pool. The gun travels along the joint in the direction of the operator.

Drag technique slope

E-Learning

Use the e-learning programme to see an animated version of the drag technique

Push Technique

Push technique

Using the push technique, the welding gun should be held at a slope angle of 75-80° and have a filler wire extension length of approximately 10mm.

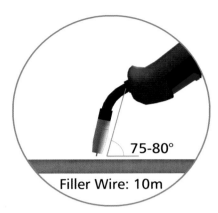

Push technique slope

Once the arc has been struck, push the welding gun forwards in the direction of travel, away from the operator. Observe the penetration characteristics which include monitoring the keyhole effect and that the build-up of weld behind the gun is sufficient. Be aware that weld penetration is higher when using this technique.

E-Learning

Use the e-learning programme to see an animated version of the push technique.

Start Stop Technique

Start stop technique

When you want to recommence a weld, you need to strike the arc within the weld zone in front of the last deposition. Then move back towards the previous weld deposit and loop around the top edge of it to ensure fusion. Then continue to move forward along the joint.

Transfer of Material

In MIG welding, filler material is transferred across the arc in four different ways.

Dip Transfer

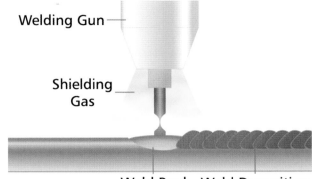

Dip transfer

In dip transfer, the filler wire dips into the molten pool, causing the wire to heat sufficiently to short circuit the power supply. This creates a pinch effect on the end of the wire which is then deposited into the weld pool as a droplet. It can be used in almost any type of application and is often used.

E-Learning

Use the e-learning programme to view an animation of dip transfer.

Spray Transfer

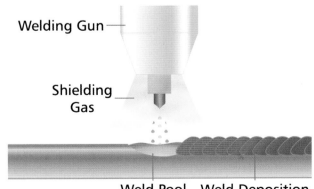

Spray transfer

Spray transfer is a high speed transfer technique due to increased amperages being used. The filler wire is heated to such an extent that end of the wire turns into a series of molten droplets. These are transferred across the arc in the form of a metallic spray and into the weld pool. This technique is used extensively on aluminium and heavy sections in flat and horizontal-vertical positions.

E-Learning

Use the e-learning programme to view an animation of spray transfer

Globular Transfer

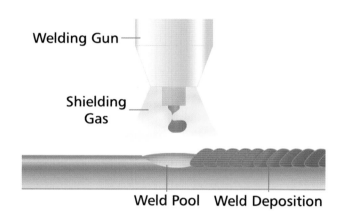

Globular transfer

Globular transfer is a method of transfer in between dip and spray. The filler wire is heated so the end of the wire drops into the weld pool in large globules.

This method of transfer is typically used in heavy structural applications, preferably in a horizontal position as the gas mixtures can help achieve relatively heavy deposition rates.

E-Learning

Use the e-learning programme to view an animation of globular transfer.

Pulse Transfer

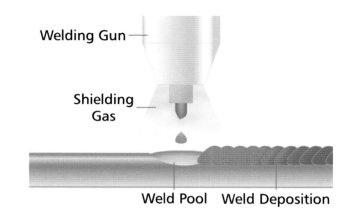

Pulse transfer

Pulse transfer occurs when a low background current is maintained in order to keep the arc stable.

An additional power impulse every few milliseconds produces a rapid heating and cooling cycle which melts the filler wire and ensures good fusion. This weld appearance is typified by a series of overlapping circles.

It is used extensively on heat sensitive materials, car body panel repair and on exotic metals.

E-Learning

Use the e-learning programme to view an animation of pulse transfer.

Weaving Technique

This is similar to the weaving techniques described in the manual metal arc welding section.

Potential Welding Failures

Potential weld failures in MIG welding can occur for a number of reasons; for example, insufficient wire speed, gas flow rates and incorrect pressures, incorrect diameter or composition of filler wire, or poor operator technique in depositing the weld bead.

One example of a welding failure is known as burnback. This is when the end of the filler wire is heated up into a ball and sticks to the contact tip of the welding gun, preventing further wire being delivered to the weld.

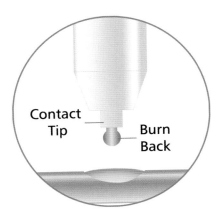

Weld failure: burnback

This can be prevented by ensuring there is sufficient wire feed speed to match the voltage set at the machine and making sure the gun isn't held too close to the weld pool.

To fix burn back, turn off the machine and strip back the contact tip. It may be hot so take care when doing so. File the tip flush and clean the hole with a nozzle cleaner of the correct dimensions. If this is not possible, do not attempt to clear the burnback by repeated operation of the control switch on the gun. The feed roll will chew and deform the wire causing a 'bird's nest' in the wire feed unit.

A bird's nest is where the surplus wire has tried to feed through the rolls of the feed unit. Because the end is fused it travels back into the casing of the feed unit and resembles a bird's nest. If it is not cleared it will cause shorting in the feed unit and effectively damage the equipment. All off-cuts of wire should be placed in the appropriate container.

To avoid a bird's nest the following procedure should be adopted:

- Release the switch on the gun immediately when burnback occurs.
- Remove the gas nozzle and try to free wire from the end of the contact tip with wire clippers.
- If wire is fused tight, release the pressure on the electrode wire feed rolls and unscrew contact tip.
- Clip wire and remove fused portion from contact tip by gripping wire in vice.

- It may be necessary to file the end of the contact tube tip to remove the fused portion of wire and clean and de-burr it with tip cleaners.
- In bad cases it may be necessary to cut off the end of the contact tip with a hacksaw to clear the fused wire.
- Replace seriously damaged contact tips that have been shortened to below the specified minimum length.
- Before refitting the contact tip, feed sufficient wire through the gun to make sure that the wire scored by the feed roll is discarded when the burnback occurred.

Cleaning the Weld

After a weld is complete it will generally need to be cleaned. Low carbon steels will require cleaning with a mild steel wire brush.

For carbon steels, clean weld using mild steel wire brush

Stainless steels and aluminium will require cleaning with a stainless steel wire brush and may also require chemical cleaning.

For stainless steels and aluminium, clean weld using stainless steel wire brush and chemical cleaner

Reinstate the Work Area

When you have finished welding, ensure all equipment is closed down correctly and turned off. Make sure the equipment is stored away safely and does not cause any hazards.

Sustainability

Cool all scrap metal and place it in the appropriate container.

Return any tools that have been used to their appropriate storage area and tidy up the work area.

Joints

There are four main types of joint in welding. Any weld on any joint should be equal to the thickness of the plate and have a smooth transition from the weld to the plate surface.

The slope and tilt angles will change with the position in which the weld is carried out. In this instance the tilt and slope angles mentioned are for the flat and horizontal vertical position only.

Outside Corner Joint

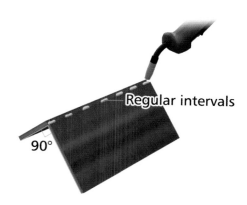

Outside corner joint

An outside corner joint is formed by two work pieces positioned with their edges next to each other at an angle of 90°. The weld is placed on the outside of this corner. The pieces should be tacked at each end and at regular intervals along the joint.

The welding gun should be tilted so it bisects the two work pieces and has a slope angle of 75-80°. Control of

the fluid molten pool is critical with this joint to prevent cold lapping of the edges.

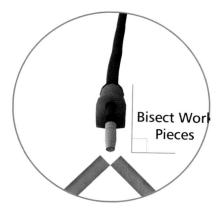

Tilt angle of welding gun

Slope angle of welding gun

Lap Joint

Lap joint

A lap joint is formed by two work pieces overlapping each other. The weld is placed where the two pieces meet. The pieces should be tacked at each end and at regular intervals along the joint.

The welding gun should be tilted so it is at 45° between the two work pieces and have a slope angle of 75-80°. The tilt will ensure that most of the heat goes into the bottom plate and both plates reach melting point at the same time. Care must be exercised to pause sufficiently to ensure no undercutting occurs.

A tee joint is formed when one work piece is positioned at 90° to another work piece. The weld is placed where the two pieces meet. The pieces should be tacked at each end and at regular intervals along the joint.

The welding gun should be tilted so it is at 45° between the two work pieces and have a slope angle of 75-80°. Like the lap, pause sufficiently on the top edge to reduce the possibility of undercutting on the vertical plate.

Tilt angle of welding gun

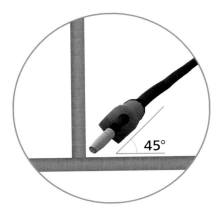

Tilt angle of welding gun

Slope angle of welding gun

Slope angle of welding gun

Tee Joint

Butt Joint

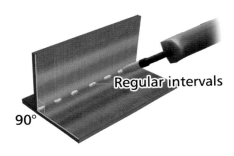

Tee Joint

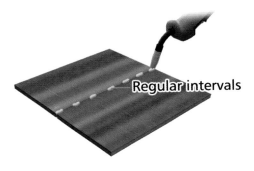

Butt joint

Activity

In the space below, sketch a tee joint and indicate the slope and tilt angles associated with working in the horizontal-vertical position.

A butt joint is formed when the two work pieces are positioned side by side with a gap between them to ensure penetration. The weld is then placed between the two pieces.

The space between the plates is called the gap, or root gap, and this can vary from 0-3mm. If the gap is too large or too small it can result in defects in the welded joint.

When welding thick plate, an edge preparation is put on the plates to ensure penetration and a sound weld deposit. The pieces should be tacked at each end and at regular intervals along the joint.

The welding gun should be tilted so that it is at 90° to the surface of the work pieces and has a slope angle of 75-80°. Manipulation should be such that pauses on the edges of the preparation ensure fusion and not cold lapping.

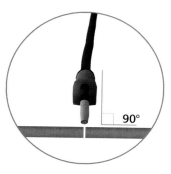

Tilt angle of welding gun

Slope angle of welding gun

Quality Control

Weld Defects

In all welding techniques there are a number of weld defects and discontinuities that can be identified once a weld is complete.

Porosity

This is created when gas becomes trapped in the weld deposit as the metal cools.

Causes: Damp filler wire or surface contamination;

Remedies: Correct storage facilities for all filler wires with particular attention being paid to temperature. This will prevent moisture build up on the filler wires to ensure weld integrity. Surface cleaning of all parent materials prior to welding.

Porosity

Inclusions

These are created when foreign matter such as oil, grease or mill scale becomes trapped within the solidifying weld deposit as irregular pores.

Causes: Inadequate cleaning of the parent metal prior to welding, failure to remove any surface coatings such as paint or protective materials;

Remedies: Ensure surface cleaning prior to all welding operations and to ensure correct storage of all filler wires prior to use.

Inclusions

Poor Weld Profile/Dimension

This is a failure to maintain design specifications.

Causes: Incorrect current settings, poor manipulation or an incorrect speed of travel;

Remedies: Selection of current settings to match material specification and thickness, correct manipulation of the welding gun and filler wire, and monitoring speed of travel to ensure weld integrity.

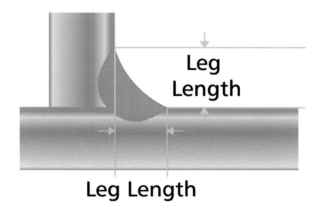

Poor weld profile/ dimension

Lack of Side Wall Fusion

This is a lack of fusion between weld metal and parent metal at the side of the weld and on the interrun deposition.

Causes: Too low a current setting or a failing to ensure fusion by moving on too quickly;

Remedies: Ensure correct manipulation of welding gun and filler wire with due regard to fusion on the side walls.

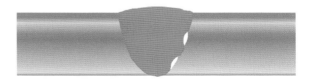

Lack of side wall fusion

Undercut

These are created when metal is removed from a joint without being replaced by weld material. This is commonly found at the toe of a run or in previously deposited weld metal.

Causes: Excessive current, insufficient filler wire, excessive speed of travel and poor manipulation of the welding gun.

Remedies: Careful control of current, matching the filler wire diameter to the weld specification, control of travel speed and manipulation of welding gun.

Undercut

Spatter

This is a surface deposition adjacent to the weld which is not fully fused into the surface of the material.

Causes: Too high a current setting, an excessive arc length, or failure to use the correct inductance setting.

Remedies: Correct use of inductance setting, checking voltage settings and correct arc length.

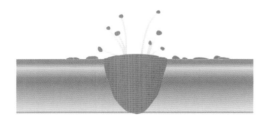

Spatter

Excessive Root Penetration

This is produced by excessive weld metal protruding through the root of a fusion weld.

Causes: Poor technique, incorrect edge preparation or too high a current setting.

Remedies: Close control of edge preparations especially root face dimension and root gap, correct selection of current settings to parent material and filler wire diameters.

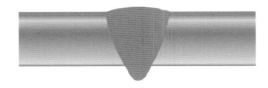

Excessive root penetration

Stray Arcing

This happens when an arc is struck outside of the weld zone and may produce a hardened zone and bring about ultimate failure of the weld.

Stray arcing

Causes: Striking the arc outside the weld zone

Remedies: Always ensure that all strikes are within the fusion zone to establish the arc.

Lack of Root Penetration

This is a failure of the weld metal to extend into the root of a joint.

Lack of root penetration

Causes: moving too quickly with not enough heat applied, incorrect joint preparation and set up with too small a gap.

Remedies: Ensure correct preparation and set up, a large enough gap, use the correct settings and adjust speed.

Underfill

This is created when the weld metal is insufficient to produce the required deposit as stated in the specification.

Possible Causes: Speed of travel is too fast, using the wrong diameter filler wire, failure to pause on the side of the weld.

Remedies: Ensure that the appropriate filler wire for the material is used and that the operator's technique is correct.

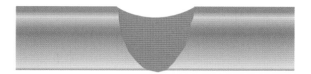

Underfill

Excessive Weld Reinforcement

This happens when the weld metal deposited is excessive and leaves the weld protruding on the surface of the weld.

Causes: The diameter of the filler wire is too large, the wire feed speed is too high or the speed of travel is too slow.

Remedies: Ensure that the appropriate filler wire for the material is used, the machine settings are on the right setting and that the operator's technique is correct.

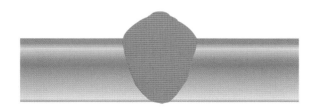

Excessive weld reinforcement

Misalignment of Plates

This is created by failing to align the plates after tacking and prior to welding, giving a stepped appearance.

Causes: Failure to tack weld prior to welding.

Remedies: Tacking at regular intervals and dressing the plates prior to welding.

Misalignment of plates

Wormholes

These are created by contaminants which may be above or below the surface and which rise up through the weld metal.

Possible Causes: Contaminants within the base metal or on the surface.

Remedies: Clean all surfaces and filler materials prior to welding with a proprietary solvent cleaner.

Wormholes

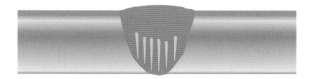

Wormholes

CHECK YOUR KNOWLEDGE

1 Which of the following applications can MIG welding be used for? Circle the correct answer.

    a.   Automotive repair
    b.   Pre-heating materials
    c.   Hard soldering
    d.   Cutting
    e.   Wind farms
    f.   Soft soldering
    g.   Robotics

2 What equipment would you need to carry out MIG welding? Circle the correct answer.

    a.   Power Source
    b.   Tungsten Electrode
    c.   Acetylene Gas Cylinder
    d.   Consumable Electrode Wire
    e.   Welding Gun
    f.   Cooling System
    g.   Welding Torch

3 Which series of pictures show pulse transfer? Circle the correct answer.

    a.

    b.

    c.

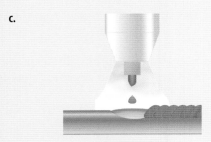

    d.

4 Can you identify these weld defects? Write a, b or c next to the appropriate diagrams.

    a.   Excessive penetration
    b.   Lack of penetration
    c.   Underfill

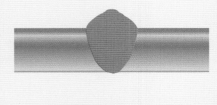

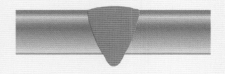

Summary

This concludes this chapter on MIG welding. You should now be able to explain the principles of MIG welding; list the specific health and safety requirements, list the equipment and explain how it should be set up; explain how to carry out the MIG welding process and list the weld defects that can occur.

End test

1. **Which of the following welders is wearing the appropriate PPE for MIG welding? Circle the correct answer.**

   ☐ a.

   ☐ b.

   ☐ c.

2. **Where should the local extraction system be placed when MIG welding? Circle the correct answer.**

   ☐ a. There is no need for extraction

   ☐ b. Above the welder's head

   ☐ c. Next to the weld zone

   ☐ d. Immediately on top of the weld zone

3. **Identify the components of the MIG equipment shown.**

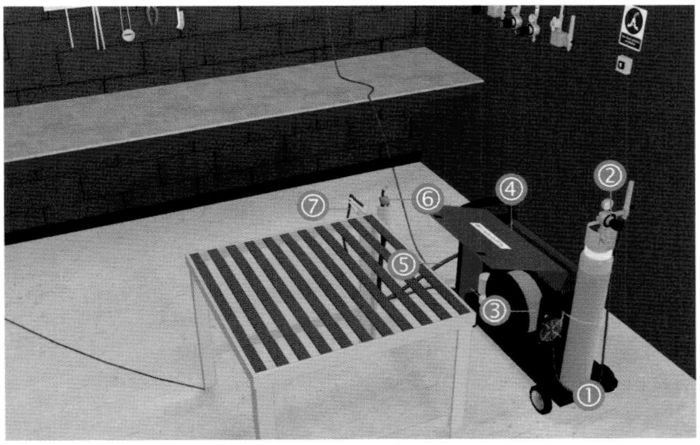

1.

2.

3.

4.

5.

6.

7.

4. **MIG welding uses a DC power supply. What does DC stand for? Circle the correct answer.**

   ☐ a. Diverted Current

   ☐ b. Distributed Current

   ☐ c. Double Current

   ☐ d. Direct Current

5. **Of the gas combinations shown here, which can be used as an inert gas shield and which can be used as an active gas shield? Put ticks in the appropriate columns.**

Gas	Inert Gas Shield	Active Gas Shield
Argon		
Helium		
Argon + Helium		
Argon + Oxygen		
Carbon Dioxide		
Argon + Carbon Dioxide		
Argon + Carbon Dioxide + Oxygen		
Helium + Argon + Carbon Dioxide		

6. **You are about to start MIG welding. Is each of the items shown in the picture in an appropriate position? Circle the correct answer.**

- ☐ a. Screening Curtains – Yes / No
- ☐ b. (B) Fire Extinguisher – Yes / No
- ☐ c. (C) Extraction System – Yes / No
- ☐ d. (D) Water Bucket – Yes / No
- ☐ e. (E) Cardboard Boxes – Yes / No
- ☐ f. (F) Welding Mask – Yes / No

7. **What slope angle should you hold the welding gun at when using the push technique? Circle the correct answer.**

- ☐ a. 65-70°
- ☐ b. 70-75°
- ☐ c. 75-80°
- ☐ d. 80-85°
- ☐ e. 85-90°

8. **Match the methods of MIG welding transfer to the brief descriptions shown. Write a, b, c or d beside each method.**

- ● Dip Transfer
- ● Spray Transfer
- ● Globular Transfer
- ● Pulse Transfer

- ☐ a. The filler wire is heated to a point where the end of the wire turns into a series of droplets that fall into the weld pool.
- ☐ b. The filler wire heats and cools in a cycle depositing the material into the weld pool at regular intervals.
- ☐ c. The filler wire heats up and forms a molten ball at the end of the wire which drops into the weld pool.
- ☐ d. The filler wire enters the molten pool causing the wire to heat and short circuit the power supply. The end of the wire drops into the weld pool.

9. **Which of these descriptions describes burn back? Circle the correct answer.**

- ☐ a. Electric arc causes a flame to travel back up the welding cable assembly
- ☐ b. Filler wire heats up into a molten ball which sticks to the tip of the welding gun

☐ c. Re-heating the weld bead back from the last deposit to restart welding

☐ d. Adjusting the angle of the gun to achieve more penetration into the weld

10. What would you use to clean a low carbon steel weld? Circle the correct answer.

☐ a. Doesn't need cleaning

☐ b. With a chipping hammer

☐ c. Stainless steel wire brush

☐ d. Mild steel wire brush

☐ e. Chemical solution

7

Tungsten Inert Gas (TIG) Welding

LEARNING OBJECTIVES

By the end of this chapter you will be able to:

- Explain the principles of TIG welding.
- List the specific health and safety requirements.
- List the equipment and explain how it should be set up.
- Explain how to carry out the TIG welding process.
- List the weld defects that can occur.

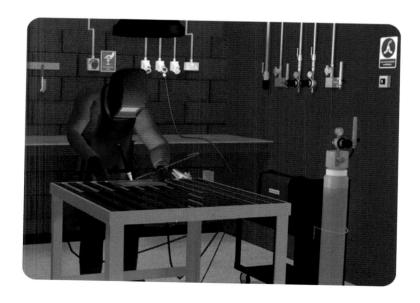

Introduction

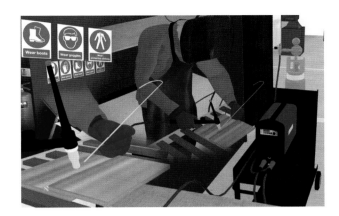

The many aspects of TIG welding

Tungsten Inert Gas (TIG) welding is a process that uses electricity to form an electric arc heat source between the tip of the tungsten electrode and the work piece.

The heat from the arc energy melts the base material as well as the filler wire which is consumed to form the filler metal for the weld. The shielding gas protects the molten weld pool and affects the electric arc and weld deposit.

Caution should be observed at all times and full personal protective equipment or PPE is recommended.

Advantages and Disadvantages

TIG welding has a number of advantages and disadvantages.

Advantages

- Small Heat Affected Zone which reduces distortion
- Suitable for a wide range of exotic metals
- Used for high specification welding due to controlled weld depositions e.g. root runs on a pipe
- Good visual appearance of the resulting weld bead

Activity

Use the internet to make a list of up to six jobs that are currently being advertised that may require TIG welding skills.

_____

_____

_____

_____

_____

_____

_____

_____

_____

_____

Disadvantages

○ Can be slow due to manual manipulation of the equipment
○ Can be expensive due to the cost of consumables and skilled labour
○ Requires good access to weld joint configuration
○ Intolerant to any surface contamination

Applications

TIG welding is used for a wide range of applications, including:

● pipeline welding;
● aerospace industry;
● motorsport;
● vehicle manifolds;
● stainless steel and aluminium applications;
● exotic metals e.g. titanium, copper alloys.

Activity

List four advantages of using TIG welding.

_____

_____

_____

_____

Health and Safety for TIG Welding

Health and Safety

Before entering a workshop environment always make sure that you are wearing the appropriate personal protective equipment or PPE for the job. Standard PPE includes fully protective, flame retardant overalls, safety boots, ear defenders and clear, safety goggles. It may also be necessary to wear an additional respirator in certain circumstances. It is advisable to remove jewellery when working with TIG and high frequency current to initiate the arc, as it is possible to end up with a burn or shock if any jewellery touches the table or component.

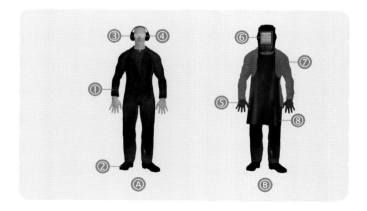

Personal Protective Equipment (PPE): A. Workshop PPE;
B. Additional PPE when MIG (Metal Inert Gas) welding;
1. Flame retardant overalls; 2. Safety boots; 3. Ear defenders;
4. Clear safety goggles; 5. Leather gauntlet style gloves;
6. Welding mask (Welding cap); 7. Flame retardant jacket;
8. Welding apron

For TIG welding you should also be wearing leather gloves, a welding cap, a welding mask (if working on metals likely to give off fumes), a flame retardant jacket done up to the neck and a welding apron. Always check to make sure the welding mask is set to the correct filter level.

E-Learning

Use the e-learning programme to download a filter lens guide that provides more information.

There are some specific health and safety issues associated with TIG welding.

Working in Confined spaces

⚠ **Warning**
Confined spaces

As with any form of welding, you must be aware of the dangers of working in confined spaces. Do not enter the area until it has been checked for suitable oxygen levels and that no poisonous gases are present.

If the oxygen in the confined space falls below 16%, then it can lead to dizziness and a shortness of breath. This can be fatal if signs are not noticed in time for the operator to get to a source of fresh air, so operators should be observed at all times when in confined spaces.

The arc welding processes produce a number of potentially harmful fumes from shielding gases, parent materials, surface coatings and contaminants. It is recommended that good extraction, close to the source of fumes be used at all times. If this is not possible due to site access, then the welding operator should be

equipped with a self-contained air supply welding shield. Because argon is an asphyxiant gas it is recommended that good ventilation and extraction are readily available.

Personal Safety

 Wear personal protective equipment

Always make sure you are wearing the correct PPE and are working in accordance with safe working practices. Harmful fumes and gases are produced in all welding processes so appropriate fume extraction should always be in place.

The heat from the welding process, sparks and hot metal can cause severe burns. The electric arc from the process also gives off a form of radiation which covers the whole spectrum from visible light, through infra-red to ultraviolet which can cause burns similar to sunburn on the skin. The light from the arc can also cause 'arc eye', a painful condition that can cause watering of the eyes, headaches and a temporary loss of vision. Long term exposure to this radiation without PPE could lead to skin cancer.

Material (MSDSs) Safety Data Sheet

Material Safety Data Sheets (MSDSs) should always be consulted before any welding is undertaken. These data sheets contain important information on items such as gases, filler wires, electrodes and degreasing solvents. They are available from the manufacturers of the products. You need to understand the properties of all the items you use, the hazards associated with them and what to do in an emergency.

Gas Cylinders

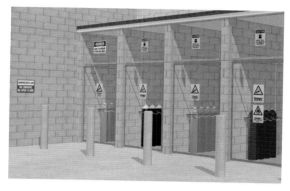

Appropriate storage of gas cylinders

In previous chapters we have described the safety procedures to take when using gas cylinders:

- Make sure you are using the correct gas or gases.
- Do not use damaged cylinders.
- Report any damage to the suppliers.
- Store cylinders upright in a cool, well-ventilated area, away from any sources of ignition.
- The correct fire extinguishers should be provided.
- Signage should show what cylinders are being stored.
- Only appropriately trained operators should have access to the area where cylinders are stored.
- Cylinders should always be transported upright and secured with chains at all times.
- If cylinders are moved in a vehicle, it should be open-backed or well ventilated.

Appropriate fire extinguishers located nearby

Electrical Safety

Always check that electrical equipment is safe to use

Before switching on the equipment and carrying out any welding, check that the equipment is not damaged, and is set up correctly and earthed appropriately. Also remember that electric arc processes present a danger to people with pacemakers.

Damaged cable insulation, incorrectly sized fuses, faulty connections and lack of a suitable earth can all cause electric shock, fire and burn hazards. Appliance testing and repairs should only be carried out by competent personnel.

Welding in conditions where water or moisture is present can be hazardous. Erect a shelter for protection and ensure the work piece is properly insulated.

Where water-cooled guns are used, additional checks should be made to ensure that there is no damage to the torch or lines. This would be indicated by a stain or a pool of water prior to operation. If there is damage, do not use. Please ensure you report this to your supervisor.

When TIG welding, the operator is also at risk of electric shock due to the process using a high frequency current and water cooled torch. Where water cooled torches are used, additional checks should be made to ensure that there is no damage to the torch or lines. This would be indicated by a stain or a pool of water prior to operation. If there is damage, do not use and proceed by reporting this to your supervisor. All cable assemblies should be laid out so that the cable does not coil as this can induce a back electromotive force (EMF) which offers resistance to the flow of electricity. It can also lead to a breakdown in the cable insulation because of the high-frequency current imposed to initiate the arc.

Fumes, Gases and Ventilation

Fume extraction should be approximately 250mm from the weld zone

In addition to general ventilation of the welding area, fume extraction should also be provided. Fumes can be produced by fluxes, surface coatings, base materials, solvents used to degrease the material and shielding gases. These fumes can cause breathing difficulties and in severe cases asphyxiation.

These fumes need to be drawn off by a localised extraction ventilation system. This should be placed close to the weld and in a position which ensures that the fumes are not drawn past the face of the welder. It should also be set to an appropriate extraction rate so it removes the fumes but not the gas shield where applicable.

Working at Height

Welders are often required to work at height. Competently erected scaffolding with earth bonding, along with a static safety harness should be used. Screening of the weld area should be erected to protect fellow workers from the effects of radiation and the area should be cordoned off with signage clearly displayed.

Activity

What additional health and safety precautions are associated with TIG welding?

_____

_____

_____

_____

_____

_____

_____

_____

_____

_____

_____

_____

Activity

Identify three ways to avoid potentially hazardous fumes when TIG welding.

1

2

3

Equipment and Set Up

Equipment

TIG welding equipment comprises of a power source which feeds gas from a cylinder, gas or water from a cooling system and an electric current to the welding torch.

An electric arc is struck between the tungsten electrode and the work piece which generates heat creating the weld pool.

The current passes through the work piece and returns to the power source via the welding clamp and welding return lead which completes the circuit.

All pressure regulating equipment including regulators, flashback arrestors and hoses are governed by a designated working life from the manufacturers and should be regularly inspected and changed if any damage is noted.

Always check your equipment before use to make sure it is in good working order.

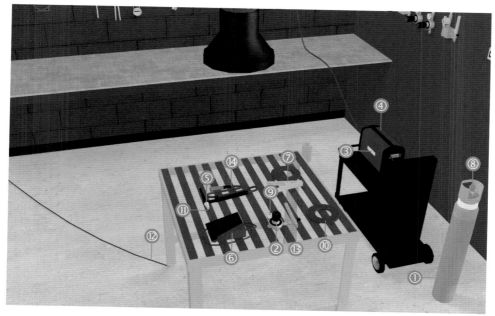

TIG welding equipment set up: 1. Shielding gas; 2. Pressure regulator; 3. Cooling system; 4. Power source; 5. Welding torch; 6. Foot pedal; 7. Welding return lead and clamp; 8. Cylinder valve; 9. Pressure gauge; 10. Flexible hose; 11. Tungsten electrode; 12. Earth connection; 13. Flow meter; 14. Welding cable assembly

Shielding Gas Cylinder

If you are using a cylinder to provide the shielding gas for the welding process then the cylinder should contain the appropriate gas for the job and should have been transported and stored correctly.

In some cases the gas may be supplied via a manifold from cylinders stored outside the welding area. Always check you are connecting to the correct gases as you can contaminate the gas lines.

1. Shielding gas

Pressure Regulator

The regulator reduces the pressure from the cylinder to a constant safe working pressure which can be maintained during different flow rates and volumes. The pressure in supplied gas cylinders has been increased over the years and it is essential that you use a regulator capable of withstanding the pressure of the cylinder you are using.

2. Pressure regulator

Cooling System

TIG welding has a low heat transfer efficiency meaning as much as 80% of the heat produced stays in the torch. This is removed via a water-based or gas-based cooling system.

Both systems have advantages and disadvantages. Gas-cooled torches are safer, lighter and easier to manipulate but water-cooled torches can operate continuously without overheating and have lower tungsten erosion rates. These factors make the gas-cooled system more practical for small workshops whereas water-cooled systems are more efficient for production welding.

Power Source

Power sources are available in a wide range of voltages and amperages with some machines capable of delivering alternating current (AC) and direct current (DC) output, while others will deliver AC or DC output only.

4. Power source

Transformer-rectifiers are the most commonly used power sources used for TIG welding, since they can provide both AC and DC welding current. With an open circuit voltage range of 80-100 volts, these machines are often referred to as having a 'drooping characteristic', meaning the voltage 'falls off' to an operating voltage of 18-22 volts once the arc has been initiated, and therefore are suitable for MMA (Manual Metal Arc) and TIG welding.

By means of a switch, the operator can change the output terminals from AC for aluminium and magnesium alloys to DC for all other metals with the added bonus of polarity. Most machines are forced-draught cooled and the larger machines incorporate a water-cooling circuit for use with water-cooled torches.

More recently, advanced solid state technology has produced a range of inverter machines. These are more versatile, lightweight and portable, and are much more efficient in the use of power to produce very stable welding conditions.

Suppressor units are used extensively in the welding of aluminium to overcome the tendency of the AC arc to be converted to DC due to a reaction between the tungsten electrode and the surface oxide. This unit will allow the passage of AC and effectively block any DC current.

Welding Torch

A TIG welding torch is made up of a number of parts. The collet fits in the body of the torch and is a tight fitting sleeve in which the tungsten electrode passes through. The collet is secured in place by the back cap. Areas for inspection prior to use include the thread pattern on the back cap and the 'o' ring which provides a gas seal, the connection where the nozzle screws to the body and the ceramic nozzle for cracks. It is also important to ensure that the correct size and length of collet matches the torch and electrode chosen, any damage to the back of the collet could result in failure to secure the electrode and stray arcing within the torch body.

5. Welding torch

The welding nozzle is ceramic in order to be able to withstand the considerable heat input from the arc. These nozzles are available in a range of diameters and designs to suit specific welding applications.

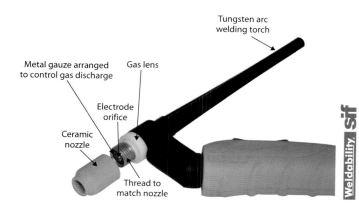

TIG gun

One device for assuring a laminar flow of shielding gas is an attachment called a gas lens. Gas lenses contain a porous barrier diffuser which regulates the gas flow into a more regular and directional flow. They are designed to fit around the electrode or collet. Gas lenses produce a longer, undistributed flow of shielding gas, and gas flow rates can be reduced if a gas lens is fitted. This enables welders to weld with increased electrode extension up to 25mm but this also reduces the current carrying capacity for that diameter electrode by approximately 25%. The advantage of this to the welder is improved visibility of the weld pool and access to limited root runs in J or U preparations on thick plate.

Foot Pedal

The foot pedal is based on a variable resistor. With the pedal fully depressed, maximum current goes into the material to establish the arc and form the molten pool. Once established, the foot can be gradually lifted to reduce the current output in line with speed of travel to ensure a consistency of deposition.

The pedal can be raised further to reduce the current and terminate the weld deposit.

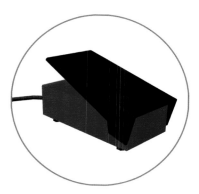

6. Foot pedal

High Frequency Control

This is used to turn the high frequency current on and off. Continuous high frequency current is used for AC welding whereas high frequency current is only used to initiate the arc when using DC and cuts out after the arc has been established.

Welding Return Lead and Clamp

The welding return lead completes the circuit by connecting the power source to the work piece via the clamp. The clamp could be bolted, swivelled or an alligator type depending on the type of job being carried out.

7. Welding return lead and clamp

Cylinder Valve

The cylinder valve allows the flow of gas from the cylinder into the regulator to be controlled so the regulator is not damaged. The cylinder valve should always be closed when not in use. If the gas cylinder valve is too tight or shows signs of damage, return the cylinder to the supplier.

8. Cylinder valve

Pressure Gauge

In TIG welding, the regulator has two pressure gauges. The first shows the pressure from the cylinder, the second shows the pressure from the regulator to the torch. Pressure readings may be shown in bars and pounds per square inch.

9. Pressure gauge

Flexible Hose

The hoses from the cylinders consist of two layers of rubber with a reinforced canvas layer which prevents them from ballooning under pressure. The canvas layer also acts as a safety indicator; if you can see the canvas layer then the hoses must be replaced and NOT repaired. The hoses should be long enough to reach your work area but not so long as to cause a trip hazard.

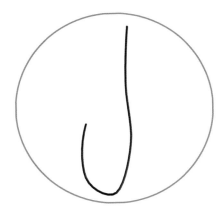

10. Flexible hose

Tungsten Electrode

The electrodes for TIG welding consist primarily of tungsten with various alloying elements to improve arc stability and tip profile. TIG welding electrodes are classified as non-consumable, which is not strictly true. What is true, however is that they should be capable of carrying the welding current and should not disintegrate at the tip whilst welding, thus contaminating the weld pool. It is virtually impossible to vaporise a tungsten electrode during welding provided the electrode is used within the current carrying capacity range for its specific type and diameter, with sufficient inert shielding gas. Tungsten retains its hardness, even at red heat and when they are alloyed with Thorium (red), Zirconium (white), Cerium (grey) and Lanthanum (black), they give increased amperage range and retain their shape. These electrodes are colour coded in the form of bands on one end of the electrode and are obtainable in rod form approximately 150mm long and from diameters starting at 0.25-6mm.

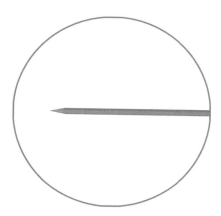

11. Tungsten electrode

Electrode preparation for thoriated electrodes is to grind a point to a length of 3 x the diameter of the electrode to ensure that there is sufficient cross-sectional area behind the point to conduct heat away from the tip. This electrode is used for welding metals on DC. All grinding should be done so that all the grinding marks are focussed towards the tip by using the face of an appropriate grinding wheel and not the side of the wheel as this will create arc wander.

When welding aluminium and magnesium alloys, AC is required which require a different electrode composition. Typical of these is the zirconiated electrode which is prepared by grinding the end to a 45° bevel to 50% of the electrodes diameter, and this will form a balled end.

Ceriated and lanthanated can be used on both AC and DC.

When the electrode becomes contaminated, if it is steel it can be ground off, however if the electrode becomes contaminated with aluminium it must be broken off before it can be ground as it will load the wheel.

Earth Connection

The work piece should be connected to a suitable earth via a clamp and earth lead. The clamp could be bolted, swivelled or an alligator type depending on the type of job being carried out.

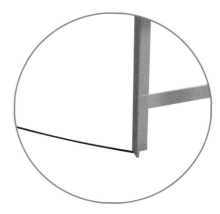

12. Earth connection

Flow Meter

The flow meter controls the flow of gas from the regulator to the welding gun. A ball in the flow meter indicates the gas flow rate and can be read with the top, centre or bottom of the ball lining up with the measurements on the meter. This provides a more accurate reading.

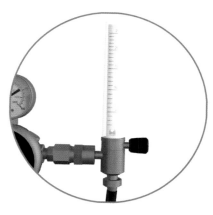

13. Flow meter

Welding Cable Assembly

The welding cable assembly connects the shielding gas hose, cooling system, the current conductor and the arc initiation mechanism to the welding torch. These sheaths are designed to protect the power cable, hoses and cooling systems from damage by being dragged across workshop floors, the best type being made of rubber, fitted at the point of manufacture. They give good resistance to abrasion, spatter and may be fire retardant. Also available as a retrofit item is a zipper cover which is normally made of nylon or glassfibre material which is zipped up over the length of cables and hoses. This type is generally more expensive but has the advantage in use as the cover can easily be removed and replaced.

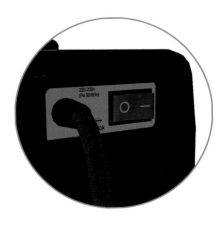

1   Ensure that the cylinder is secured in an upright position.

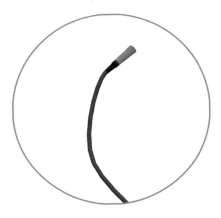

14. Welding cable assembly

Set Up Procedure

2   Check the thread patterns on the cylinder for damage or debris, then attach the regulator with the flow meter.

When setting up TIG welding equipment, first ensure you have a safe work environment and that the power supply is off.

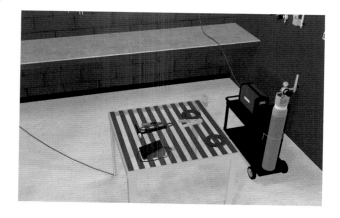

5 Finally, assemble the torch and install the tungsten electrode. Connect the torch to the welding cable assembly. If the tungsten electrode is touching the work piece or table when the power is switched on it could result in an arc being created.

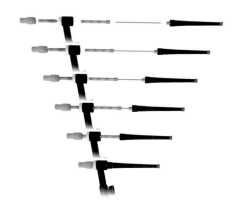

3 Attach the gas feed hose to the power source and gas cylinder.

4 Connect the foot pedal, the welding cable assembly and welding return lead to the power source, then attach the welding return clamp to the work piece.

6 Finally, turn the power on and select the polarity and current setting for the material to be welded. For example, AC for aluminium or magnesium and DC for all other materials.

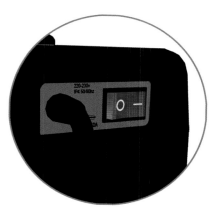

Key for Valve Actions:
Close   Open

Equipment Checks

Before commencing TIG welding, there are a number of equipment checks that should be carried out.

These include a visual inspection of the welding torch including back caps and nozzle seals, checking for damage to the assembly or insulation, or leakage of the cooling fluid hose and gas hose, and a functional check on the regulators and flow meters. You should also ensure the equipment has been purged.

Check that the cables being used are of the correct diameter for the amperage being used.

Check that the appropriate filler wires and tungsten electrode is being used and are in good condition.

Closing Down Procedure

When you have finished TIG welding, the equipment should be closed down properly. Turn off the power, gas and water or air supply where applicable. Check the equipment for any damage and ensure you roll up and store all hoses and leads that have been used during the process. Make sure the equipment is left in a safe position and that the torch is secure to prevent damage.

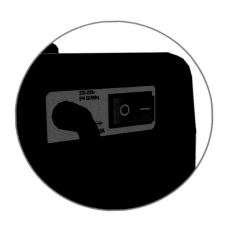

Consumables

2% Throiated
Zironiated
Pure Tungsten
Ceriated
1% Lanthanated
1.5% Lanthanated
2% Lanthanated

Types of tungsten electrodes used in TIG welding

TIG welding uses a filler wire and tungsten electrodes. The filler wire adds material to the weld and can be made from a number of different materials and come in a range of diameter sizes.

The type of filler wire needed depends on conditions such as its compatibility with the materials to be welded, any need for additional mechanical properties and to add any de-oxidising elements to the weld pool.

Filler wires should be stored in clean and dry conditions and packages should be clearly labelled. You should not mix different types of filler wires.

Always handle filler wires with care and make sure they are free from contamination such as moisture, oil, grease and rust before use.

The tungsten electrode in the welding torch can also come in different forms and can be identified by their tip colour. Check your local regulations for more information and always consult Material Safety Data Sheets for each before use.

E-Learning

Use the e-learning programme to download some information about TIG consumables.

Shielding Gases

A shielding gas protects the molten weld zone and the tungsten electrode from gases in air. It also has an effect on the electric arc and the appearance of the weld deposit.

The shielding gas comes out of the torch and provides a bell-like shape coverage of the weld area.

TIG welding generally uses inert gases such as argon and helium. An inert gas is a gas that will not readily combine chemically with other gases. However they can be mixed with other gases such as hydrogen and nitrogen to improve certain characteristics of the welded material. For example, the addition of hydrogen to argon for stainless steel improves the surface penetration characteristics.

Gas selection is dependent upon the material being used and any additional requirements.

	Shielding Gas	Typical Applications	Information
1	Argon(Pure)	Mild steel, carbon steel, low alloy steel, stainless steel, aluminium, copper, nickel alloys, titanium, magnesium	Initiates arc easily. Stable Arc Performance. Effective shielding gas. Comparatively low cost. Limited heat input.
2	Argon + (1 – 5%) Hydrogen	Stainless steel, nickel alloys	Hydrogen improves heat input, surface deposition and weld bead profile. Hydrogen % must be controlled to prevent hydrogen cracking with some sensitive materials.
3	Helium (Pure)	Stainless steel, aluminium, copper, titanium, magnesium	High heat input by increased arc voltage. Doesn't initiate the arc easily.
4	Helium + (25 – 80%) Argon	Carbon steel, low alloy steel, stainless steel, aluminium, copper, nickel alloys	Compromise between pure argon and helium. Gives good heat input for aluminium castings and alloys.
5	Nitrogen (Pure)	Copper	Good heat input and surface deposition qualities. Not suitable for a large range of other materials.
6	Argon + (0.5 – 15%) Nitrogen	Copper	Initiates arc easily. Good heat input. Limited range of materials.

Activity

Use your preferred method (paper and pencil, calculator, online converter, mobile phone app.) to calculate the gas flow difference between 20 l/min and 40cfm (cubic feet per minute)

Activity

In the space below, sketch the TIG welding equipment in your shop, label each part of the equipment and indicate the polarity terminals, current regulation and arc initiation system

Welding Parameters

Some of the settings that an operator can change in TIG welding are: the amperage used, the type of tungsten electrode, the shielding gas flow and the composition of the filler wire.

The settings for these parameters can change depending on the conditions of the job. For example: the weld position, joint configuration, the thermal conductivity, thickness and type of material and any need for additional alloying elements.

Back Purging

Back purging relies on an inert gas shield being present on the underside of stainless steel when welding butt and outside corner joints. The shielding gas prevents the penetrating weld metal from oxidising.

Trailing Shields

For some reactive materials such as titanium and zirconium, trailing shields are required if other chambers or shielding techniques are not available or practical. The trailing shield will ensure that there is inert gas coverage over the weld area until the molten metal has cooled to the point that it will not react with the atmosphere. This is supplied with a separate gas supply to the torch by means of a 'Y' connection on the flowmeter.

The Welding Process

TIG welding uses an electric current to generate an electric arc between the tip of a tungsten electrode and the work piece. An electric arc is when electricity jumps across a gap between two conductors. This gap is known as the arc length. The arc can create a heat in excess of 4 000°C.

The arc causes instant heating of the parent material and a molten weld pool is formed, into which additional material is added in the form of the filler wire to complete the weld.

As the process moves along the joint the deposited material cools and solidifies leaving a weld bead. The weld zone is protected from atmospheric contamination by a gas shield.

This process can also fuse the parent metal together without the need for filler wire; this is known as an autogenous weld.

When the TIG torch is being operated correctly it makes a humming sound. This is due to the high frequency.

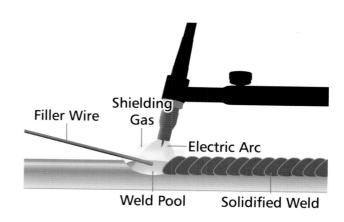

Welding process diagram

Preparing to Weld

Before commencing welding, there are a number of checks you need to make.

Preparation of Work Area

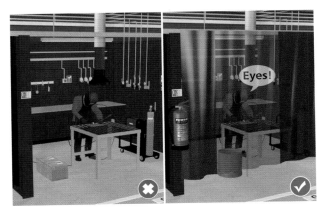

Correct and incorrect ways of preparing the work area

Health and Safety

Before carrying out any welding or fabrication operation you should carry out a risk assessment. This can include:

- Checking for hazards, for example slips, trips, obstructions and flammable materials.
- Checking the existing safety procedures and equipment, for example fire extinguishers, water buckets (for hot metal only), containment vessels and screening provision.
- Making people in the vicinity aware of what work is being carried out, restricting access to the work area and giving a verbal warning of when you are about to strike up an arc.

Material Preparation

Familiarise yourself with the relevant MSDSs before using any equipment, materials, solvents or chemicals.

It is good practice to deburr and degrease the material to prevent contamination of the weld and remove any flammable substances.

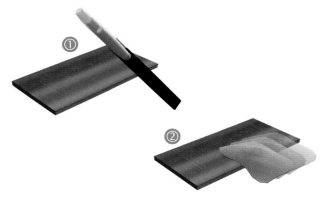

Material preparation: 1. Deburring; 2. Degreasing

Prior to any weld deposition, it is recommended that the joint is tacked to aid alignment and distortion control.

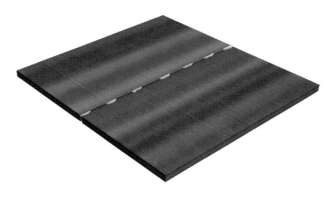

Tacking the joint

Position of Welder

Before welding, you should get into a comfortable and balanced position that can be maintained throughout the period of welding. You will need to able to see the weld develop and be able to weld along the joint in one continuous movement.

Striking the Arc

There are a number of techniques that can be used to strike the arc when TIG welding. The position of the strike is also important as a strike outside the weld joint may produce a weld defect.

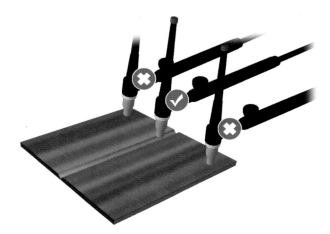

Correct and incorrect strike positions

A scratch start is when the tungsten electrode is initially lightly scratched on the surface of the parent material to initiate the arc.

A lift arc is when the tungsten electrode physically touches the parent material and is gradually lifted away to initiate the arc.

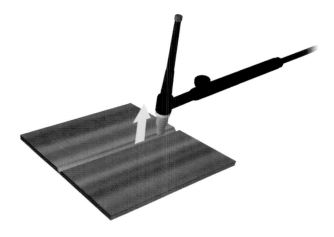

It is also possible to use a high frequency unit to initiate the arc. This sends a high frequency current superimposed on the standard current to initiate the arc.

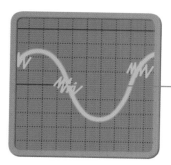

HF Current superimposed on standard current

High frequency unit

Once the arc has been struck and the arc length established, it must be maintained.

Techniques

Each welding process has specific techniques which require the understanding of the tilt angle and slope angle.

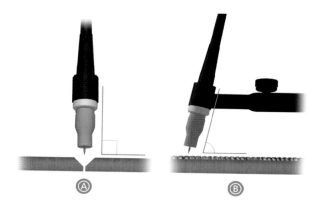

Techniques: A. Tilt angle; B. Slope angle

The tilt angle is the angle the welding torch is held at between the two pieces of material to be welded.

The slope angle is the angle the welding torch is held at between the joint to be welded and a 90° angle from the joint.

TIG welding uses the leftward technique and has a specific technique for starting and stopping a weld.

Leftward Technique

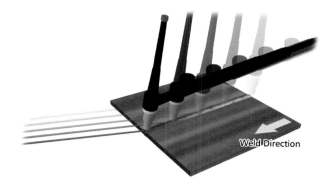

Using the leftward technique, the filler wire is fed into the front edge of the molten pool at a slope angle of 10-15°. It is held within the shielding gas to prevent weld defects such as atmospheric contamination and inclusions in the weld deposit.

The torch follows at a slope angle of 75-80° to the material being welded. This is followed by the solidifying weld metal.

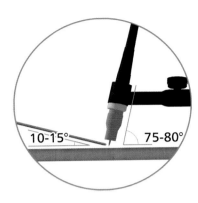

Leftward technique slope

Keep the filler wire as close to the plate as possible to prevent potential high frequency shock.

The welder should maintain a consistent arc length and access for filler wire in front of the weld and observe the deposit behind the torch to ensure a good weld.

Start Stop Technique

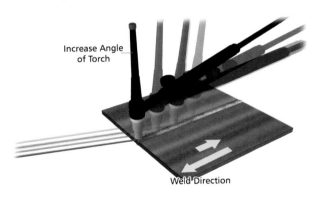

When you want to recommence a weld, you need to re-heat the weld back from the point at which you stopped. When the molten pool has been established, move forwards and apply the filler material as and when required.

As you work towards an open end, you need to increase the amount of filler wire and slightly increase the slope angle of the torch to prevent a crater forming. This would lead to potential weld failure if the crater was not filled.

Alternatively you can use slope in slope out controls or add additional pieces of metal to the end of the weld run to terminate the weld on. This is known as a run-off tab.

Additional Settings

There are some additional controls available when TIG welding, including slope in slope out controls, pre and post flow and pulse control.

Slope In/Slope Out Controls

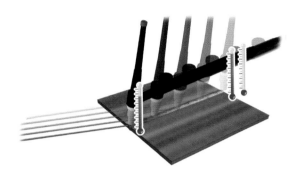

Slope in slope out technique

Slope in and slope out controls are designed to slowly build and reduce the arc temperature. This establishes the molten pool and prevents burn through of both the start position and termination position of the weld.

The controls also allow the termination point of the weld to be filled to the weld profile and prevent crater cracking.

If the machine you are using does not have these facilities, a good technique is to use run-on and run-off tags or plates.

Pre-flow and Post-flow

Pre-flow technique

Pre-flow is designed to ensure the initial purging of the gas line and the start of the gas flow for arc welding conditions.

Post-flow technique

Post-flow provides an additional period of time when the cooling weld and tungsten is shielded within the inert atmosphere.

Pulse Control

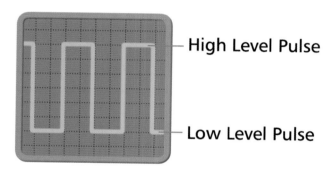

Pulse control technique

Pulse control allows welding to be carried out at a sufficient current to melt the parent material and filler material without overheating the joint and causing unnecessary distortion.

It provides a low background current with a high heat input for a few milliseconds before dropping back to the lower background current. This heating and cooling cycle creates a weld appearance that is typified by a series of overlapping circles.

Potential Welding Failures

Potential weld failures in TIG welding can occur for a number of reasons, for example, tungsten contamination.

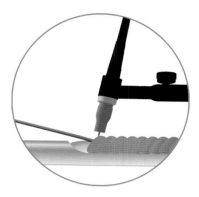

Excess deposition of filler material

If there is an excess deposition of filler material beyond the front edge of the molten pool it could contaminate the tungsten electrode. If this occurs, the power source should be turned off and the hot tungsten carefully removed and examined for the degree of contamination.

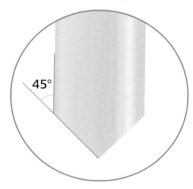

Prepare the tip of the electrode appropriately

If working with aluminium, the electrode contamination will need to be severed and the end prepared by grinding the electrode at an angle of 45° bevel to half the thickness of the electrode.

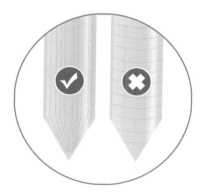

Grind the electrode in the appropriate direction

If working with low carbon steels and stainless steels these electrodes should be cleaned up on a grinding wheel. The grinding marks should run along the electrode towards the tip and not around the tip in a circle. This ensures a stable arc.

In both instances the electrode should only be ground on one end so it can be identified by type and is easier to remove from the collet assembly.

Cleaning the Weld

After a weld is complete it will generally need to be cleaned. Low carbon steels will require cleaning with a mild steel wire brush.

Stainless steels and aluminium will require cleaning with a stainless steel wire brush and may also require chemical cleaning.

Reinstate the Work Area

When you have finished welding, ensure all equipment is closed down correctly and turned off. Make sure the equipment is stored away safely and doesn't cause any hazards.

Sustainability
Cool all scrap metal and place it in the appropriate container.

Return any tools that have been used to their appropriate storage area and tidy up the work area.

Joints

There are four main types of joint in welding. Any weld on any joint should be equal to the thickness of the plate and have a smooth transition from the weld to the plate surface.

The slope and tilt angles will change with the position in which the weld is carried out. In this instance the tilt and slope angles mentioned are for the flat and horizontal vertical positions only.

Outside Corner Joint

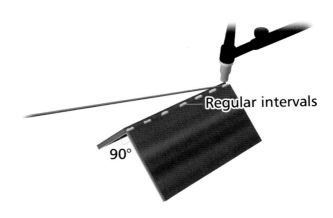

Regular intervals

90°

An outside corner joint is formed by two work pieces positioned with their edges next to each other at an angle of 90°. The weld is placed on the outside of this corner. The pieces should be tacked at each end and at regular intervals along the joint.

The welding torch should be tilted so it is halfway between the two work pieces and have a slope angle of 75-80°.

The filler wire should be tilted so it is halfway between, bisects the two work pieces and have a slope angle of 10-15°.

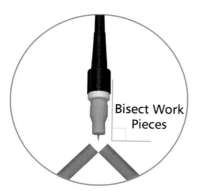

Tilt angle of torch

A lap joint is formed by two work pieces overlapping each other. The weld is placed where the two pieces meet. The pieces should be tacked at each end and at regular intervals along the joint.

The welding torch should be tilted so it is at 45° between the two work pieces and have a slope angle of 75-80°.

The filler wire should be titled so it is at 45° between the two work pieces and have a slope angle of 10-15°.

The tilt will ensure that most of the heat goes into the bottom plate and both plates reach melting point at the same time.

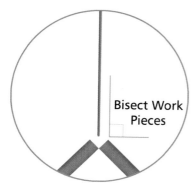

Tilt angle of filler wire

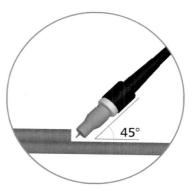

Tilt angle of torch

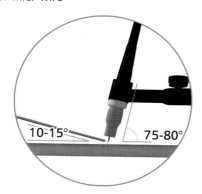

Slope angle of torch and filler wire

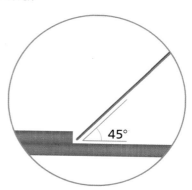

Tilt angle of filler wire

Lap Joint

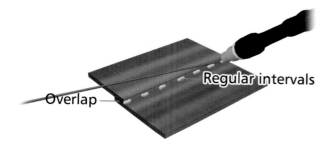

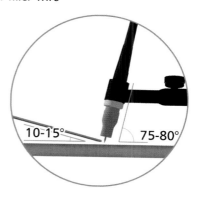

Slope angle of torch and filler wire

Tee Joint

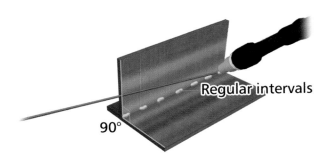

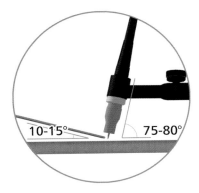

Slope angle of torch and filler wire

A tee joint is formed when one work piece is positioned at 90° to another work piece. The weld is placed where the two pieces meet. The pieces should be tacked at each end and at regular intervals along the joint.

The welding torch should be tilted so it is at 45° between the two work pieces and have a slope angle of 75-80°.

The filler wire should be titled so it is at 45° between the two work pieces and have a slope angle of 10-15°.

Tilt angle of torch

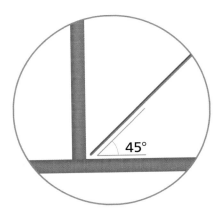

Tilt angle of filler wire

Butt Joint

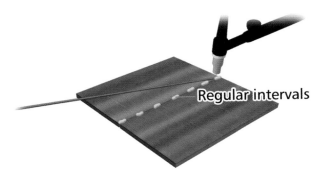

A butt joint is formed when the two work pieces are positioned side by side. The weld is placed between the two pieces.

Depending on the thickness of the material a gap between the two pieces is not always required. Where it is required, it is referred to as the root gap, and this can vary from zero to three millimetres. If the gap is too large or too small it can result in defects in the welded joint.

When welding thick plate, an edge preparation is put on the plates to ensure penetration and a sound weld deposit. The pieces should be tacked at each end and at regular intervals along the joint.

The welding torch should be tilted so it is at 90° to the surface of the work pieces and have a slope angle of 75-80°.

The filler wire should be titled so it is at 90° between the two work pieces and have a slope angle of 10-15°.

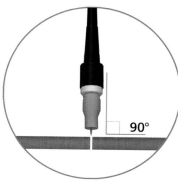

Tilt angle of torch

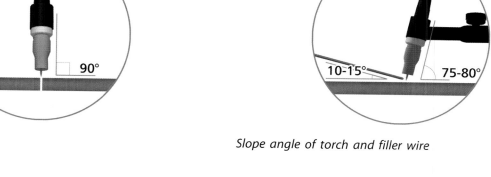

Slope angle of torch and filler wire

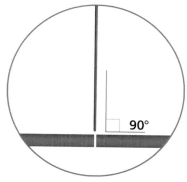

Tilt angle of filler wire

Activity

In the space below, sketch a butt joint on stainless steel and show the purging arrangements

Quality Control

Weld Defects

In all welding techniques there are a number of weld defects and discontinuities that can be identified once a weld is complete.

Porosity

This is created when gas becomes trapped in the weld deposit as the metal cools.

Causes: Lack of shielding gas, damaged hoses or poor seals, surface contaminants or oxidised or contaminated filler wire.

Remedies: Check flow rates and seals prior. Clean surface with suitable solvent and allow to evaporate. Filler wire is kept within the protective gas shield at all times.

Gas Pockets

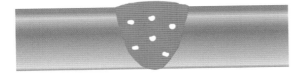

Porosity

Inclusions

These are created when foreign matter such as the electrode, oil, grease or mill scale becomes trapped within the solidifying weld deposit as irregular pores.

Causes: Contaminated electrode or using to high amperage which causes vaporisation of the electrode, which transfers into the weld pool.

Remedies: Careful selection of amperage settings to meet thickness of the material. Ensure that any electrode contamination is removed immediately and the area previously welded is cleaned to ensure weld integrity.

Non-metallic Materials

Inclusions

Poor Weld Profile / Dimension

These are caused by failure to maintain design specifications.

Causes: Using incorrect current settings, poor manipulation of torch or an incorrect speed of travel.

Remedies: Correct the current settings for material and weld configuration, maintenance of slope and tilt angles and observation of weld pool characteristics/fusion on side walls.

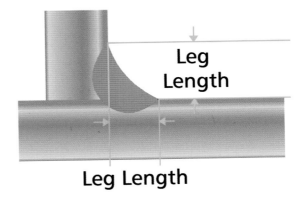

Poor weld profile / dimension

Lack of Side Wall Fusion

This is lack of fusion between weld metal and parent metal at the side of the weld and on the interrun deposition.

Causes: Using too low a current setting or a poor operator technique (slope and tilt angles).

Remedies: Establish correct torch and filler rod angles, ensure surface melting and deposition technique and speed of travel.

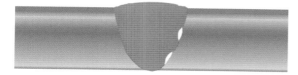

Lack of side wall fusion

Undercut

This is created when metal is removed from a joint without being replaced by weld material. This is commonly found at the toe of a run or in previously deposited weld metal.

Causes: Excessive current, insufficient filler wire, excessive speed of travel and poor manipulation of the torch.

Remedies: Careful control of current, matching the filler wire diameter to the weld specification, control of travel speed and manipulation of torch.

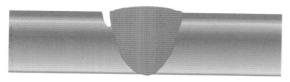

Undercut

Excessive Root Penetration

This is produced by excessive weld metal protruding through the root of a fusion weld.

Causes: Using a poor technique, incorrect edge preparation or too high a current setting.

Remedies: Close control of edge preparations especially root face dimension and root gap, correct selection of current settings to parent material and filler wire diameters.

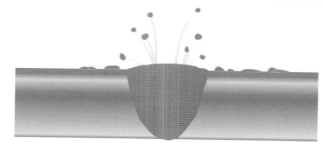

Excessive root penetration

WormHoles

These are created by contaminants which rise up through the weld metal.

Causes: Contaminants within the base metal or on the surface.

Remedies: Clean all surfaces and filler materials prior to welding with a proprietary solvent cleaner.

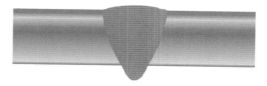

Wormholes

Stray Arcing

This happens when an arc is struck outside of the weld zone and may produce a hardened zone which may bring about ultimate failure of the weld.

Causes: Striking the arc outside the weld zone.

Remedies: Always ensure that all strikes are within the weld zone to establish the arc.

Stray arcing

Lack of Root Penetration

This is a failure of the weld metal to extend into the root of a joint.

Causes: Incorrect joint preparation and set up, with too small gap, moving too quickly with not enough heat applied.

Remedies: Ensure correct preparation and set up, a large enough gap, use the correct settings and adjust speed.

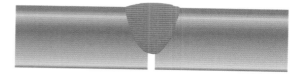

Lack of root penetration

Underfill

This is created when the weld metal is insufficient to produce the required deposit as stated in the specification.

Causes: Speed of travel is too fast, using the wrong diameter filler wire, failure to pause on the side of the weld.

Remedies: Ensure that the appropriate filler wire for the material is used and that the operator's technique is correct.

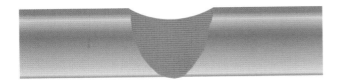

Underfill

Excessive Weld Reinforcement

This occurs when the weld metal deposited is excessive and leaves the weld protruding on the surface of the weld.

Causes: The diameter of the filler wire is too large, the speed of travel is too slow.

Remedies: Ensure that the appropriate filler wire for the material is used and that the operator's technique is correct.

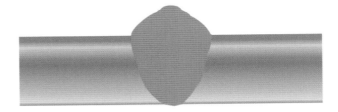

Excessive weld reinforcement

Misalignment of Plates

This is created by failing to align the plates after tacking and prior to welding, giving a stepped appearance.

Causes: Failure to tack weld prior to welding.

Remedies: Tacking at regular intervals and dressing the plates prior to welding.

Misalignment of plates

CHECK YOUR KNOWLEDGE

1   Which of the following applications can TIG welding be used for? Circle the correct answer.

   a.   Cutting
   b.   Motorsport
   c.   Pre-heating materials
   d.   Aerospace industry
   e.   Hard soldering
   f.   Exotic metals

2   What type of current can be used in TIG welding? Circle the correct answer.

   a.   AC
   b.   DC
   c.   AC or DC

3   In TIG welding, into which part of the molten pool is the filler rod fed? Circle the correct answer.

   a.   The centre of the molten pool
   b.   The front edge of the molten pool
   c.   The back of the molten pool

4   Can you identify these weld defects? Write a, b or c next to the correct diagram.

   a.   Porosity
   b.   Wormholes
   c.   Inclusions

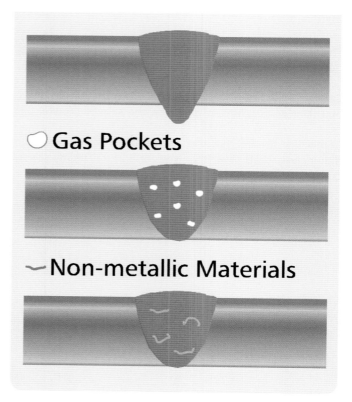

○ Gas Pockets

⌣ Non-metallic Materials

Summary

This concludes this chapter on TIG welding.

You should now be able to explain the principles of TIG welding; list the specific health and safety requirements; list the equipment and explain how it should be set up; explain how to carry out the TIG welding process and list the weld defects that can occur.

End test

1. **Which of the following welders is wearing the appropriate PPE for TIG welding? Circle the correct answer.**

   ☐ a.

   ☐ b.

   ☐ c.

2. **Identify the components of the TIG equipment shown.**

   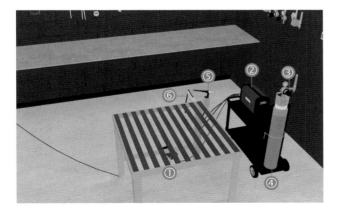

   1.
   2.
   3.
   4.
   5.
   6.

3. **Identify the different types of TIG electrodes by the colours of their tips. Write a, b, c or d next to the correct diagram.**

   ☐ a. Zirconiated

   ☐ b. 1% Lanthanated

   ☐ c. Thoriated

   ☐ d. Ceriated

4. **Which of these gases can be used in some form when TIG Welding? Circle the correct answer(s).**

☐ a. Argon

☐ b. Carbon Dioxide

☐ c. Helium

☐ d. Hydrogen

☐ e. Nitrogen

5. **What material would you use a trailing shield on? Circle the correct answer.**

☐ a. Aluminium

☐ b. Titanium

☐ c. Stainless Steel

☐ d. Carbon Steel

6. **What is the main technique used in TIG welding? Circle the correct answer.**

☐ a. Push Technique

☐ b. Drag Technique

☐ c. Leftward Technique

☐ d. Rightward Technique

☐ e. Start Stop Technique

7. **What would be the ideal slope angles for the welding torch and filler wire when TIG welding? Circle the correct answer.**

☐ a. Welding torch held at a slope angle of 45-50° and filler wire held at a slope angle of 40-45°

☐ b. Welding torch held at a slope angle of 55-60° and filler wire held at a slope angle of 25-30°

☐ c. Welding torch held at a slope angle of 65-70° and filler wire held at a slope angle of 15-20°

☐ d. Welding torch held at a slope angle of 75-80° and filler wire held at a slope angle of 10-15°

8. **When TIG welding, what are the slope in and slope out controls designed to do? Circle the correct answer.**

☐ a. Prevent burn through at start and end position of the weld

☐ b. Provide controlled gas flow at the start and end position of the weld

☐ c. Provide a pulsed current which causes a regular heating and cooling cycle

9. **When working on stainless steel, which two joints will require back purging? Circle the correct answers.**

☐ a. Outside Corner Joint

☐ b. Lap Joint

☐ c. Tee Joint

☐ d. Butt Joint

10. **Which of these weld defects could be caused by an oxidised filler wire? Circle the correct answer(s).**

☐ a. Slag Inclusions

☐ b. Porosity

☐ c. Excess weld penetration

☐ d. Lack of side wall fusion

Part 3

Engineering materials, metal fabrication and quality control

8

Engineering Materials

LEARNING OBJECTIVES

By the end of this chapter you will be able to:

- Describe the mechanical properties of materials
- List the metals used in engineering
- Describe the structure, properties and uses of metals used in engineering

Mechanical Properties

The mechanical properties of materials enable them to resist external forces without failing. It is very important to understand the mechanical properties of different materials to ensure that they meet the requirements of the engineering specification.

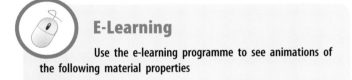

E-Learning

Use the e-learning programme to see animations of the following material properties

The following sections describe eleven properties of materials and give examples of where these characteristics are important.

Hardness

Ability to resist indentation, cutting and abrasion, the sort of qualities that would be expected of gear teeth and the contact faces of agricultural machinery.

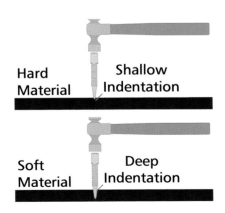

Brittleness

Ability to resist being significantly deformed when cracked or broken. A typical material that displays this property would be cast iron, which is hard but brittle.

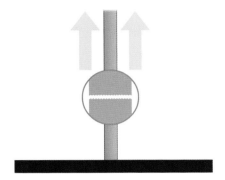

Ductility

Ability to be drawn out along its length, bent or twisted under a tensile load without fracturing, useful in wire, bar or tube manufacture.

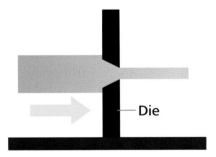

Toughness

Ability to resist shock and impact loading as in the case of a hammer hitting the end of a chisel. Toughness can be controlled by heat treatment or by work hardening.

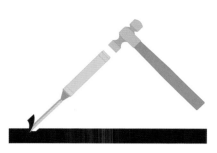

Strength

There are five types of strength:

1   Tensile: resistance to being pulled apart
2   Compressive: resistance to being crushed
3   Shear: resistant to being cut or sliced
4   Torsional: resistance to being twisted
5   Impact: resistance to a rapidly applied load

These abilities are put to good use in the form of high-tensile bolts, rivets, and rotating members that would be found in most cars or factory components.

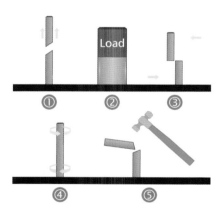

Different types of strength properties

Malleability

Ability of a material to deform under compressive stress. A property very much sought after in presswork where the material must flow to shape under the force of the press without fracture.

Elasticity

Ability of a material to return to its original dimension upon the load being removed, a property that quite a few engineering materials possess to some degree. A typical application would be in the manufacture of springs.

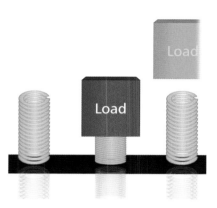

Plasticity

Ability of a material to be deformed and retain the shape of the load once it has been removed. A property most sought after with forgings.

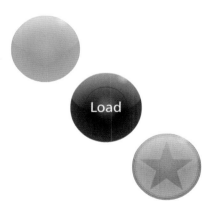

Conductivity

Ability of a material to conduct heat or electricity. It is this property that ensures the correct selection for conductors such as electric plugs, and circuitries for a whole host of electronic devices. It is also used in insulators (made from plastics, ceramics and glass) which oppose the flow of current and heat.

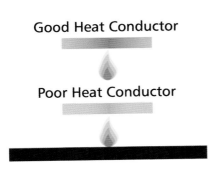

Source of metals

Weldability

The ease with which a material or materials can be welded to give an acceptable joint.

Corrosion Resistance

The ability to resist oxidation or chemical attack from substances such as acids, alkalis and solvents. This property is looked for in architecture, cryogenic applications and marine environments.

Introduction to Metals

The most common engineering material is steel. Today's materials owe a lot to the early pioneer, such as Sir Henry Bessemer who revolutionised the industry by developing the converter process for steel making in 1856. The open-hearth process arrived a decade later, followed by a series of advances in steel-making processes which led to the complex industry we have today.

Metals have to go through a number of processes before they end up in everyday items that you use and see around you.

Source

Most metals are found within the earth's crust in the form of solid rock minerals called ores. These ores are mined from the ground, and sometimes huge quantities are required to make useable amounts of pure metal. Metal mining takes place all over the world and consumes vast resources.

Processing

Production of iron starts with iron ores being melted in large blast furnaces using coke as a fuel and limestone as a fusible slag. These are heated by high pressure blasts of hot air which results in the coke being partially burnt and the hot carbon monoxide produced reduces the oxides of iron to the metal. Both the slag and iron are tapped separately at regular intervals and the iron that is produced is impure. It contains approximately 4% carbon derived from the coke, 2% silicon and 1% manganese reduced from the ore and anything up to 2% phosphorous and sulphur which are the by-products of the ore. At this stage it is often referred to as 'pig iron' because of the shape of the ingots that the hot iron solidifies as. In this condition it has very few possible applications and requires further refining. This is done by oxidation, inserting an oxygen lance to reduce the carbon, phosphorous and sulphur content of the molten ingots in a kaldo converter which is continuously rotated to ensure good mixing of the charge and efficient refining.

Metals are either ferrous or non-ferrous but can also be combined with other metals to form alloys.

Processing of metals

Forms of Supply

Metals can be formed and supplied in almost any shape depending on the requirements.

- Plate is measured in millimetres and is usually 3mm or thicker and available in widths from 300mm up to 2.4m, lengths from 2.4m–6m. and thickness ranges up to 300mm.

- Sheets are measured in millimetres or Standard Wire Gauge (SWG) and are usually up to 3mm.

- Pipe is dimensioned, or measured, by its diameter and schedule or strength. Pipe that is smaller than 300mm is dimensioned by its inside diameter, and the outside diameter is given for pipe that is 300mm in diameter and larger. The strength of pipe is given as a schedule. Schedules 10 through to 180 are available and schedule 40 is often considered a standard strength. The wall thickness for pipe is determined by its schedule (pressure range). Pipe is available in welded (seamed) and extruded (seamless) forms.

- Hollow section sizes are always given as the outside diameter. The desired shape of hollow section, such as square, round or rectangular, must be listed with the ordering information. The wall thickness is measured in millimetres, although conversion can be done for imperial measures or as manufacturer's Standard Wire Gauge (SWG). Tubing should also be specified as rigid or flexible. The strength of hollow section may also be specified as the ability to withstand compression, bending or twisting loads.

- Structural sections are available in a range of sections which include beams, joists, channels, angles, tee-stalks and z-sections. All of these are produced by hot rolling and rely on their shape to resist loads or buckling. They are available in a wide range of dimensions and thickness ranges.

- Angles are dimensioned by giving the length of the legs of the angle and their thickness, stock lengths of angles are available in 6m, 9.1m, 12.2m, and 18.3m lengths.

- Extrusions offer a lightweight alternative to sectional sections. The shape determines strength under load. They are used extensively where weight is a critical factor, especially in automobile and aircraft manufacture.

- Wire and rod are produced by drawing down the material to produce a range of wire, rods and bars for electrical purposes, filler wires and electrodes, as well as a multitude of engineering applications.

- Forgings are used to meet an increasing range of applications from aircraft, automobile, and marine manufacturing industries.

Forms of supply of metals

Applications

Metals can be used for almost anything, depending on their individual properties. Some metals are particularly suitable for high strength structures; some are good conductors of heat and electricity while others are used in specialist areas such as oil refineries, catering and brewing and all forms of transportation from commercial aircraft, military vessels to space travel.

Applications of metals

Activity

Select a suitable material for the following components and indicate the reasons for your selection.

Component	Material selected	Reasons for selection
Machine Bed		
Aircraft Panel		
Catering Equipment		
Car Body Panel		
Heating System		
Nuts and bolts		

Sustainability

The production of metal from its extraction and processing to its final use consumes vast resources. It can be a very expensive process and it uses huge amounts of energy and contributes significant amounts of greenhouse gases to the environment.

Almost all metals can be reused and recycled into high quality metal. This is a more eco-friendly alternative to the production of new metals and provides environmental, energy and financial benefits. By recycling everyday objects such as aluminium cans, household appliances or even cars, we are able to contribute to protecting our environment and saving our resources for future generations. This now has such a high profile that it is incumbent on manufacturers to use materials that can be recycled. A typical example of this is in the manufacture of motor vehicles with some manufacturers claiming that 90% of their new ranges are recyclable.

Recycling of metals

http://en.fotolia.com/id/21355739 © thieury #21355739

The grains in metal can reach a point when they virtually lock-up; the grain boundaries are compacted and any further work would eventually bring about failure. This is where heat treatment comes in to play. By applying heat to a specified temperature we are able to release the locked in stresses in the grains and bring about what is known as 'recrystallization'. This is a form of relaxation that allows the grains to return to their original form, which allows us to perform further forming operations. This is 'process annealing', one of the mechanisms made possible by the use of heat treatment. Other processes associated with heat treatment include hardening, tempering, annealing and normalising. Heat treatment also has an important part to play in non-ferrous materials.

In the welding process the input of heat, and the reaction of the parent metal to it, can have an immense effect upon the resulting weld metal, the structure as a whole and to the service conditions under which it is able to operate. In the final chapter you will learn more about these effects and understand why they need to be controlled. What we hope to achieve is a rounded 'equiaxed' grain structure, which has the best mechanical properties and reduce the formation of elongated 'columnar' grains, which could bring about failure.

The input of heat over a period of time can affect the composition of a structure and can play a major part in determining the physical, chemical and mechanical properties of the material. Knowledge of a metal's grain structure is essential to ensure that the materials comply with production requirements.

When a metal is subjected to heat over a certain period of time, the grain structure alters. This is known as grain growth and it can be controlled in a number of ways.

Metal Grain Structure and Growth

All metals are crystalline in nature. It is these crystals, or grains as they are also known, that make up the structure of the metal. The way in which the crystals or grains form during initial manufacture of plate, sheet or any other market form will, to a large extent, determine the form of heat treatment or consideration that needs to be taken into account when manufacturing. The grain structure can be altered by cold working, in which the grains become elongated in the direction of rolling, imparting a degree of hardness and toughness, sometimes referred to as 'tempering'. Some metals that are relatively soft in their natural form, such as aluminium, need to be tempered in order to have a commercial use.

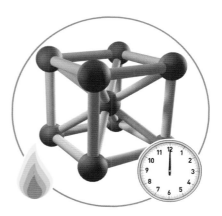

Metal grain structure alters when subjected to heat over time.

Grain Growth

When a heat source is applied over time to a section of metal, the grains in this section that make up the structure of the metal start to grow.

At the start of the heating process the grains are small and positioned next to each other.

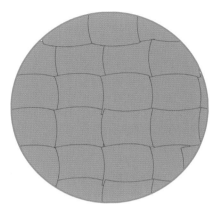

As the temperature of the heat source increases the grains grow larger in size by absorbing neighbouring grains.

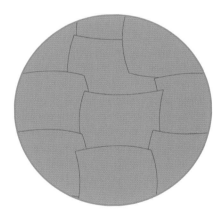

As the temperature increases further still, the grains forming the structure are significantly larger and fewer in number than before the heating process.

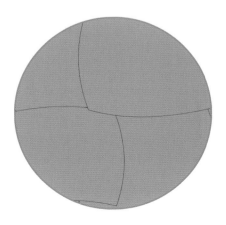

An enlarged grain structure can lead to a marked reduction in its mechanical properties. For example, a crack in a larger grain structure will have more impact than in a small grain structure.

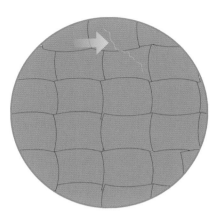

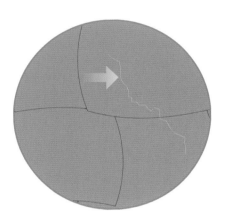

E-Learning

Use the e-learning programme to see an animation of grain growth.

Controlling Grain Growth

Grain growth can be controlled in a number of ways, two of which are annealing and normalising.

Annealing is heating the metal to a pre-determined temperature to bring about recrystallization and controlling the rate of cooling in 'still air', which is free of draughts, or an inert atmosphere to keep the surface of the steel bright. This will reduce the stresses within the material and return some ductility.

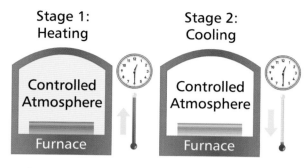

Annealing process

Normalising is heating the metal to a pre-determined temperature, again to bring about recrystallization, and allowing it to rapidly cool in air to bring it back to its 'normal' structure (tensile strength, hardness, and toughness) without greatly affecting its ductility.

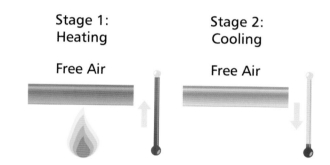

Normalising process

The Effects of Heat

When a metal is heated, the heat will conduct through the metal a certain distance from the source point. The area affected by the heat is known as the Heat Affected Zone or HAZ and it is in this area where grain growth occurs and the mechanical properties alter.

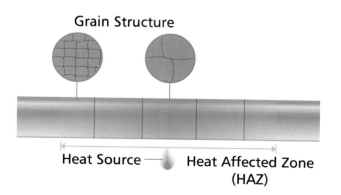

The size of the HAZ can be dependent on a number of variables and their combinations, some of which are listed in the following text.

Heat Input

A heat input can be formed using two main sources of energy, arc energy or gas energy.

Arc energy processes, such as manual metal arc, tungsten inert gas shielded welding (TIG) and metal inert gas shielded welding (MIG), are just three of the most commonly recognised processes which use the combination of an electric arc and gas shield to produce an extremely efficient method of joining materials.

Electric arc energy can also produce high temperatures for welding by means of:

- an electric arc (arc welding);
- the resistance to the flow of an electrical current (resistance welding);
- an induced electrical current (induction welding);
- light emission in an ionised gas (laser).

An arc energy heat input, for example MIG welding, will tend to give a narrower HAZ due to its higher temperature that it is concentrated on a specific area over a shorter period of time.

Gas energy is a thermo-chemical process where the energy for welding is derived from the combustion of a fuel gas aided by pure oxygen. The ratio of fuel gas to oxygen is one part fuel gas to two parts oxygen. One part of the oxygen required is supplied from a cylinder and the other part from the surrounding atmosphere.

A gas energy heat input such as oxyacetylene welding uses a lower temperature and therefore takes a longer time to heat the area, giving more time for the heat to spread, giving a larger HAZ.

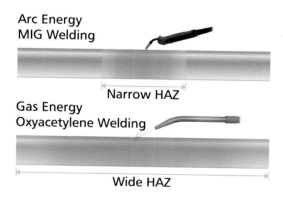

Two main sources of heat input: Arc energy and Gas energy

Thermal Conductivity

The amount of thermal conductivity a metal has will affect how much heat passes through it and the distance it reaches. In large structures, such as bridges, designers incorporate expansion joints to take account of this expansion. Failure to provide these release mechanisms could eventually lead to failure of the structure. In welding terms a metal with a high level of thermal conductivity such as aluminium or copper will give a larger HAZ. A metal with lower thermal conductivity such as stainless steel will give a narrower HAZ, but will be more susceptible to distortion and therefore requires distortion control techniques to be employed to reduce stresses within the structure.

Material Mass

The mass of a material affects how heat is distributed. The source of heat and the conductivity of the material will also play a part but generally, a thicker material will absorb more heat than a thin piece of material but may exhibit considerable forces on the weld which could lead to failure. To counter this effect pre-heating is often used to maintain a thermal balance into the weld deposit and parent material and thereby reduce the effects of residual stresses. Due to the absorption of heat in a thicker material, there tends to be a narrow HAZ, whereas the opposite is true in a thinner material.

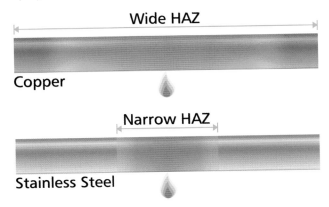

Thermal conductivity of copper and aluminium

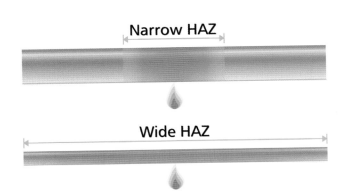

Material mass's impact on heat distribution

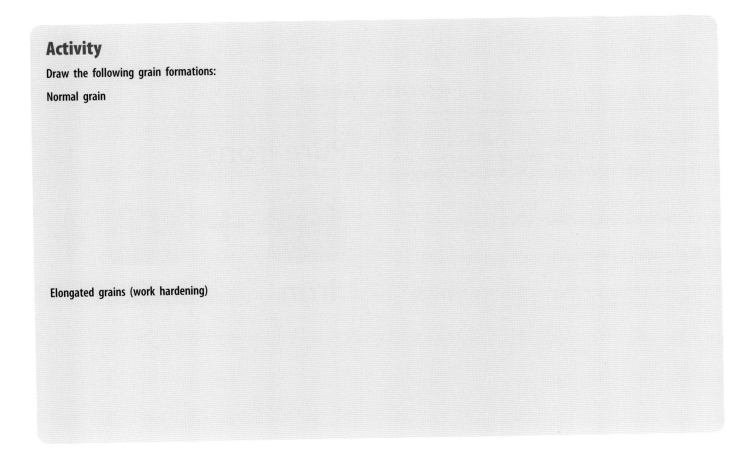

Activity

Draw the following grain formations:

Normal grain

Elongated grains (work hardening)

Recrystallised grain structure

Grain growth

Ferrous Metals

A ferrous metal is a metal whose main component is iron. There are a number of different types of ferrous metals and they can generally be grouped into the following categories:

- Pure irons are ferrous metals with a small carbon content.
- Cast irons are ferrous metals with a high carbon content.
- Plain carbon steels are alloys of iron, carbon and manganese.
- Stainless steels are alloys of carbon steel with other elements such as chromium and nickel.

Pure Irons

Fe + C

Iron   Carbon

Cast Irons

Iron   Carbon

Plain Carbon Steels

Iron   Carbon   Manganese

Stainless Steels

Iron   Carbon   Chromium   Nickel

Carbon Steels

Carbon steels owe their properties chiefly to the carbon content of the metal rather than to the presence of any other elements. Commonly used carbon steels have carbon contents in the range of 0.05% to 1.2%. For most constructional and engineering applications the maximum carbon content is typically 0.6%. Steels containing more carbon than this are usually only used for tools.

Chemical Analysis of Carbon Steels

All carbon steels contain the following elements in addition to iron and carbon:

- silicon;
- manganese;
- sulphur;
- phosphorous.

These elements occur in all steels, either as the result of their presence in the original iron ore or as a residual effect of the steel making process. While sulphur and phosphorous are deliberate additions in free cutting steels, in carbon steels they are regarded as impurities and

should be kept to a maximum of typically 0.040% to 0.050%.

Manganese occurs naturally in most iron ore deposits. During steel making more is added to give a total content within the range 0.5% to 1%. It improves the toughness by combining with any sulphur present to form discrete particles of manganese sulphide. In the absence of manganese, the sulphide would combine with iron to form a continuous film of iron sulphide at the grain boundaries, which would embrittle the steel and result in 'hot shortness'. Manganese is also used as a deoxidizer; it is added to the steel to combine with any dissolved oxygen preventing it from reacting with carbon to form the gas carbon monoxide which would result in blowholes during solidification. Finally, manganese increases the hardenability of steel, which is a measure of how quickly steel has to be cooled to fully harden. Low hardenability steels require rapid cooling, for example by quenching in brine or water to fully harden.

Silicon occurs in all steels naturally, but it is also deliberately added during steel making. Once again it is a deoxidiser and amounts up to 0.35% are added for this purpose. The majority of steels for engineering applications are fully deoxidised with silicon contents within the range of 0.15% to 0.35%.

Sulphur is regarded as an impurity in carbon steels and is consequently minimised to levels below 0.05%. When present, sulphur tends to embrittle steel by collecting at the grain boundaries as iron sulphide which has a low melting point. This leads to a lack of cohesion between the grains of the metal, or hot shortness, when it is subjected to hot-working. In free cutting steels a higher sulphide content is permitted in combination with higher manganese sulphide particles which significantly improves machinability.

Phosphorous is an undesirable impurity in carbon steels and is limited to below 0.05%. A high phosphorous content causes failure in steel when subjected to cold working, a condition known as 'cold shortness'. In free cutting steels marginally higher contents are desired to improve machinability.

Plain carbon steel is a steel containing up to 1.7% carbon, together with not more than 0.05% of silicon and phosphorous and not more than 1% manganese, and with only traces of other elements. It can be susceptible to cracking and distortion when quench-hardened and for this reason the content should be kept low, below 0.5% in medium carbon steels. Within the plain carbon steels it is further divided into sub categories of dead mild steel, mild steel (or low carbon steel), medium carbon steel, and high carbon steel.

Ferrous Metal Fact Sheets

Wrought Iron

This cannot be classified as a carbon steel due to insufficient carbon (less than 0.05%) being present. It is used extensively for crane hooks, lifting tackle, and architectural ironwork.

Low Carbon Steel (Mild Steel)

Dead mild steel has the carbon content left deliberately low (0.1–0.15%), so that the steel will have high ductility. This enables it to be pressed into complicated shapes even while it is cold, which makes it ideal for deep pressings such as motor car body panels or for extruded components such as thin wire, rod, and drawn tubes.

Mild steel or low carbon steel is relatively soft and ductile containing 0.15–0.3% carbon. It can be forged and drawn in both the hot and cold conditions which makes it ideal for the manufacture of constructional sections, bars or boiler plate.

Medium Carbon Steel

Medium carbon steel contains between 0.3–0.8% carbon, this is harder, tougher and less ductile than mild steel, and cannot be bent or formed, to any extent in the cold condition, without cracking. It is used extensively for forgings, axles, leaf springs, and cold chisels.

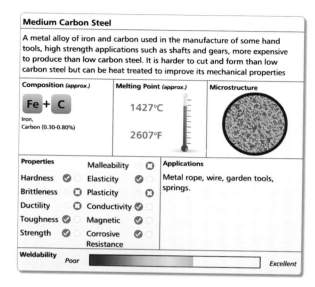

High Carbon Steel

These steels contain between 0.8–1.4% carbon which means that the ductility is once again reduced, as is the toughness, and cold forming is not recommended. However, high carbon steel does hot forge well, providing the temperature is closely controlled between 700°–900°C. Applications include cold chisels, knives, drills and metal cutting tools.

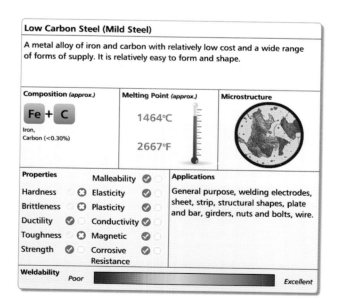

Carbon Manganese Steel

Steels in this group have a manganese content usually between 1.3% to 1.7% with a carbon content in the range 0.15% to 0.04% depending on the specification. Typical applications are welded structures and components where reasonable tensile strength and toughness are important.

Stainless Steel

This is a term generally applied to a group of steels with more than 10-12% chromium. Other elements such as nickel, molybdenum, niobium and titanium are used to provide additional operating characteristics which extend the range of applications that they can be used for. The corrosion resistant properties come from the invisible protective coating which is always present on the metal's surface. If the surface is scratched and the oxide film is damaged it will immediately reform in the presence of oxygen in the atmosphere, and as a result the metal's corrosion resistance is unaffected. Sheets can be supplied with a protective PVC or polythene coating to protect against damage during storage and handling. It is available in four classifications; ferritic, martensitic, austenitic, and duplex, all of which refer to the metallurgical structure that they form.

Ferritic stainless steels contain 13–20% chromium and less than 0.1% carbon and may be strengthened by work hardening. They are tough, ductile, are easily worked in the hot or cold condition and they are also magnetic. Their low strength prohibits these steels from being used for highly stressed components. Typical applications include domestic and automotive trim, exhaust systems, food processing and catering equipment and architectural cladding panels.

Martensitic stainless steels contain between 11–18% chromium with a carbon content between 0.1–1.5%. They do not normally contain nickel in appreciable quantities. These steels possess good corrosion resistance, are magnetic and can be hardened and tempered by heat treatment. They are not so easily formed and welding of martensitic stainless steel is not recommended. Typical applications include cutlery, surgical instruments, fastenings, valves, spindles and shafts.

Austenitic stainless steels contain both chromium and nickel with the carbon content below 0.15%. One of the best known is the 18/8 stainless steel containing 18% chromium and 8% nickel. This range of stainless steels has excellent corrosion resistance properties and remain tough and ductile even at sub-zero (cryogenic) temperatures. They are capable of being cold worked and although they work-harden, they can be softened by annealing and are non-magnetic in the annealed state. This group of stainless steels are readily welded and the addition of 'stabilising' elements such as molybdenum, titanium and niobium greatly increases their weldability. The austenitic group are designated in the ISO standards by the '300'series while the ferritic and martensitic groups are denoted by the '400'series. The purity of product and ease of cleaning make it highly suitable for use in the food processing industry as well as for hospital and domestic uses. It is also extensively used in the petro-chemical industry.

Duplex stainless steels covers a group of high-strength, corrosion resistant steels that contain higher chromium percentages and lower nickel percentages than their equivalent austenitic stainless steels, and have nitrogen and manganese as important alloying elements. These steels are called 'duplex' because the metallurgical structure consists of a mixture of 50% ferrite and 50% austenite. Typical applications include increasing use in the oil and chemical processing industries because of its ability to maintain corrosion resistance and toughness under extreme working conditions.

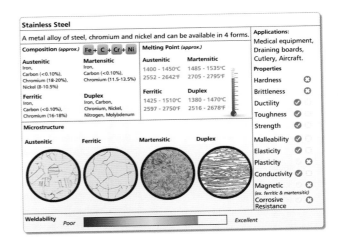

Grey Cast Iron

This is a cast iron containing 3.2–3.5% carbon which is present as free carbon flakes of graphite which gives the material its characteristic grey colour when fractured. This graphite is self-lubricating which means it promotes good machining characteristics and has a dampening effect upon vibrations, which makes it ideal for machine frames. It does, however, have a very low resistance to tensile loading.

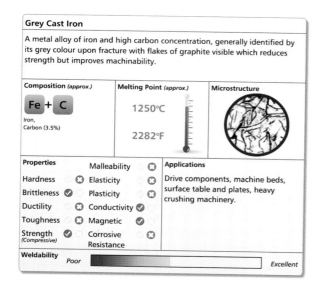

Grey Cast Iron

A metal alloy of iron and high carbon concentration, generally identified by its grey colour upon fracture with flakes of graphite visible which reduces strength but improves machinability.

Composition (approx.): Fe + C, Iron, Carbon (3.5%)
Melting Point (approx.): 1250°C / 2282°F

Properties:
- Hardness ✗
- Brittleness ✓
- Ductility ✗
- Toughness ✗
- Strength (Compressive) ✓
- Malleability ✗
- Elasticity ✗
- Plasticity ✗
- Conductivity ✓
- Magnetic ✓
- Corrosive Resistance ✗

Weldability: Poor ——— Excellent

Applications: Drive components, machine beds, surface table and plates, heavy crushing machinery.

chosen to produce fittings for pipework. Joining of these cast irons is usually done by braze welding or the use of low hydrogen electrodes due to their sensitivity to cracking, or porosity by other joining processes.

Malleable Cast Iron

A metal alloy of iron and high carbon concentration, used when a stronger, less brittle material than grey cast iron is required.

Composition (approx.): Fe + C, Iron, Carbon (3.5%)
Melting Point (approx.): 1250°C / 2282°F

Properties:
- Hardness ✗
- Brittleness ✗
- Ductility ✗
- Toughness ✓
- Strength ✓
- Malleability ✓
- Elasticity ✗
- Plasticity ✗
- Conductivity ✓
- Magnetic ✓
- Corrosive Resistance ✗

Weldability: Poor ——— Excellent

Applications: Pipe fittings, elbows, bends.

White Cast Iron

These are cast irons that are traditionally regarded as hard and unmachinable due to the combined carbon content. They are normally 'cast to shape', so that final finishing is kept to a minimum. The composition of white cast iron (2.2–3% carbon, 0.4–1.5% silicon, 0.1% phosphorous) and the lack of alloying additions make it a relatively cheap material. The industrial applications of this material are applications such drag line buckets, crushing and grinding equipment and nozzles for shot blasting.

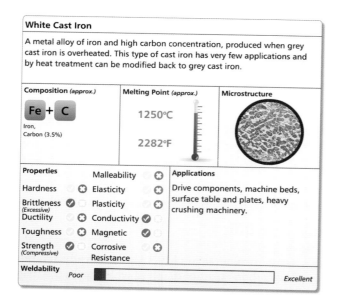

White Cast Iron

A metal alloy of iron and high carbon concentration, produced when grey cast iron is overheated. This type of cast iron has very few applications and by heat treatment can be modified back to grey cast iron.

Composition (approx.): Fe + C, Iron, Carbon (3.5%)
Melting Point (approx.): 1250°C / 2282°F

Properties:
- Hardness ✗
- Brittleness (Excessive) ✓
- Ductility ✗
- Toughness ✗
- Strength (Compressive) ✓
- Malleability ✗
- Elasticity ✗
- Plasticity ✗
- Conductivity ✓
- Magnetic ✓
- Corrosive Resistance ✗

Weldability: Poor ——— Excellent

Applications: Drive components, machine beds, surface table and plates, heavy crushing machinery.

Malleable Cast Iron

Malleable cast irons have a reduced carbon content 2.5–3.0% and because of their high malleability are often

Spheroidal Cast Iron

Spheroidal graphite (SG) cast iron is a cast iron in which traces of magnesium or cerium are added to ordinary grey cast iron in order to redistribute the graphite flakes as very fine spheroids or balls of carbon. This greatly improves the mechanical properties of the metal so that it can be used for more highly stressed components

Spheroidal (SG) Cast Iron

A metal alloy of iron and high carbon concentration, which is also known as a high duty cast iron. When traces of the metal's magnesium or cerium are added to ordinary grey cast iron the graphite flakes become redistributed throughout the mass of the metal as fine spheroids.

Composition (approx.): Fe + C, Iron, Carbon (3.5%)
Melting Point (approx.): 1250°C / 2282°F

Properties:
- Hardness ✗
- Brittleness ✗
- Ductility ✗
- Toughness ✓
- Strength (Tensile) ✓
- Malleability ✗
- Elasticity ✗
- Plasticity ✗
- Conductivity ✓
- Magnetic ✓
- Corrosive Resistance ✗

Weldability: Poor ——— Excellent

Applications: Forged crank shafts, water mains, manhole covers.

Abbreviations used in Stock Control

Abbreviation	Material
GFS	Ground flat stock
CI	Cast Iron
M	Mild steel, low carbon steel
CRCA	Cold-rolled, close annealed
LCS	Low Carbon Steel
HRPO	Hot-rolled, pickled and oiled
BDMS	Bright drawn mild steel

Sometimes steel is referred to by different names depending on how it has been processed such as:

- bright bar: same as BDMS;
- black bar: hot rolled mild steel;
- silver steel: centreless ground high carbon steel rod.

Material treatment

Many of the materials described above are supplied having had some form of treatment, and it is these processes which can govern their operational efficiency.

- **Hardened** means that they have been heated to a predetermined temperature and quenched in a medium such as water, oil or brine. Not all metallic materials can be hardened by heat treatment but all can be work hardened.
- **Tempered** refers to the material being re-heated after hardening to reduce some of the hardness and increase the toughness. This is done by heating to a predetermined temperature and observing a colour change and then quenching in some medium.
- **Cold rolled** is one method of work hardening. The material is passed back and forth through rollers to increase its tensile strength, temper or just to increase the hardness.
- **Close annealed** means that the material is heated in a container in which an inert rich gas is circulated, and then allowed to cool at a controlled rate within this inert environment.
- **Annealed** means that the material is heated to a predetermined temperature, to bring about re-crystallization, which will reduce the stresses within the material and return some ductility. It is held at this temperature to ensure full soaking of the material and then allowed to cool in still air.
- **Normalised** is also a heat treatment process where the material is heated to a predetermined temperature to bring about re-crystallization and relieve stresses. It is then allowed to soak followed by rapidly cooling in air, to bring the structure of the material back to its 'normal' structure without greatly affecting its ductility

E-Learning

Use the e-learning programme to download a copy of these fact sheets.

Activity

Match these heat treatment definitions to their processes.

tempering	They have been heated to a predetermined temperature and quenched in a medium such as water, oil or brine. Not all metallic materials can be hardened by heat treatment but all can be work hardened.
hardening	The material has been re-heated after hardening to reduce some of the hardness and increase the toughness. This is done by heating to a predetermined temperature and observing a colour change and then quenching in some medium.
normalising	The material is heated to a predetermined temperature, to bring about re-crystallization, which will reduce the stresses within the material and return some ductility. It is held at this temperature to ensure full soaking of the material and then allowed to cool in 'still air' (free of draughts).
annealing	A heat treatment process where the material is heated to a predetermined temperature to bring about re-crystallization and relieve stresses. It is then allowed to soak followed by rapidly cooling in air, to bring the structure of the material back to its normal structure.

Non-Ferrous Metals

A non-ferrous metal is a metal that does not contain any iron. This group includes pure metals such as copper, aluminium, zinc, tin and lead and also alloys of two or more non-ferrous metals, such as copper-based alloys or aluminium-based alloys.

Pure Metals

Cu   **Al**   **Zn**
Copper Aluminium Zinc

Sn   **Pb**
Tin   Lead

Copper Based Alloys (e.g. Bronze)

Cu + **Sn**
Copper   Tin

Aluminium Based Alloys (e.g. Aluminium Silicon)

Cu + **Si**
Aluminium Silicon

Non-Ferrous Metals Fact Sheets

Aluminium

Aluminium is produced from the ore bauxite, a hydrated alumina mineral which has iron oxides and other minerals associated with it. The bauxite has to be purified before electrolytic reduction can take place. Aluminium has a melting point of 660°C and possesses a number of properties which make it an extremely useful engineering material. Its good corrosion resistance and low density make it particularly useful for transportation purposes by land, sea and air. This corrosion resistance is due to the fact that aluminium has a high affinity for oxygen and any fresh metal surface will rapidly oxidise. High purity aluminium (99.5% and above) is too weak to be used for many purposes. The term 'commercially pure aluminium' is, in reality, an aluminium-silicon-iron alloy (0.5%) which gives

a considerable increase in strength, although there is some reduction in ductility. Typical applications for this material are in thin foils for packaging, kitchenware, rod and wire for electrical transmission. Aluminium alloys are commonly alloyed with manganese, magnesium, copper, silicon and zinc to produce a series of useful engineering materials. The alloys of aluminium may be further subdivided into non-heat treatable and heat treatable.

Non-heat treatable alloys are made up of three main alloy systems:

- **Aluminium – manganese** (1.25%) has a higher tensile strength than commercially pure aluminium and is easily welded by oxyacetylene, manual metal arc, or resistance welding. It has good ductility and therefore is readily formed by rolling and pressing operations.

- **Aluminium – magnesium** (2–5%) alloys have higher tensile strengths than the previous group and extremely good resistance to corrosion by sea water. These alloys are subject to work hardening and may be softened by annealing. Typical applications are in marine and automobile engineering.

- **Aluminium – silicon** (10–13%) alloys have good flow characteristics and are ideal for casting. They have considerable strength, ductility and resistance to corrosion, with small contraction on solidification.

Heat treatable alloys are those that contain elements such as copper, magnesium, silicon and nickel. Typical of this group are:

- **Aluminium – *copper*** (4%) alloy, which goes under the trade name of Duralumin, requires heat treatment prior to working the material. This is because the copper content needs to be taken into solution to reduce its hardening effect. This is done by heating to a predetermined temperature (425°–540° C) to allow the copper to disperse within the structure (**solution treatment**) and then quenching in water. There is then a limited time (approx 2 hours) in which the material can be worked before the constituents precipitate into a more uniform pattern in the alloy, which will increase the strength and hardness.

- **Nickel-aluminium and copper-aluminium.** The alloy with the highest strength is one containing aluminium-zinc (5-7%), with the addition of smaller amounts of magnesium, manganese, and copper. These alloys are used primarily where strength is important such as structural aircraft components, rivets, extruded sections, forgings, and automobile components such as pistons and cylinder heads.

The International Organization for Standardization (ISO) has a four digit system series which identifies the alloy group. The first digit indicates the alloy group according to the major alloying elements. The second digit shows modifications in impurity limits or the addition of alloying elements. If the second digit is zero, then the alloy has only natural limited impurities. The last two digits show the maximum percentage of aluminium. Thus 1050 is an aluminium with a purity (minimum) of 99.5%. In group 2xxx to 8xxx the last two digits only serve to identify the different alloys in the groups.

Aluminium alloy designations are shown here:

1xxx	Aluminium of 99.00% minimum purity and higher
2xxx	Copper
3xxx	Manganese
4xxx	Silicon
5xxx	Magnesium
6xxx	Magnesium and silicon
7xxx	Zinc
8xxx	Other elements
9xxx	Unused series

sheet, strip, wire, and tube. Beta brass, 60% copper and 40% zinc, is often referred to as yellow or Muntz metal and has a high tensile strength but lower ductility than alpha brass and therefore these materials are usually hot worked. Brasses can be cast, rolled, pressed, drawn and machined. They have good resistance to atmospheric and sea water corrosion and are therefore extensively used in catering, brewing, and marine industries.

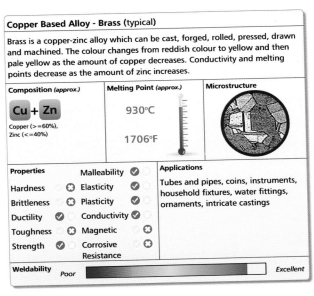

Bronze

Bronzes containing 88% copper, 10% tin and 2% zinc are often referred to as gunmetals and were chiefly used for admiralty work where resistance against corrosion together with strength were required. Lead was added to the bronze to improve the properties of bearing materials and to increase its machinability.

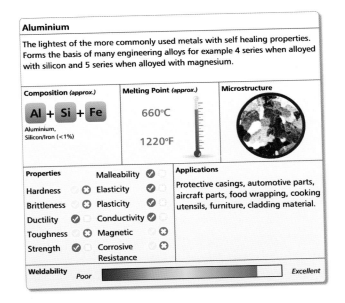

Brass

Brasses are available as 'alpha brass', 70% copper and 30% zinc, sometimes referred to as cartridge brass, which has good strength and ductility when cold and is used for

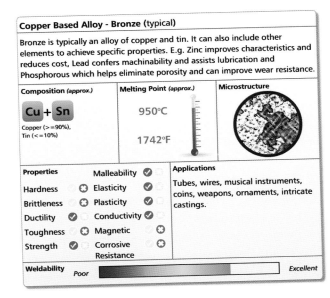

Aluminium Bronze

Aluminium bronzes containing approximately 9% aluminium have very good corrosion resistance, particularly in marine environments. Typical applications include marine propellers, pumps, valves, condenser tubes and heat exchangers.

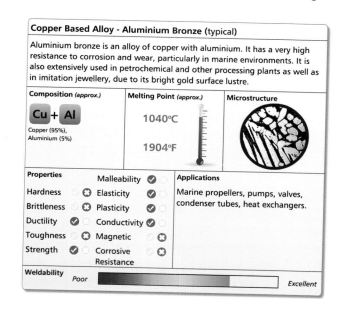

Copper Based Alloy - Aluminium Bronze (typical)

Aluminium bronze is an alloy of copper with aluminium. It has a very high resistance to corrosion and wear, particularly in marine environments. It is also extensively used in petrochemical and other processing plants as well as in imitation jewellery, due to its bright gold surface lustre.

Composition (approx.)

Cu + Al

Copper (95%),
Aluminium (5%)

Melting Point (approx.)

1040°C

1904°F

Microstructure

Properties

Hardness	✗	Malleability	✓
Brittleness	✗	Elasticity	✓
Ductility	✓	Plasticity	✓
Toughness	✗	Conductivity	✓
Strength	✓	Magnetic	✗
		Corrosive Resistance	✗

Applications

Marine propellers, pumps, valves, condenser tubes, heat exchangers.

Weldability   Poor ▬▬▬▬▬▬▬ Excellent

Cupro Nickel

Cupro nickels give a range of materials which are ductile and can be hot or cold worked and are extensively used for coinage (75% copper 25% nickel). They have excellent corrosion resistance and are very good conductors of heat and electricity. The 68% nickel alloy with the addition of approximately 2% iron is known as Monel metal and has good resistance at moderately high temperatures which lends itself to turbine blades, valves, and surface coating applications.

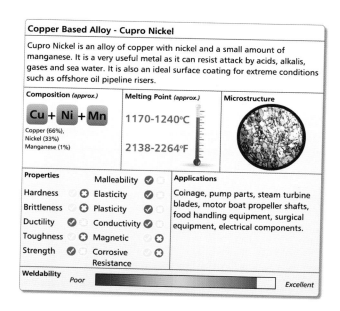

Copper Based Alloy - Cupro Nickel

Cupro Nickel is an alloy of copper with nickel and a small amount of manganese. It is a very useful metal as it can resist attack by acids, alkalis, gases and sea water. It is also an ideal surface coating for extreme conditions such as offshore oil pipeline risers.

Composition (approx.)

Cu + Ni + Mn

Copper (66%),
Nickel (33%)
Manganese (1%)

Melting Point (approx.)

1170-1240°C

2138-2264°F

Microstructure

Properties

Hardness	✗	Malleability	✓
Brittleness	✗	Elasticity	✓
Ductility	✓	Plasticity	✓
Toughness	✗	Conductivity	✓
Strength	✓	Magnetic	✗
		Corrosive Resistance	✗

Applications

Coinage, pump parts, steam turbine blades, motor boat propeller shafts, food handling equipment, surgical equipment, electrical components.

Weldability   Poor ▬▬▬▬▬▬▬ Excellent

Phosphor Bronze

Phosphor bronzes containing up to 8% tin and up to 0.4% phosphorous have good corrosion resistance combined with reasonably high tensile strength. They are used extensively in the marine engineering, and in the form of rod, strip, and wire to form springs and bi-metal strips.

E-Learning

Use the e-learning programme to download a copy of these fact sheets.

Activity

Identify the alloying elements and give a typical use for each material.

Material	Alloying Elements	Typical Use
Austenitic stainless steel		
Brass		
Spheroidal cast iron		
Duralumin		
Bronze		
Monel		

CHECK YOUR KNOWLEDGE

1   Match these descriptions to the correct mechanical property. Write a, b, c or d next to each description.

    a.   elasticity
    b.   plasticity
    c.   toughness
    d.   tensile strength

Ability to resist to being pulled apart

Ability to resist shock and impact loading

Ability of a material to return to its original dimension upon the load being removed

Ability of a material to be deformed and retain the shape of the load once it has been removed

2   What percentage of carbon does cast iron contain? Circle the correct answer.

    a.   3.5%
    b.   4.5%
    c.   5.5%

3   Which of these options are some typical applications of brass? Circle the correct answer(s).

    a.   coins
    b.   musical instruments
    c.   girders
    d.   ornaments
    e.   medical equipment
    f.   metal rope or cable

Summary

This concludes this chapter on engineering materials. You should now be able to demonstrate a knowledge of the mechanical properties of materials and the metals used in engineering, their structure, typical properties and applications.

End test

1. **Match these mechanical properties of materials to their correct definition. Write a, b, c or d next to each description.**

☐ a. brittleness

☐ b. ductility

☐ c. hardness

☐ d. toughness

a material's ability to resist cutting and surface penetration

a measurement of how much a material deforms when it cracks

a measurement of a material's ability to be permanently re-shaped without cracking

a material's ability to resist shock and impact

2. **What is the definition of tensile strength? Circle the correct answer.**

☐ a. Resistance to being crushed

☐ b. Resistance to being cut or sliced

☐ c. Resistance to being pulled apart

☐ d. Resistance to a rapidly applied load

3. **What happens to the grain structure of a metal when it is heated? Circle the correct answer.**

☐ a. Grains break down and get smaller.

☐ b. Grains collapse and discolour.

☐ c. Grains grow larger and merge.

4. **Which of these descriptions explain the annealing process? Circle the correct answer.**

☐ a. Heating the metal to a pre-determined temperature and allowing it to rapidly cool in still air.

☐ b. Heating the metal to a pre-determined temperature and controlling the rate of cooling in an inert atmosphere.

☐ c. Heating the metal to a pre-determined temperature and then cooling it in water.

5. **What does HAZ stand for? Circle the correct answer.**

☐ a. Heat Acclimatised Zone

☐ b. Heat Area Zone

☐ c. Heat Affected Zone

☐ d. Hot Affected Zone

6. **How much carbon does each of these plain carbon steels contain? Write a, b or c next to each type of steel.**

☐ a. 0.80-1.4%

☐ b. 0.30-0.80%

☐ c. <0.30%

high carbon steel

low carbon steel

medium carbon steel

7. **Can you match the carbon content and approximate melting points to the correct type of carbon steel? Write a, b or c and d, e or f next to each type of steel.**

☐ a. 0.80-1.4%

☐ b. 0.30-0.80%

☐ c. <0.30%

☐ d. 1464°C / 2667°F

☐ e. 1427°C / 2600°F

☐ f. 1353°C / 2467°F

high carbon steel

low carbon steel

medium carbon steel

8. **What other metals are added to iron and carbon to make stainless steel?**

9. **Which of the following properties make aluminium a useful material? Circle the correct answer.**

☐ a. brittleness

☐ b. conductivity

☐ c. hardness

☐ d. magnetic

☐ e. non-magnetic

10. **Which metals are combined with copper to make these copper based alloys? Write a, b, c or d next to each alloy.**

☐ a. aluminium

☐ b. nickel

☐ c. tin

☐ d. zinc

Brass

Bronze

Aluminium bronze

Cupro nickel

Fabrication and Cutting

9

Introduction

The many aspects of fabrication and cutting

Fabrication is the use of materials to manufacture objects using forming, shaping and joining. Virtually everything that surrounds you, be it furniture, lighting, white goods, your vehicle or the plane that takes you on holiday, was manufactured using some form of fabrication.

In this chapter, we will be concentrating on the fabrication of metals, although fabrication also uses other materials such as plastics, ceramics, composites and timber products. A classic example of this use of several different

materials would be in shop fitting, where metals combine with plastics and timber to display a wide range of products. Take a look around you and see how many objects you can see that were manufactured using metal fabrication.

Wear personal protective equipment

Wear PPE sign

Health and Safety

Fabrication is like many other engineering activities where appropriate personal protective equipment must be worn. This can include clothing, eye protection, ear defenders, safety boots and in certain cases, gloves.

Observation of safe working practices is essential in any workshop and is especially applicable when using guillotines, presses and while carrying out welding or joining processes.

Measuring and Marking Out

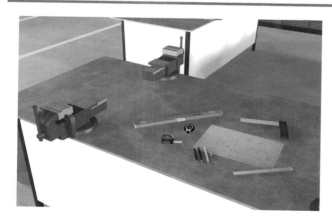

Measuring and marking out

Measuring and marking out is dependent upon the operator correctly interpreting the specifications laid down in the engineering drawing. If there are any issues with the drawing or anything you do not understand it is essential that you seek guidance.

Sustainability

Failure to ask questions about a drawing you do not understand fully will produce inaccurate work and unnecessary waste.

No matter what level of work is being undertaken, some form of measurement is required in order that the component produced complies with a standard or specification, this is standard proceedure all over the world.

Measuring instruments can be 'indicating', meaning that a readable measurement of a component can be made using a steel rule, tape, laser, vernier height gauge, protractor, calliper, or micrometer. The choice of instrument will be determined by the type of work. In general work, there is a tolerance of around 2mm and in fine limit work the tolerance may be as little as 0.05mm. 'Non-indicating' instruments merely show acceptance or rejection of a component. They include plug gauges, which are used to check a hole or gap, weld profile gauges, and gap gauges which are used to check shafts. The advantage of these non-indicating instruments is that they can be adapted to production and provide an easy check on conformance which keeps costs to a minimum.

In terms of measurement and in strict accordance with international agreed recommendations, the International System of Units (SI units, abbreviated from the French Système international d'unités) is the regulatory body. The advantage of having a system of standards is that there is a level of conformity which means that parts sourced from different suppliers will go together and it is possible to use standard off the shelf: bolts, bearings, wire sizes or electrodes.

Tools

There are many tools used in the measuring and marking out process for metal fabrication.

Measuring Tools

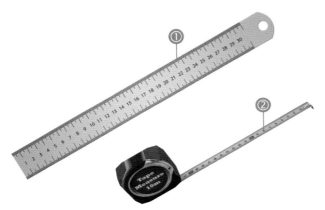

Measuring tools: 1. Steel rule; 2. Steel tape

Measuring tools for metal fabrication include steel rules and steel tapes.

Precision Steel Rules are made from hardened and tempered stainless steel. They are available in 150, 300 and 600 mm lengths with graduations on both edges. When marking out it is essential that datums are established from which all measurements are carried out. When measuring out a distance, line the rule up so that the distance to mark is in line with the datum edge. With both

graduation lines now aligned, and with a scriber angled to scratch the end of the rule at the designated distance, mark the material and, using an engineer's square, continue the line to the drawing destination. Rules are precision measuring instruments and should be treated as such. They should not be used to scrape paint or grease off surfaces, or to prise off tin lids or used as a screwdriver. Where approximate measurements are required over greater distances both steels and fabric tapes are available. The disadvantage of using fabric tapes is that they can deteriorate and stretch, which makes accurate measurement more difficult.

Angular Measurement

Angular measurement tools: 1. Engineer's square; 2. Protractor; 3. Combination set

Tools to measure angles include the engineer's square, protractor and combination set.

- The engineer's square is used to measure a 90° angle in the vertical and horizontal planes and can be used to transfer lines at 90° to an edge on sheet material.
- A protractor is used to measure a range of angles between 0 and 180°.
- Vernier protractors are marked off in degrees on the main scale and the vernier scale is marked off in spaces 1 degree 55 minutes apart. As the space on the vernier scale are 5 minutes less than two spaces on the main scale, the vernier protractor can be read to the nearest 5 minutes, and must be read in the same direction as the main scale. Vernier tools are discussed in more detail below.
- Combination sets consists of a graduated steel rule on which is mounted three separate heads: 90° square with 45° mitre face and bubble level, centre finder, and

a protractor. The rule has a slot in which each head can be locked at any position along its length. This gives the advantage of being able to mark accurately any dimension lines at 90° to the datum edge, 45° to the edge and any angle between 0-180° accurately. The centre finder relies on the V faces touching the cylindrical surface to identify a common centre. This tool is especially useful for fabricators needing to mark square, mitred and angular measurements, and to check folds against designated angles. The blade can also be used to measure depth measurements against the stock of the square. Care needs to be exercised in storage especially with the locking screw mechanisms, which can easily fall on the floor if they are not being used in conjunction with the rule.

Marking out tools

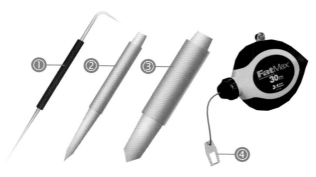

Marking out tools: 1. Scriber; 2. Dot punch; 3. Centre punch; 4. Chalk line

- A scriber consists of a hardened steel rod with a sharp point. This the basic marking out tool. It is essential that it is sharpened regularly on a grinder or oil stone to maintain accuracy. The point of the scriber should always be in contact with the edge of the square or template being used. Never carry a scriber in the top or side pocket of your overalls as this could cause a major injury, either to your eye or to your arteries, when you are working in cramped conditions.

- Punches are designed to make an indentation on the surface of a piece of metal. A dot punch creates a very fine point which can be used to mark the position of instruments. A centre punch creates a heavier indentation which can be used for marking the point of a drill and is available as either an automatic tool or manual tool.

- Chalk lines are chalk covered string lines which, once in place, can be snapped to mark a chalk line on the surface of a piece of material.

Vernier tools

Vernier tools covers a category of fine precision measuring tools which includes height gauges, callipers and protractors. All vernier instruments consist of two scales; one fixed and one moving. The fixed scale is graduated in millimetres, every 10 divisions equalling 10mm, and is numbered 0,1,2,3, up to the capacity of the instrument. When taking a measurement, note how many millimetres is on the main scale and then check on the vernier scale for a line that coincides with a line on the main scale and add together the two dimensions to get the total dimension. For example if the main scale registers 40 and the vernier scale registers 5 we have: 5 x 0.02 = 0.10 + 40 = 40.10mm.

All vernier tools should be satin chromed finished to prevent corrosion and to improve the ease of reading by reducing glare when working in artificial light.

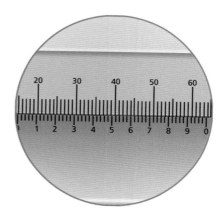

Vernier scale

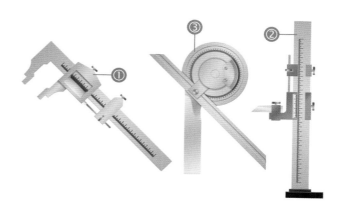

Vernier tools: 1. Vernier calipers; 2. Vernier height gauge; 3. Vernier protractor

- Vernier callipers are used to measure internal, external and depth measurements and are available from 150-1000mm. To measure, slacken both locking screws and move the sliding jaw until it touches the work surface to be measured. Tighten the locking screw on the main scale and adjust the wheel nut on the vernier scale until the correct 'feel' is obtained and lock the second locking screw to read the measurement. A variant of this is the dial calliper. Electronic callipers give a digital readout with a resolution of 0.001mm, but care must be exercised to zero the gauge before taking any reading.

- A vernier height gauge consists of a precision machined base with a perpendicular graduated blade on to which a slide mechanism with two locking nuts is attached. Once again a precision graduated scale is available to give infinite measurement. Attached to the slider mechanism is a coupling onto which a scriber point is attached which is used both to measure height and to scribe lines on components. Readings are taken as previously described and once again are available in a digital format.

- Vernier depth gauges come supplied with a machined T-bar in which a graduated blade slides up and down to record the depth.

Circles and Parallel Lines

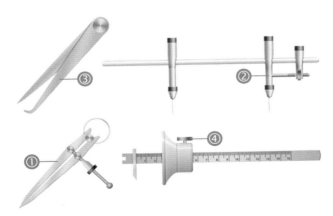

Circles and parallel lines: 1. Dividers; 2. Trammels; 3. Hermaphrodite calipers; 4. Scratch gauge

- Dividers are used to mark circles and arcs. One leg is placed in a centre dot mark and the other leg marks the circle or arc. They can also be used to mark the centre of holes along a line or around a pitch circle diameter (PCD). When adjusting the dividers, it is recommended practice to place one point in the graduation of the rule and adjust to the required measurement, taking into account where measuring from. For example, put the point in 10mm graduation on the rule and adjust to 60mm if you require a 50mm dimension.

- Trammels consist of two pointed locators which slide on a bar section and are used to scribe radial distances and arcs, with the second pointer acting as a scribing point.

- Hermaphrodite calipers or odd leg calipers are used to mark lines parallel to an edge where one leg is machined to follow the edge of the material and the second holds a scribing point. A scratch gauge is used to mark lines parallel to a datum edge or back marks for drilling.

Marking Blue

Marking blue is used to mark the flatness of a surface or edge. The blue ink is rubbed onto a reference surface and then the piece of work is rubbed against the blue surface. Areas that touch will be marked in blue so any distortions or imperfections can be easily seen. It is also applied to materials prior to marking out to highlight fold lines, machining lines or cutting lines.

Marking out from Datum Lines

A datum line is a single line from which all measurements are taken. In metal fabrication, the most commonly used datum line is called the 'edge datum'.

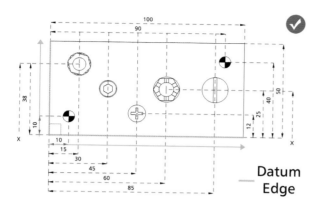

Progressive marking

Two edges of a piece of material are prepared so they are at exactly 90° to each other these will then become datum edges from which all measurements will be taken.

After the first measurement, all subsequent measurements in the same dimension should be taken from the datum line and not the previously marked line. This is known as progressive marking out and ensures greater accuracy. Measuring from a previously marked line or chain measuring can result in cumulative error, meaning that an error at one point is exaggerated along the whole line of marking out. Inaccurate marking out can mean that the whole sheet of metal has to be discarded causing unnecessary waste.

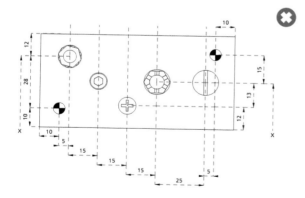

Cumulative marking

E-Learning

Use the e-learning programme to see an animation of marking out from a datum line.

Marking Out from a Pitch Circle Diameter

The pitch circle diameter, or PCD is usually the centre line between an external and internal circle and is measured and marked with either dividers or trammels. A PCD is used when marking out on circular co-ordinates, for example when marking out a flange with bolt holes which would have a PCD based on the centre point of a circle.

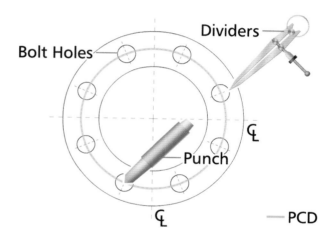

Pitch Circle Diameter (PCD)

If holes are to be drilled along a pitch circle diameter, the pitch of the holes is calculated and then measured on the pitch circle with dividers. The centre of each hole is then marked with a punch.

E-Learning

Use the e-learning programme to see an animation of marking out from a PCD.

Activity

You are required to mark out the following shape. Construct a tool list you will require in order to produce the component.

_____

_____

_____

_____

_____

_____

_____

_____

_____

_____

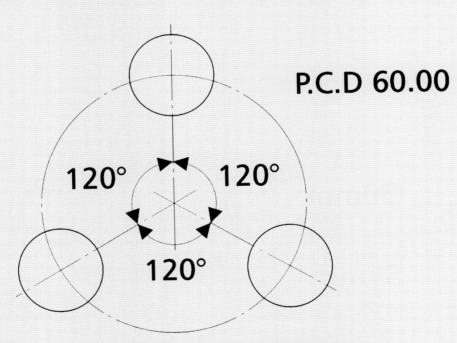

P.C.D 60.00

120°   120°

120°

Polar coordinates applied to
holes on a pitch circle

Folding Allowances

When material is folded there are tensile and compressive stresses placed on the fold. In a material such as paper, this will have no effect on the overall size but with metal the thickness of the material needs to be taken into consideration.

If a 100x100 by 1mm thick steel sheet is folded at a right angle along its centre line, this 1mm is added to the external dimensions of the folded piece. The internal dimensions remain unchanged. When there are multiple folds, every fabrication will be oversize by one material thickness for each fold. For example, a steel sheet 2mm thick folded twice at 50mm intervals will increase its external dimensions to 52mm x 54mm x 52mm.

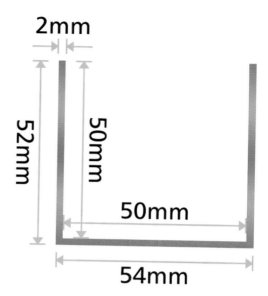

2mm steel sheet folded at 50mm intervals

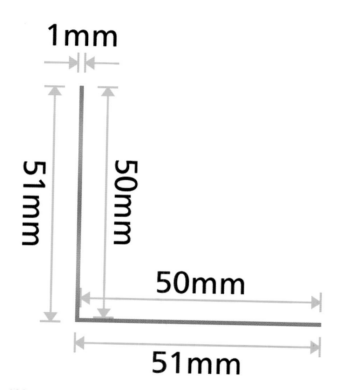

100 x 100 x 1mm steel sheet folded at right angle

When a metal sheet or plate is bent, tensile (stretching) forces are created on the outside of the bend and compressive forces on the inside. Where these forces are equal within the sheet or plate is known as the neutral line.

It is up to the fabricator to make allowances for folds by subtracting one material thickness for each fold in the finished piece up to a certain thickness. However when the thickness increases significantly you need to take account of the 'neutral-line' formula.

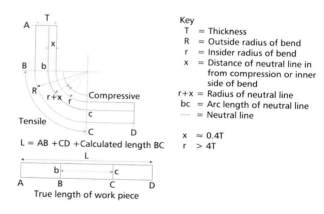

Key
T   = Thickness
R   = Outside radius of bend
r   = Insider radius of bend
x   = Distance of neutral line in from compression or inner side of bend
r+x = Radius of neutral line
bc = Arc length of neutral line
—   = Neutral line

x ≈ 0.4T
r > 4T

L = AB +CD +Calculated length BC

Bending sheet metal

To avoid fractures, the inside bend radius of the fold must be no less than four times the thickness of the plate.

E-Learning

Use the e-learning programme to see an animated explanation of folding allowances and the neutral line formula.

Material Removal Techniques

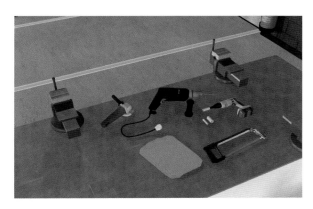

Materials removal techniques

Once we are satisfied that we have marked out according to the design specification given, we are now ready to remove any surplus material prior to forming the component. This can be done both mechanically and manually.

Health and Safety

All equipment used should be checked prior to use to ensure it is in good working order. These tools can present a hazard and care should be taken when operating them.

Sustainability

All material removed should be stored in appropriate containers to recycle and reuse where possible.

All edges should be de-burred (removing any sharp edges from cutting process) where material has been removed.

De-burr sharp edges after cutting process

Tools

There are many tools used to remove material in metal fabrication.

Saws

Saws for material removal are available as hand tools and power tools. They cut using a chip-forming principle. In other words, the material is removed as 'chips' as it is cut. The chart below summarises the main features of some commonly used saws.

Hacksaw

- a general purpose saw used for cutting metals, plastics and composites
- can be used with a range of blades from 18 – 24 teeth per inch (tpi)
- appropriate blade should be selected for the type of metal to be cut (soft or hard)
- also available in a small frame and referred to as a 'junior hacksaw'

Hacksaws: 1. Hacksaw; 2. Junior Hacksaw

Mechanical power saw

- designed to cut thick sections and box sections
- used on a wide range of materials
- can be used at 90° or at a range of angular adjustment

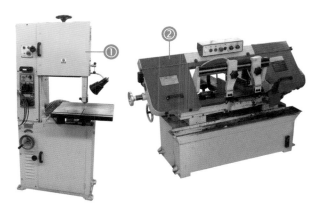

Band saws: 1. Vertical band saw; 2. Horizontal band saw

Rotary saw

- consists of a rotating circular blade or abrasive disc
- used to cut components at 90° and a wide range of angular cuts
- often referred to as 'chop saws'
- available in most fabrication workshops

Hole saw

- designed with a central drill mandrel and a circular band saw blade
- used for designated circular diameter holes, such as in light fittings

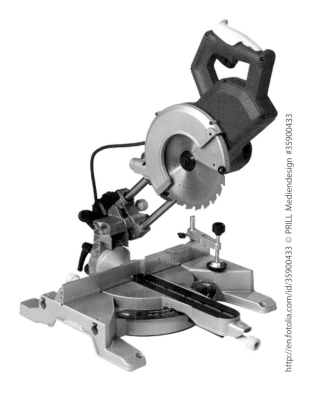

Band saw

- available as vertical or horizontal versions
- each has specific uses
- vertical band saws are used for cutting profiles and shapes
- horizontal band saws are used in much the same way as a power saw

Cutting Tools

Cutting tools include the power guillotine, hand guillotine, reciprocating shears, nibblers, snips and the universal steel worker, which all work using a non-chip forming principle. When pressure from the cutting edge is applied it penetrates the material to a certain distance after which the material shears, leaving a cut edge. The chart below summarises the features of some common cutting tools.

Guillotines

● available as hydraulic and pneumatic
● mechanical machines are limited by the amount of pressure they can apply
● hydraulic machines are preferred for cutting thick metal

Universal steel worker functions: 1. Shearing; 2. Punching; 3. Section shear; 4. Notching

Universal steel worker

● shearing blade
● punch and nibbler
● section shearing tool
● cropping tool for notching

Flypress

● Versatile piece of equipment for blanking out shapes, piercing holes, notching corners and forming operations

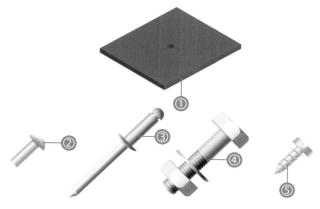

Whitney punch functions: 1. Piercing; 2. Solid rivet; 3. Blind rivet; 4. Nut and bolt; 5. Self-tapping screw

Selection of Cutting Machines

When selecting a cutting machine for a particular use in the workshop, the primary factor affecting the decision will probably be the size and section of the material to be cut. The following factors will determine the capacity of the machine required, and will also influence the type of machine selected:

- the capacity range;
- material to be cut;
- maximum thickness to be cut;
- maximum length to be cut;
- sectional shape;
- type of cut: straight or radius.

In terms of production, the following considerations need to be taken into account:

- rate of cutting;
- degree of accuracy;
- quality of cut edge;
- labour cost (skill in operating);
- attachments required.

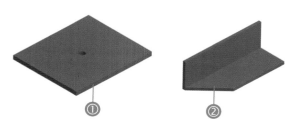

Flypress functions: 1. Piercing; 2. Notching corners

Whitney punch

- Used for rapid piercing of holes for riveting, nuts and bolts, self-tapping screws and other fastening systems

Manual Cutting Tools

Portable shears and nibblers have a fixed lower blade and a moving upper blade which operates at high speed. The blades are removed for replacement or sharpening. This

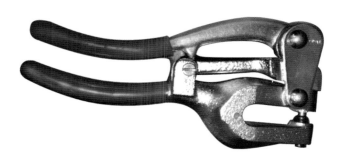

type of machine will easily cut to straight or curved lines. The portable nibbler is very similar in construction but uses a punch and die for cutting the metal, producing a half moon nibblet.

Bench shears or knives are used for cutting heavy gauge metal sheet up to 3mm. The cutting action is made easier by the use of a long handle to provide the leverage. Once again the lower blade is fixed and the top blade moves. They are available for straight line cuts with a curved base plate for cutting circular or irregular shaped components. Always ensure that the handle is locked when not in use.

Snips are available in different configurations: straight, curved, universal and aeronautical (American). They all work on the shear principle with the leading edges of the blades giving a clearance angle similar to scissors. The force is exerted against a 'fulcrum point' (rivet) to provide the leverage for shearing. They are available in different lengths to meet metal specification thickness ranges up to 1.5mm thick plate. The use of extension arms is not recommended as this puts undue force on the fulcrum point and can bring about failure. When using snips it is essential that the shear faces are kept parallel to one another; any twisting of the cutters will reduce their efficiency and bring about wear on the shear faces.

Drills

A variety of hand and power drills are used in metal fabrication. The features of some frequently used drills are summarised here.

Health and Safety

Battery operated hand drills are increasingly being used on site for safety reasons, especially in confined spaces as the voltage is low.

Bench drilling machine

● most commonly used drill

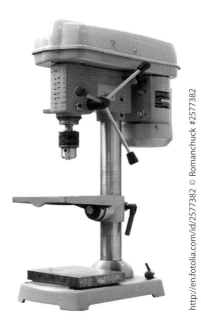

http://en.fotolia.com/id/2577382 © Romanchuck #2577382

Pillar drilling machine

● more rugged version of bench drilling machine
● uses either a chuck or larger morse taper drill

Column drilling machine

- has a work table that can be raised and lowered for different length tools

Radial arm drilling machine

- allows the drilling head to be moved rather than the work piece
- gives greater flexibility especially when dealing with large jobs which can be fixed to the floor
- the head of the drill can be rotated out from the base

Oxyfuel Gas Cutting

Oxyfuel gas cutting

Oxy-fuel gas cutting can be used on thin sheet, thick plate or structural sections of ferrous metals. The equipment used is similar to oxy-acetylene welding equipment but with some significant differences in the torch design and the use of specially designed nozzles.

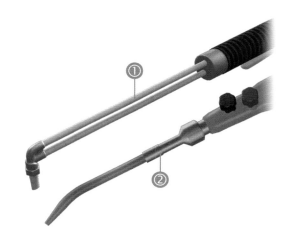

Torches: 1. Oxyfuel gas cutting torch; 2. Oxyacetylene welding torch

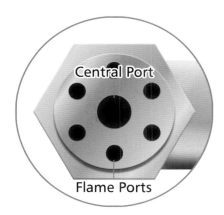

Cutting torch nozzle design

Activity

Tool: _____

Use: _____

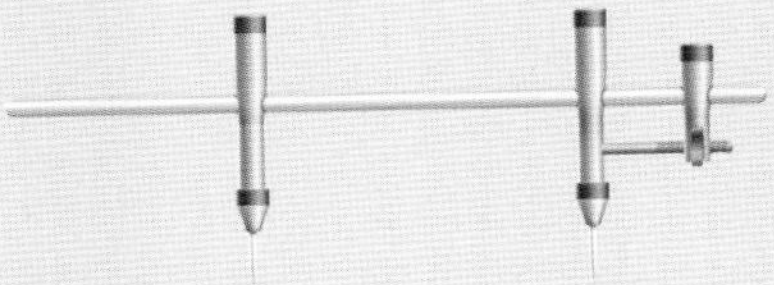

Tool: _____

Use: _____

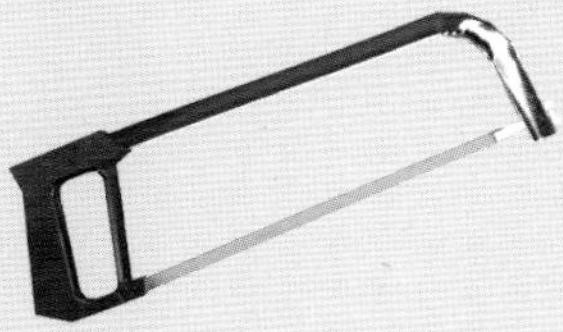

Tool: _____

Use: _____

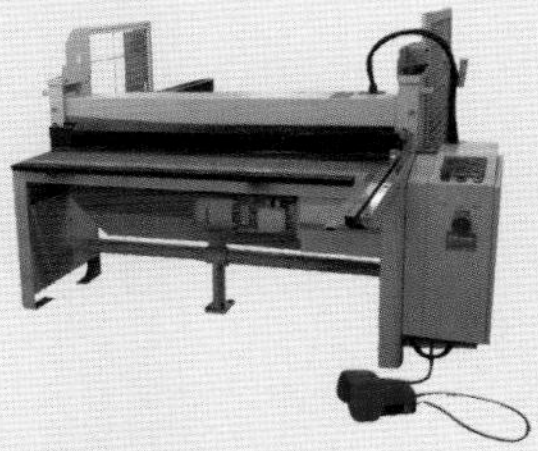

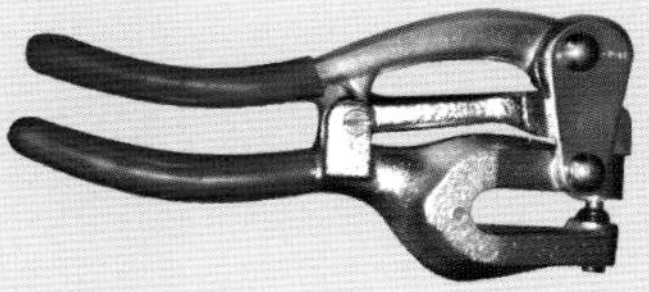

Tool: _____

Use: _____

Tool: _____

Use: _____

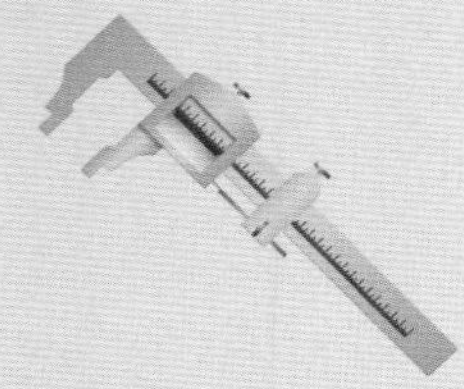

Tool: _____

Use: _____

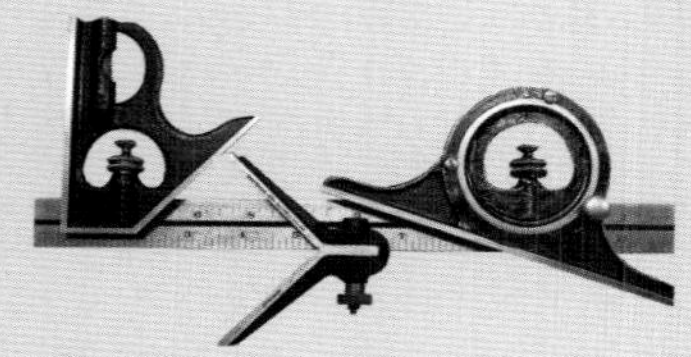

Tool: _____

Use: _____

Tool: _____

Use: _____

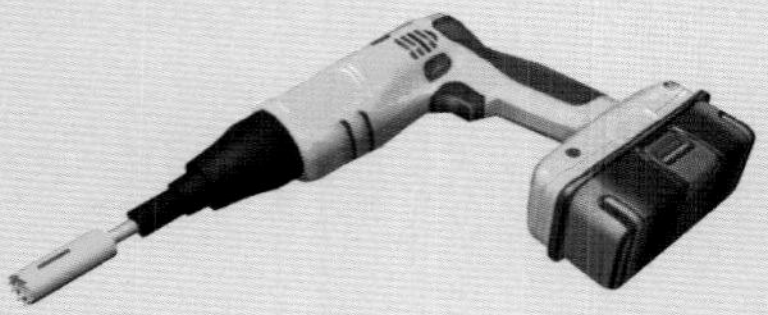

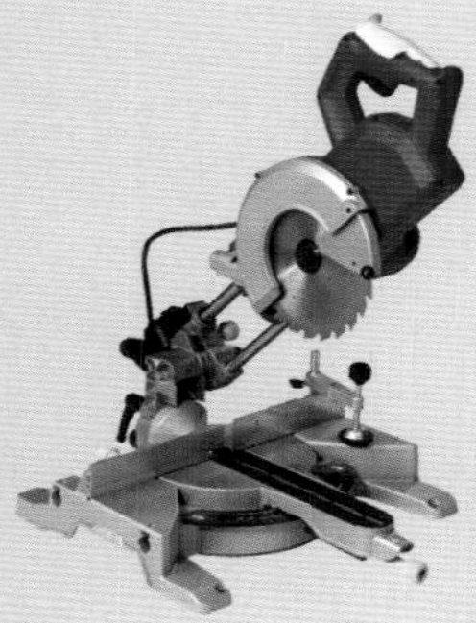

Tool: _____

Use: _____

Tool: _____

Use: _____

The conventional nozzle provides a number of flame ports which pre-heat the metal and a central port which provides a high pressure supply of oxygen to initiate the cutting or burning process. When used with acetylene, the flame can reach up to a temperature of 3,500°C. The metal is heated to between 870° and 900°C which is the ignition temperature for steel. At this point a reaction occurs causing oxidation of the metal's surface to form metal oxides. These oxides are then blown away by the oxygen jet in the centre of the nozzle, and the metal is cut by chemical severance rather than by conventional cutting mechanisms. The iron or steel is not actually melted in this process, but is severed by chemical action. Because the cutting is essentially an oxidising process, little or no steel is melted, the kerf should therefore be quite clean and the top and bottom edges should be square. On examining the melted oxides after cutting, it can be seen that up to 30% of unmelted steel has been scoured from the sides of the cut by the high pressure oxygen stream. This scouring is represented by 'drag lines' faintly etched on the faces of the metal. In an incorrect cut, these drag lines will be more pronounced. The only area, which is not heated in this way, is the top surface of the plate, since the heat generated there is carried down to the kerf. The preheat flame must keep the surface of the plate above the ignition temperature, otherwise the reactions do not take place and the cutting ceases.

If this sequence of events is to proceed at a regular rate, it is imperative that the cutting oxygen must come into contact with clean hot metal. There must not be any barrier which could prevent the oxygen from freely reaching the steel, or the reaction will slow down or even stop. This could happen because of the presence of the other alloying elements in steel which oxidize to form gases. Carbon produces a mixture of carbon monoxide and carbon dioxide, while sulphur when oxidized produces sulphur dioxide. These gases are generated at the interface between the cutting oxygen and the steel, and must be swept away by the velocity of the oxygen jet. If they are allowed to collect, they form a boundary layer through which the oxygen diffuses slowly or not at all.

Another factor which can affect the cutting process is the presence of laminations which are areas in the plate in which trapped oxides are present from the hot rolling process. When the cutting stream hits these locations, the plate opens up to produce a delamination and this results in a break in the oxidation process typified by an expulsion of hot sparks and molten oxide. When this occurs it is important to stop the cutting operation and check the extent of the lamination. If in doubt, you should consider starting over again on a new piece of plate.

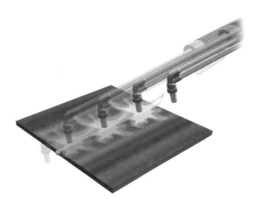

Oxyfuel gas cut process

A large volume of oxygen is required for this process to provide the pre-heating flames and the central cutting jet. The purity of the oxygen stream is very important as a drop in purity can affect the cutting speed dramatically. Cuts will not be achieved if the oxygen jet is insufficient or the movement of the nozzle is too fast.

When cutting thin sheet, a specially adapted nozzle is used. It has a step design to ensure that the oxygen stream is maintained at a designated height. This has only two ports, one to pre-heat the other to supply the cutting oxygen stream.

Cutting Gases

Acetylene produces the highest flame temperature of all the fuel gases and generates a highly focused flame. As the pierce time is approximately one third that achieved with propane, it should be used when the pierce time is a significant proportion of the total cutting time, for example, for short cuts and multi-pierce cutting operations. The high temperature, highly focused flame makes the oxy-acetylene flame ideal for cutting thin sheets with minimum distortion and for bevel cutting. However, the high cost and low heat generation makes it less suitable for general heating of large plates. On long cuts, the storage, availability and cost of the fuel gas and the quantity of oxygen required will be more important, and gases such as propane may be preferred.

Propane has low cost and has the advantage of being available in bulk supplies. The flame temperature is lower than that for acetylene (2,810°C compared with 3,200°C) which makes piercing much slower. However, it can tolerate a greater nozzle-to-work piece distance which reduces the risk of molten metal splashing back onto the nozzle and causing a 'backfire'. For similar nozzle designs, cutting speeds for oxy-propane and oxy-acetylene are similar. Advantages claimed for propane are smoother cut edges, less dross adhesion and lower plate edge hardening because of the lower flame temperature. The heat affected zone however is much wider than that for oxyacetylene.

Cutting Torch

A combined head is ideal for maintenance work as it is can be converted for welding and cutting. When the cutting attachment is used, control of the heating gases is made by the fuel gas valve on the shank (handle) of the torch, but the cutting oxygen is controlled by the fine adjustment valve on the attachment. To enable this to be done, the oxygen valve on the shank must be fully open when the attachment is in use. Control of the cutting oxygen is by depressing the cutting lever, or by turning the cutting oxygen control valve if this is fitted instead of a lever.

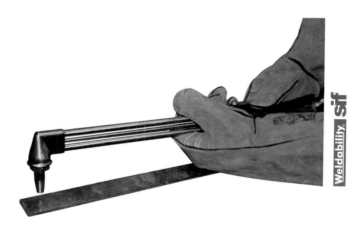

Hand cutters are intended for heavy cutting operations from 100mm upwards. They are designed with a longer distance to the cutting nozzle and larger shank which protects the operator and are available in three variations:

- In nozzle mix cutters the oxygen and fuel gas are kept separate and are only mixed in the actual cutting or gouging nozzle, which means that the amount of mixed gas in the system is minute. Nozzle mix cutters are both simple and efficient, and tend to stand up better to aggressive environments. The ease of lighting up, durability, and availability make this the preferred choice for many.

- **Injector cutters** were first designed to be used with low pressure acetylene, which is no longer a problem. With the use of natural gas for cutting, which again is at low pressure, an injector cutter will be required.

Some operators will claim that injector cutters give greater control of cutting oxygen velocity, which is a critical factor in some gouging operations and therefore also prefer to use a cutter with the injector built into the body.

- Pre-mix cutters were introduced to enable injectors to be employed, but with the least possible amount of mixed gas in the system. The injector is placed in the head, enabling the gas in the cutter tubes to remain separate. Because of the need to place the injector in the head, it becomes larger than a nozzle mix cutter, which makes it top heavy and badly balanced, leading to operator fatigue if used for long periods.

Cutters

Cutting Nozzles

Most cutting in the UK is done with either acetylene or propane as the fuel gas. The central orifice diameter is always stamped on some part of the nozzle for matching to plate thickness. Too small a nozzle size results in frequent failure of the cut, whereas too large a nozzle produces a poor cut with rounded top edges, in addition to excess consumption of gas. A dirty nozzle will divert or distort the gas stream, again producing a rough cut. If the nozzle is too close to the plate, the top edges may be fused and failure of the cut will take place. If the nozzle is too far away, heat is lost to the surrounding plate, causing a rounded top edge and partial penetration. Pre-heating time is longer and the cutting operation is slowed down. The nozzle distance increases with thickness of plate and nozzle size, but the tips of the blue heating cones should be just above the plate (3-5mm).

Acetylene Nozzles (ANM)

Acetylene cutting nozzles are mainly drilled from solid copper and their design will depend on the cutter they are manufactured for. Nozzle mix nozzles are mainly three seated, to ensure the heating gases are kept separated until they mix within the nozzle. The number of heating gas channels may vary, but the most commonly used in the UK is six and is denoted as ANM-6 nozzle.

Acetylene nozzle

Propane Nozzles (PNM)

The propane nozzle has a brass inner part which is fluted and grooved around the outside and provides the pre-heat flame and a central hole for the cutting oxygen, with an outer copper surround.

Propane nozzle

The design slows down the gas through the nozzle, producing turbulence to ensure good mixing of propane and oxygen. The inner part of the nozzle is brass so that the gas passages may be formed by an accurately cut channel, which is fluted or grooved, with a central hole for oxygen. The outer surround is made from copper, with the inner wall scoured to encourage turbulence. The outer nozzle exit stands proud of the inner to form a skirt that will retain the flame on the end of the nozzle.

Nozzle Variants

Gouging nozzles (AGNM) are designed to produce a neat controlled back gouging of welds and defects as well as removing cleats, lugs and weld defects. They incorporate a hard wearing tungsten shoe that prolongs the life of the nozzle when running along a gouge and makes the operation easier.

Gouging nozzle

Sheet nozzles (ASNM) are for light cutting of sheet or thin plate with one preheating orifice and the cutting orifice. The nozzle is shaped with a standard stand-off distance for the cutting oxygen. This gives a very fine cut ideal for bodywork, thin sheet or box section up to 3mm.

Sheet metal cutting nozzle

The condition of the seats of all cutting nozzles is critical, to avoid cross head leaking which leads to serious backfiring. Great care needs to be taken when removing a hot nozzle from a cutting torch, for hot copper will easily mark or indent if the nozzle is dropped or thrown on to a hard surface. When removing a cutting tip that is stuck in the torch head, gently tap the back of the head with a plastic hammer. Avoid any tapping on the side of the seating or nozzle as this will damage the seating and could lead to gas leakage and backfiring. The gas entry and exit ports should always be at 90° to the end of the nozzle and should be cleaned with the correct sized nozzle cleaner, which should be inserted and withdrawn straight out. If it is twisted or used like a file the orifice will become enlarged and the flame shape distorted. Nozzles with bell shaped orifices are more likely to backfire. To check the assembled torch nozzle for a good seal, turn on the oxygen valve, and spray the nozzle tip with an oil free leak-detecting solution.

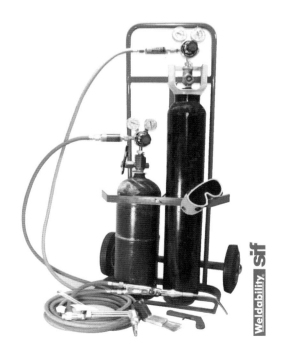

Activity

Sketch these nozzles and describe their typical use.

Acetylene nozzle showing ANM

Sheet metal nozzle showing ASNM

Propane nozzle showing APM

Gouging nozzle showing AGNM

Lighting Technique

Wearing the appropriate PPE and with the equipment safely assembled you are now ready to light up the torch. It is imperative that prior to lighting up, the hoses and torch are 'purged' to prevent back-pressure in the system with the possibility of explosions. Remember the longer the length of hose, the greater the time required to purge it.

- If using acetylene, point the torch upwards, as it is lighter than air, and away from any other equipment or fellow workers. Turn the acetylene valve on and using a spark lighter, light from behind the torch, thereby ensuring you do not get burnt. If using propane point downwards, as it is heavier than air (this is to ensure that the fuel gas does not enter an oxygen outlet prior to the gas being lit).

- If the flame is small it will produce heavy black soot and smoke. Increase the acetylene until the black smoke just disappears.

- Open the oxygen valve on the cutter or on the cutter attachment slowly and adjust to give a neutral flame on the pre-heating cones in the case of multi-port type nozzle, or a short white conical ring if the nozzle is of the annular port type (propane). Note that if there is another valve on the cutting attachment controlling the oxygen flow, the oxygen valve on the shank should be left fully open during all cutting operations.

- When the cutting oxygen lever is depressed, the flame may become slightly carburising. This may occur because of a drop in line pressure due to the high flow of oxygen through the cutting orifice.

- With the cutting lever depressed re-adjust the pre-heat flame to a neutral setting. The flame will become slightly oxidising when the cutting lever is released.

- To turn off the cutting torch, close the acetylene valve first and then the oxygen valve.

When using oxy-propane the properly adjusted pre-heating flame will be indicated by a small non-luminous central cone with a pale blue envelope.

If a sustained backfire occurs, identified by a rapid machine gun effect, quickly followed by a squealing noise with black smoke and sparks being emitted from the nozzle (flashback), it is essential that the flame within the system be starved of oxygen immediately. In this case, the oxygen valve should be closed first followed by the fuel gas valve. The torch should then be plunged into a bucket of water with the oxygen valve open to prevent water entering the nozzle. Allow to cool and thoroughly check before re-using. Also remove the nozzle from the head and check the seatings for carbon build-up or damage.

Oxy-Fuel Gas Gouging

This is a variant of oxy-fuel gas cutting used to remove defects from welds, to prepare a 'U' preparation or to remove heads from rusted rivets or bolts. Flame gouging uses a special curved nozzle to modify the oxy-fuel cutting process. This nozzle delivers a high volume of oxygen at relatively low velocity and by varying the nozzle angle and travel speed, grooves of various width and depth can be produced. The pre-heat is obtained by just touching the inner cones of the pre-heat flames to the work with the torch at an angle of 25°-30°. When the oxygen lever is depressed and gouging begins, the torch angle is lowered to approximately 5°-10° and gouging then progresses.

Hand Cutting

In manual hand cutting the rate of travel is not as uniform as it is with mechanised cutting. It is therefore advisable to have a slightly larger pre-heat flame with rather higher oxygen pressures and a slower speed of travel. A certain latitude is allowed for flame adjustment, but too low a heat value will cause the flame to stop cutting, and too high will spoil the cut finish. The best adjustment is one which will give a reasonably quick start and maintain a clean cut at maximum speed.

Less heat is required near plate edges, but dirty plate needs more heat than clean plate. Rust, paint, scale and protective coatings make starting difficult and slow down the rate of cutting. Plate with open laminations stop the cut altogether. Tight laminations will hardly affect the cut, provided there is no appreciable amount of mill scale and slag inclusions (rolled in to the surface during hot rolling). Flame cleaning, grinding or trial runs over the line to be cut (pre-heat) help when cutting scaled or dirty plate.

When making a cut with a hand torch, it is important for the operator to be steady in order to make the cut as smooth as possible. The operator must be comfortable and free to move the torch along the line of cut and it is good practice to always do a 'dummy run' to ensure that your angles of approach and travel are established before you light up. Even when the operator and the torch are braced properly, a tiny movement such as breathing will cause a slight ripple in the cut. Attempting to brace oneself without leaning on the work is tiring and can cause inaccuracies. The torch should be braced with the left hand if the operator is right-handed. The torch may be moved by sliding it towards you over your supporting hand as shown.

Pivot guide with torch

Circle cutting guide with torch

The torch can also be pivoted on the supporting hand although care must be taken to ensure that the cut does not become a series of arcs. In this instance the use of trammel guides or circle cutting guides would be advisable.

Circle cutting with no guide

A slight forward torch angle helps the flame pre-heat the metal, keeps some of the reflected flame off the tip, aids in blowing dirt and oxides away from the cut, and keeps the tip clean for a longer period of time because slag is less likely to deposit on it. The forward angle can be used only for a straight line square cut. If shapes are cut using a slight angle, the part will have bevelled sides.

When making a cut, the inner cones of the flames should be kept 3-10mm from the surface of the plate, sometimes referred to as the 'coupling distance'. To start on the edge of a plate, hold the torch at right angles to the surface or pointed slightly away from the edge, this is to ensure that the cut is started at the very edge. The edge of the plate heats up more quickly and therefore allows the cut to be started sooner. Also, fewer sparks will be ejected on to the nozzle or blown around the workshop/area. Once the cut is started, the torch should be rotated back to a right angle to the surface or to a slight leading angle. If the correct conditions have been achieved the cut portion should drop away without adhesion, leaving a light oxide (dross) on the cut face. The top and bottom edges should be square with slightly noticeable vertical drag lines.

Always plan your cutting sequence so that the portion to be detached falls away from you.

Cut Face Characteristics

The following problems can be diagnosed by examining the appearance of the cut face:

Speed too fast:

- top edge not sharp with undercutting;
- bottom edge slightly rounded;
- drag lines have excessive backward drag.

Speed too slow:

- melted and rounded top edge;
- rough bottom edge;
- irregular gouging on lower half of cut face;
- heavy scale difficult to remove.

Nozzle too high:

- excessive melting and rounding of top edge;
- sharp bottom edge;
- undercut at top of the cut edge.

Nozzle too low:

- top edge slightly rounded and beaded;
- square cut face with sharp bottom corner.

Cutting oxygen pressure too high:

- a regular bead along top edge;
- a wider kerf at the top edge with undercutting of the face.

Pre-heating flame too high:

- a rounded top edge;
- the melted metal running into the kerf;
- smooth cut face tapered from top to bottom with lightly adhering slag (dross).

Piercing

If a cut is to be started in a place other than the edge of the plate, a hole should be either drilled or produced with the cutting torch. The inner cones should be held as close as possible to the metal to speed up the pre-heat time. When the metal is hot enough to allow the cut to start, the torch should be raised as the cutting lever is slowly depressed. When the metal is pierced, the torch should be lowered again. By raising the torch tip away from the metal, the amount of sparks blown into the air is reduced and the tip is kept cleaner. If the metal being cut is thick, it may be necessary to move the torch nozzle in a small circle as the hole goes through the metal. If the metal is to be cut in both directions from the spot where it was pierced, the torch should be moved backward a short distance and then forward. This prevents slag from refilling the kerf at the starting point, thus making it difficult to cut in the other direction.

Starts and stops can be made more easily if one side of the metal being cut is scrap. When it is necessary to reposition yourself before continuing the cut, the cut should be turned out into the scrap side. The extra space this gives the operator allows for a smoother start with less chance that slag will block the kerf.

If neither side of the cut is to be scrap, the forward movement should be stopped for a moment before releasing the cutting lever. This action will allow the 'drag', or the distance that the bottom of the cut is behind the top, to catch up before stopping. To restart, use the procedure that was given for starting a cut at the edge of the plate.

The proper alignment of the pre-heat holes will speed up and improve the cut. For a straight line square cut, the holes should be aligned so one is directly on the line ahead

of the cut, and another is aimed down into the cut. You can use French chalk to put a chalk mark on the nozzle centre and align this with the line. Also, if you 'witness mark' the line with a centre punch and load the indentations with French chalk it makes it easier to see the line during the cutting operation.

Stack Cutting

Stack cutting is a process in which as many as 100 sheets may be cut simultaneously to produce regular or irregular shaped thin plates. Stack cutting involves piling a number of thin plates one on top of the other, fusing the edges together at discrete points, clamping them tight together and making the cut as if the clamped plates were one piece of solid metal. With a stack not exceeding 50mm, a cut edge tolerance of 1mm is obtained, while stacks from 50-100mm can be cut with an edge tolerance of 1.6mm. The edges of the stack cut sheets are square and full with none of the burrs that are often present on sheets pre-fabricated by shearing methods.

Cutting Aids

Cutting aids are frequently used to ensure consistent and accurate work. They help to remove guesswork from the process and produce better results with less operator fatigue. The items that are available include:

- **spade guide:** an inexpensive guide which attaches to the cutting nozzle and ensures the cutting of straight lines. It is adjustable for height and can be used with most nozzles.
- **circle cutting attachments:** available for flange and circle cutting and designed for specific cutting nozzles. The circle cutting attachment is simply a pivot which is attached to the shank of the torch at a particular distance from the nozzle. Check for compatibility before attempting to use.
- **double roller guides:** available in different designs, some with the use of a radius bar so that it can be used to aid the cutting of circles. When cutting bevels in the vertical plane, they are indispensable as they reduce operator fatigue and improve the quality of cuts made.
- **angle iron:** can be used to guide the torch for both square and bevel cuts.

Controlling Distortion

During thermal cutting, as in welding, the expansion and contraction of the material causes distortion. As the cut progresses through the plate, the plates tend to move apart behind the nozzle unless restrained. On straight line cuts or bevels this may not be detrimental, but when cutting circular blanks this causes a flattening of the circle towards the end of the cut when the circle blank is small relative to the plate. To eliminated this movement, wedges can be placed in the cut after cutting has commenced. Alternatively use a zig-zag entry technique to reduce movement of the plate.

Other techniques used involve the use of tags, bridges and ties of uncut material being distributed around the circle or cut. Cutting is carried out between the tags and these are finally removed when the material has sufficiently cooled to prevent movement.

To utilise plate and produce minimum scrap, components are often nested, that is fitted close together so that only sufficient space for cutting is left between components. By using this technique all distortion passes into the scrap metal.

Plasma Cutting

Plasma cutting

Plasma cutting can be used on ferrous and non-ferrous metals and works on a non-chip forming principle which gives a more accurate and cleaner cut than oxy-fuel cutting.

Health and Safety

It is essential with this process that a head shield with an appropriate filter lens is used as ultra violet rays are produced which can cause arc eye and burning.

To begin cutting, an arc is formed between the torch and the work piece by holding the torch against the work piece. An inert gas is passed at high speed through a specially designed nozzle which holds up and energises this gas so that it turns into a plasma gas with a temperature in excess of 20,000°C. This plasma is hot enough to melt any metal and is delivered at a high enough velocity to blow the molten metal away from the cut. Plasma is a state of matter that is found in the region of an electrical discharge (arc). The plasma created by an arc is an ionized gas that has electrons and positive ions whose charges are nearly equal. A plasma consists of charged particles that conduct the electrons across the gap between the work and an electrode which is either copper or hafnium.

>20,000°C

Plasma cut process

The process differs from the oxy-fuel process in that the plasma operates by using the arc to melt the metal. In oxy-fuel gas cutting it is the oxygen that oxidises the metal and the heat from the exothermic reaction that melts the metal. Therefore, unlike the oxy-fuel process, the plasma process can be applied to cutting metals which form refractory oxides such as stainless steel, aluminium, cast iron, and non-ferrous alloys.

Plasma cutters can be automated and used to cut predefined shapes on programmable machines.

E-Learning

Use the e-learning programme to download a filter lens table.

Equipment

The power source required for the plasma arc process must have a drooping characteristic and a high voltage.

Although the operating voltage to sustain the plasma is typically 50–60V, the open circuit voltage needed to initiate the arc can be up to 400V DC. On initiation, the pilot arc is formed within the body of the torch between the electrode and nozzle. For cutting, the arc must be transferred to the work piece in the so called 'transferred' arc mode. The electrode has a negative polarity and the work piece a positive polarity so that the majority of the arc energy (approximately two thirds) is used for cutting.

A plasma torch supplies electrical energy to a gas to change it into the high-energy state of plasma. On a manual torch the body is made of a special plastic that is resistant to high temperatures, ultraviolet light and impact, and is available in a variety of lengths and sizes. The torch and head may be connected at any angle (90°, 75°, 45° etc.) or the head can be flexible. The 75° and 90° angles are popular for manual machines and the 180° straight torch heads are most often used for machine operations. Because of the heat produced, some provision for cooling is needed. For low power torches this cooling may be either by air or water; high power torches are predominately water-cooled. All torch heads can be replaced if they become worn or damaged.

Most hand-held torches have a manual power switch that is used to start and stop the power source, gas, and cooling water. Most often, this is a thumb switch located on the torch body, but it may be a foot control or located on the panel for machine equipment. Some equipment has an automatic system that starts the plasma when the torch is brought close to the work. The electrode tip (copper or hafnium), nozzle insulator, nozzle tip, nozzle guide and nozzle are parts of the torch that must be replaced periodically as they wear out or become damaged from use. The metallic parts are predominately made out of copper and may be plated to reduce spatter adherence.

The electrode tip is often made of a copper alloy with an embedded tungsten tip or hafnium. Copper allows the heat generated at the tip to be conducted away faster. Keeping the tip as cool as possible lengthens its life and allows for better quality cuts for a longer time.

The nozzle insulator is situated between the electrode tip and the nozzle tip and provides the critical gap spacing and the electrical separation of the parts. The spacing is called electrode setback and is essential to the safe operation of the system.

The nozzle tip has a small, cone-shaped, constricting orifice in the centre. The electric current forms the plasma in the setback space between the electrode tip and nozzle tip. Changes in the diameter of the orifice affect the action of the plasma arc, while changes in the setback distance alter arc voltage and current flow.

The nozzle, sometimes called the cup, is made of ceramic or any other high-temperature resistant substance. This helps prevent the internal electrical parts from accidental shorting and provides control of the shielding gas or water injection, if used.

The water shroud nozzle is attached to some torches. The water surrounding the nozzle tip is used to control the potential hazards of light, fumes, noise or other pollutants produced by the process.

The water filter is essential when using compressed air as some moisture is carried in the air stream and this can cause an arcing effect on air-cooled torches and reduce the effectiveness of the cutting torch.

The gas composition in the conventional system using a tungsten electrode is usually an inert gas such as argon, argon-hydrogen or nitrogen. Oxidising gases such as compressed air or oxygen can be used but the electrode must be copper with hafnium nozzle bore diameter. If the gas flow is too low for the current level, or the current level too high for the nozzle bore diameter, the arc will break down, forming two arcs which is usually catastrophic, melting the nozzle.

Using a plasma cutter, a body repairer can cut thin, low-alloy sheet metal of a damaged car with little danger of distortion. On thicker sections, the hardness zone along the edge of the cut will be so small that it is not a problem.

The quality of cut is similar to that achieved with the oxy-fuel gas process. However, as the plasma process cuts by melting, a characteristic feature is the greater degree of melting towards the top of the metal, resulting in top edge rounding, the edges not being square or a bevel on the cut edge. As these limitations are associated with the degree of constriction of the arc, several torch designs are available to produce more uniform heating at the top and bottom edge of the cut. One of the major advantages of this process is the reduced heat-affected zone (HAZ), which means that the work cools down rapidly allowing you to handle the cut plates.

Forming Techniques

Forming techniques

Forming techniques include bending, folding and shaping metal sheet and plate. Sheet is defined as being metal up to 3mm thick and plate as being more than 3mm thick.

How we form and what equipment we use can determine the working life of a component. within a given environment. For example by shaping the material to a given profile we can ensure that it remains rigid under severe operating conditions.

How we form and what equipment we use can determine the working life of a component. For example, by shaping the material to a given profile we can ensure that it remains rigid under severe operating conditions.

Some materials exhibit a higher tensile strength and therefore an allowance needs to be considered to prevent spring back. After the metal has been formed, the residual tensile and compressive forces will combine to create 'spring back' where and the metal will try to return to its original form. The amount of spring back will depend on the composition and mechanical properties of the metal and the fabricator will need to over bend in order to achieve the required form.

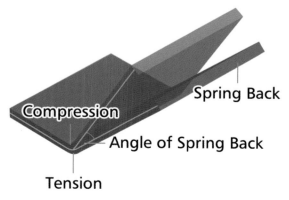

Springback

Selection of Forming Machines

It takes considerable experience to select the most suitable equipment for forming operations if the maximum production rate, quality and operational safety are to be achieved. Consideration should be given to the following factors:

- capacity range. Material to be formed, thickness of metal, maximum length, and sectional shape required;
- type of forming. Straight line folding or bending, single or double curvature bends;
- production. Rate of forming, insertion and removal of work, degree of accuracy, shape to be formed, attachments required, and the labour cost (skill level);
- administration. Safety implications, maintenance, demand and capital cost of machine.

Machine Forming

Machine forming tools cater for a variety of shapes and material thicknesses and provide an accurate and efficient way of repetitively forming metal. However, their size and price can make them uneconomic for small workshops. Machine forming is commonly used to form box sections, panels, small clips and brackets.

Press Brake (Air Bending)

Press brakes are available as mechanical or hydraulic. They can be used for an extensive range of forming operations and use one of two forming techniques: air bending or coining. With air bending, forming is carried out by 'three point location', one point on the line to be folded and the other two points where the forming tool touches the sides of the bottom die. This leaves an 'air gap.' The material will have a greater tendency to spring back and this must be compensated for. However, it requires a smaller force to bend materials and can be used on heavy materials.

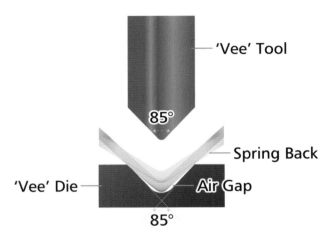

Air bending

Press Brake (Coining)

Coining requires a higher force than air bending and involves the tool following the bottom die so that no gap is left. This removes the elasticity from the metal and means that it retains the exact bend required.

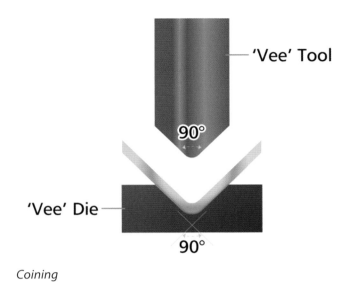

Coining

Comparisons of Machines

The choice of which machine to use is dependent upon the manufacturing requirements of the work. Mechanical machines are designed to deliver the maximum force on the bottom of the stroke and this is usually the initial contact with the metal, pressure then falls off. Movement of the beam can be stopped at any point and inching of the beam can also be achieved which gives the operator maximum control over the forming operation.

Hydraulic machines are connected to the pistons of two hydraulic chambers. These are co-ordinated to ensure that the beam remains parallel during forming. Full force is available at any point throughout its stroke, and the ease with which the pressure can be controlled on these machines makes them very accurate. The movement of the beam can be stopped and reversed at any point. The beam is operated by a foot pedal and removal of the foot at any stage during the bending cycle automatically returns the beam to its top position. Inching of the beam can be achieved quickly and easily.

Both mechanical and hydraulic machines are dangerous and require guarding to safeguard the operators. Guards are either mechanically operated or of the photo-electric type in which, if you break the beam, the machine instantly trips out and has to be re-set. Access to the back of these machines should be prevented when the machine is in operation. This is usually done by controlled automatic locking systems which come into play the minute the machine is operated.

Lockformers

Lockformer

Lockformers are double-sided forming machines with a series of rollers which manipulate the material to produce a designated shape in sheet metal up to 1.6mm. They are limited to light gauges (0.9-1.6mm) and are used to produce self-secured joints (Pittsburgh Lock and double seam, a form of mechanised grooved seam).

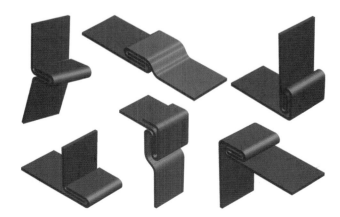

Self-secured joints produced by lockformers

Stretching and Shrinking Machines

Stretching and shrinking machine

Stretching and shrinking machines are hydraulically powered machines which consist of two jaw plates in either steel or plastic to prevent surface damage. They are available as either large static machines of the C-frame type or mobile forming units. Forming that can be carried out on this machine include stretching, shrinking, flattening, planishing, doming, flanging, notching and punching.

The work piece is inserted between the top and bottom tools. Pressure is brought to bear from either side, gripping the metal and shrinking the metal in extremely small increments. Wrinkling is eliminated due to the small increments deformed. Stretching is done in a similar operation.

By changing the heads you can planish, which involves using the reciprocating heads to remove high spots from a formed component. Doming is shaping a flat sheet into a domed shape by reciprocating heads specifically shaped to match the required dome. The degree of doming is determined by the pressure applied and movement of the sheet.

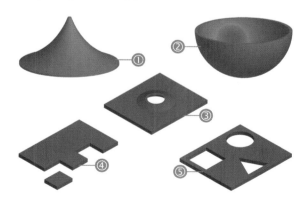

Formings created by stretching and shrinking machine: 1. Planishing; 2. Doming; 3. Flanging; 4. Notching; 5. Punching

Powered Rollers and Folders

Powered rollers and folders use a controlled pressure to shape metal. They are capable of exerting a considerable force on the component to overcome the natural spring back of the material and ensure that it meets the specification. However allowances must be given to the thickness of plate and the degree of rolling and forming required.

Powered rollers and folders can be electric, pneumatic, or hydraulically driven and are generally used for plate work. A hydraulically operated vertical plate bending machine is capable of either hot or cold forming plate up to 4m wide and from 20-160mm thick. When vertical plate bending, the weight of the plate has very little effect on the bending accuracy as no sagging occurs. Vertical machines offer more power for edge setting than horizontal machines and can take the place of two machines, a press brake and pyramid rollers. A reciprocating beam is brought forward to exert maximum force on the plate edge until the required pre-set is formed. The beam is retracted, the plate is run through the machine and the trailing edge pre-set in the same manner. Rolling of plate can then be completed to the required diameter. The upper bearing on the main feed roller is swung up for removal of the cylinder. These machines are capable of forming cylinders and cones, plate straightening and flanging. Horizontal power folders work on a similar process but are limited by the width of plate that they can deal with.

Manual Forming

Manual forming tools generally are used in smaller workshops where space is at a premium and the range of work is limited. They include folders, rollers, jennies, stakes and the use of mallets, sandbags, wheeling machines and hammers.

Manual folding machines

Manual folding machines are designed to fold metal sheet up to 1.6 to 2mm thick by adjusting the top bed to take account of the thickness of material and prevent cracking. The sequence of folds should be carefully planned to ensure that the work can be easily removed from the machine once the folding is complete. They are available in several formats: swing beam, box and pan, bench type flat bed and roll type folders, all designed to fold metal within given constraints of length of forming blade and capacity of thickness of metal.

The frame of the folder is available in either cast iron or as an all steel model. The all steel frame is cheaper and easier to repair but should not be overloaded by material thickness as it is possible to get deflection or distortion over the length of the blade. The clamping action on both versions is by eccentric levers or geared top blade with wheel adjustment.

Swing beam folders are so called because of the weights attached to the vertical arms which provide the folding force. Care needs to be exercised when using this type of folder to allow sufficient space for the beam to swing upwards under your control.

The box and pan type of folder is designed with a segmental top blade which allows each segment to be withdrawn or arranged to give a clearance for specific forming operations, such as boxes and pans or other shapes which require 90° folds in two planes or more.

'Flat-bed' folders are suitable for preparing the edges for self-secured joints and beadings. The folder is designed for production work and the guide is used for repeat folds without any further measurement. This type of folder has no provision for clamping the metal and is limited in its width and thickness capacity. It is predominately used with thin metal as the folding force is delivered by a single lever. There is also a bench mounted set of folders for forming thick plate with either a flat or curved profiles.

Manual sheet rollers

Manual sheet rollers are known as pinch rollers because the two front rollers are designed to pinch the sheet while the back roller shapes the sheet. These are available in two variants which can be made to roll the sheet up or down by changing the position of the back roller. The minimum diameter of cylinder which can be rolled on bending rollers is approximately 1.5-2 x the diameter of the roller around which it is being formed. During rolling there is always some tendency for the rollers to deflect away from the metal under the action of the bending forces. This is particularly so with long rollers of small diameter. The maximum deflection will be in the centre, resulting in the production of a barrel-shaped cylinder rather than a parallel cylinder. Most pinch type rollers are supplied with slip rolls, which are designed to slip out sideways and allow for extraction of the rolled cylinder or shape. The position of the back roller will determine if the metal is formed around the top or bottom roller. The majority of these machines are un-geared hand operated with a capacity up to 1.5-3mm. Another form of roller is the pyramid roller which, as its name suggests, has the rollers arranged in a pyramid. These rollers are designed to form circular shapes in thick metal or angle sections.

Jennies

These are the simplest form of rotary combination machines used for turning up an edge, wiring and joggling, putting a step-like form into the metal to provide a flat joint connection.

Stakes

Stakes: 1. Funnel stake; 2. Bick iron; 3. Creasing iron; 4. Bottoming stake; 5. Crescent stake

Where custom bends and folds are required, and conventional machines are limited, stakes are available in a range of shapes. The stake is fitted into a bench socket and the metal can then be bent and folded to the required shape with a suitable mallet or hammer.

Mallet and Sandbag

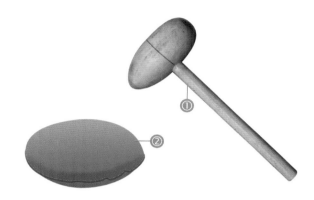

Mallet and sandbag: 1. Bossing mallet; 2. Sandbag

To create a hollow shape in a metal sheet manually a mallet and sandbag can be used to gently form the shape. Hollowing and raising techniques are used to produce bowl-like shapes and domed fabrications which are usually the precursor to further forming in wheeling machines used to create specified shapes. When hollowing and raising, adopt a technique which consists of an inverted spiral to work the outer edges and move towards the centre, taking care to put a uniform distribution of blows to maintain the desired shape. This process is designated as a work-hardening as the material changes due to distortion of the initial grain structure. If this was to continue unabated, cracking would occur as the grains would have nowhere to move to. This is where process annealing comes into play, to bring about recrystallization and thereby reduce the residual stresses and render the work capable of being further worked.

Wheeling Machine

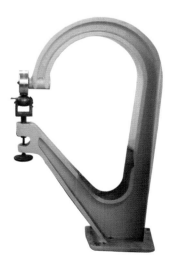

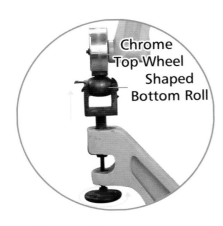

Wheeling machine operation

A wheeling machine, or English wheel, is another way of creating a curve manually in a sheet of metal. This is a highly skilled process. The wheeling machine consists of a shaped bottom roll and a fixed flat chromed top wheel. Pressure is applied by turning a screw and wheel arrangement on the bottom roller to raise the bottom wheel and engage the top wheel. The amount pressure exerted should be controlled to produce a minor change in the gap between the rollers and metal so that the metal does not become 'stretched' but simply evened out. The piece of metal is rolled back and forth between the wheels. It is essential that the path of the wheels is changed with every pass to ensure that there is no uneven pressure applied in one place. The operator needs to gain a feel for the pressure being applied and the movement of the sheet to achieve the required shape. The frame consists of a large 'C' form casting and the throat distance (the capacity of sheet it can deal with) determines the specification, which is usually given in Imperial measurements of 10-42in. A quick release action by cam and lever enables metals to be instantly released when desired, reinserted at another location and the bottom roller returned to its working position with the original pressure maintained.

Hammers

- Planishing hammers are generally used to smooth out distortion or bumps on the metal's surface without leaving indentations known as dressing out. This is achieved by the two faces of the hammer having crowned surfaces which help prevent indentations.
- Stretching hammers are designed to thin out the metal and increase the surface area so that a flange can be maintained, or to provide a slip joint on thin gauge cylinders.
- Paning down hammers are used to tuck in an edge on a self-secured joint.
- Blocking hammers are designed with two rounded profile faces to help in the hollowing and raising processes. They are available in a range of sizes, weights and profiles to match specified dimensions.
- Ball pein hammers are general engineering hammers used for marking out using dot and centre punches and general hammering activities.

Mallets

Mallets are used to dress or shape material, leave no or minimal marking and are available in a range of materials from boxwood, plastic, cow hide, aluminium, and copper. The bossing mallet is a wooden pear shaped head mallet with two different profiles at each end and is used for hollowing and raising. The cow hide mallet is a general purpose mallet often used for dressing out dents or imperfections on metals where surface finish is a consideration. The boxwood mallet is another mallet used for planishing a raised profile, with faces machined square it provides a flat surface area face. Plastic mallets are often used as an alternative to the hide mallet while aluminium and copper mallets are used where a degree of weight is required to dress out or move some component.

Thermal Joining Techniques

There are seven main thermal joining techniques, most of which have been explored in some detail earlier in this book. They are summarised here.

Oxyacetylene Welding

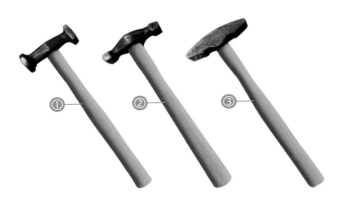

Hammers: 1. Planishing hammer; 2. Stretching hammer; 3. Panning down hammer

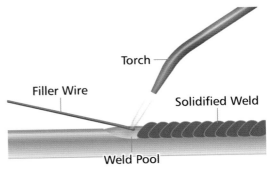

Wheeling machine operation

Activity

Name each of these forming and material removal machines.

_____

_____

_____

_____

_____

_____

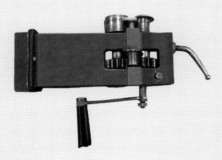

The oxyacetylene process is made up of two elements which are carried out simultaneously. The first is penetration of heat via the torch and the second is the deposition of filler metal via the filler rod. This joins the base materials together.

When the oxyacetylene flame impacts upon the base materials, localised heating occurs and a molten weld pool is created. A filler material is added to the weld pool via a filler rod to complete the weld. As the process moves along the joint the deposited material cools and solidifies leaving a weld bead. This process can also fuse the parent metal together without the need for filler wire, this is known as an autogenous weld.

Manual Metal Arc (MMA) Welding

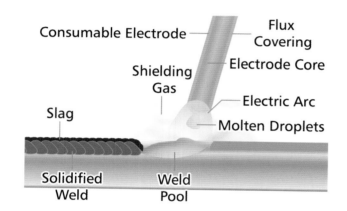

Manual Metal Arc (MMA) welding

Manual Metal Arc or MMA welding uses an electric current to generate an electric arc between the tip of an electrode and the work piece. The arc can create a heat in excess of 4000°C.

The arc causes instant heating of the parent material and a molten weld pool is formed, into which additional material is added in the form of the filler wire contained within the electrode. The metal is transferred from the tip of the electrode across the arc into the weld pool in the form of droplets by electromagnetic forces.

As the process moves along the joint the deposited material cools and solidifies leaving a weld bead. The weld zone is protected from atmospheric contamination by a gas shield created by the flux coating. The flux coating also provides a slag which protects the weld bead. When the MMA electrode is being operated correctly it makes a quiet crackling sound.

MIG Welding

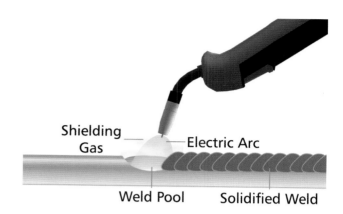

MIG welding

MIG welding uses an electric current to generate an electric arc between the tip of a filler wire and the work piece.

The arc causes instant heating of the parent material and a molten weld pool is formed, into which additional material is added in the form of the filler wire to complete the weld.

As the process moves along the joint the deposited material cools and solidifies leaving a weld bead. The weld zone is protected from atmospheric contamination by a gas shield.

When the MIG gun is being operated correctly it makes a loud crackling sound.

TIG Welding

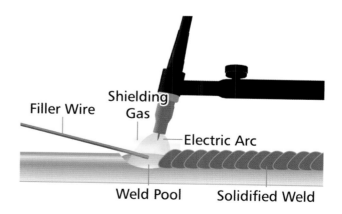

TIG welding

TIG welding uses an electric current to generate an electric arc between the tip of a tungsten electrode and the work piece.

The arc causes instant heating of the parent material and a molten weld pool is formed, into which additional material is added in the form of the filler wire to complete the weld.

As the process moves along the joint the deposited material cools and solidifies leaving a weld bead. The weld zone is protected from atmospheric contamination by a gas shield.

This process can also fuse the parent metal together without the need for filler wire.

When the TIG torch is being operated correctly it makes a humming sound.

Resistance Welding

Resistance welding provides a fast way of joining metals. As no holes need to be drilled, it also maintains the strength of the sheet metal. The surfaces to be joined should be clean and free of corrosion; they are then joined by passing a current through the material to produce welds at designated intervals. The advantage of using resistance welding is the speed of production that can be achieved. The fact that the thermal input is in the 'plastic stage' (not fully melted) means that thermal disturbance to the material is minimal, and this allows temperature sensitive materials to be joined. Also because the thermal input is not continuous, distortion is virtually non-existent.

Spot welds are created by passing a heavy current, at low voltage through the two pieces of metal at the point they are to be joined. Resistance to the current at the interface between the two pieces creates heat which then forms a weld nugget. As the weld is not continuous, the joint then has to be sealed to prevent leakage and corrosion.

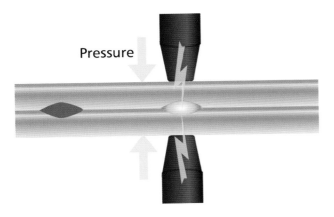

Spot welding

Seam welding consists of two circular electrodes, one of which is powered and rotates to produce a series of overlapping spot welds which are leak proof. Typical applications would be on radiators and fuel tanks.

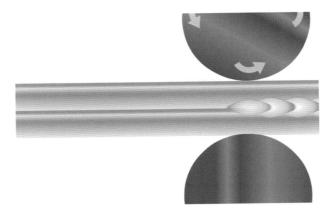

Seam welding

Projection welding is where one of the components to be joined has a projection raised on its surface. The other component to be joined is then placed in contact and special shaped electrodes apply the current. The projection heats up and collapses into the other component under applied pressure. It is used extensively for captive nuts.

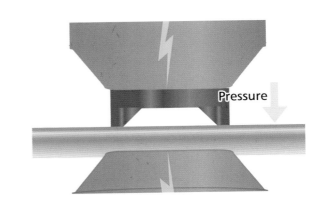

Projection welding

Soft Soldering

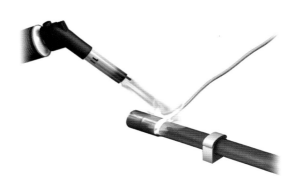

Soft soldering

Soft soldering is a low-temperature process, typically 180-300°C dependent upon the composition of the solder. The process relies on capillary attraction (vacuum effect) to draw a low viscosity metal alloy through closely matting surfaces. The parent metals are not melted, but a solder alloy is used to form a bond between them. The alloy reacts with the surface layers of the parent metals to form an intermetallic compound which cannot be physically removed and is often referred to as tinning the parent metal surfaces.

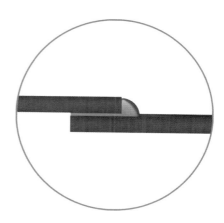

Filler material drawn into the joint by capillary attraction

Braze Welding

Braze welding differs from brazing in the mode of deposition. It forms a metallic bond between the surfaces but the resulting bead is similar to that of a fusion welded bead with no fusion taking place.

Solder alloy used to form a bond

Brazing

Distortion Control

When heat is applied to a metal during a thermal joining technique, distortion occurs in a number of directions. Longitudinal distortion is a bowing effect along the length of the weld; transverse distortion is shrinkage across the face of the weld and angular distortion is where the cooling weld pulls across the face of the weld and reduces the angle of the welded joint.

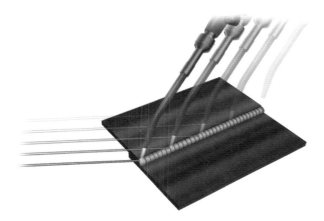

Brazing (Hard soldering)

Distortions: 1. Longitudinal distortion; 2. Transverse distortion; 3. Angular distortion

In brazing, the filler material being used is drawn into the joint by capillary attraction. The surfaces being joined should be clean, parallel and with a tight fitting surface throughout the joint for the capillary attraction to occur and secure the joint. This process is often referred to as a hard soldering process.

A variety of aids can be used to control the distortion including magnetic clamps, wedges, jigs, fixtures and G-clamps. Weld sequences are used to distribute heat around the joint and reduce its thermal heat impact. Typical sequences include intermittent and skip welding.

Weld sequences: A. Skip welding; B. Intermittent welding

Alternative Joining Techniques

In addition to thermal joining techniques, there are a large number of alternative joining techniques.

Nuts and bolts

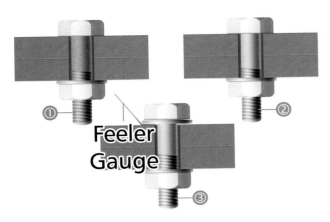

Nuts and bolts: 1. Black barrel; 2. Turned barrel; 3. High strength friction grip

Nuts and bolts provide a joint that can be removed without damage to the parent metal. They are available as black barrel, turned barrel and high strength friction grip bolts.

Black barrelled bolts are general purpose bolts produced by cold or hot forging of a mild steel diameter bar to produce the hexagonal head. They are usually used with loose tolerance holes with low tensile stresses.

Turned barrel bolts are accurately machined and parallel throughout the length of the shank or barrel, with the underside of the head machined to ensure a good contact face. These are usually used with close tolerance holes that have been reamed out for size.

High strength friction grip bolts (HSFG) are made from high tensile steel, hardened and tempered and used with special nut and hardened washer. These bolts are tightened to a predetermined load to give a minimum tension in the bolt shank at least equal to the load of the bolt. A high clamping force is developed in the joint, transferring the load on the joint by friction between the connecting parts. Once tightened the bolt remains permanently tight maintaining the strength of the joint. HSFG bolts are used extensively on site work enabling joints to be made more easily and quickly and unaffected by vibration. HSFG bolts can be recognised by three radial marks on the bolt head; spaced 120° apart.

They are available in many different sizes, materials and types and the correct one should one selected to meet the requirements of the fabrication and to prevent galvanic corrosion. All metals posses a voltage and you have to be careful when putting dissimilar metals together as those that are lower in the galvanic series will be corroded by the higher value metals by means of electrolytic action. A good example of this is steel studs in a cast aluminium block. The problem can be reduced by placing a intermediary substance, such as a mastic or graphite grease, between the abutting surfaces to break the electrical path and reduce or remove corrosion.

Self-tapping screws

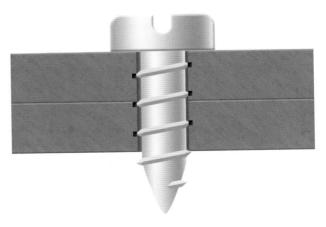

Self-tapping screw

A self-tapping screw creates its own thread as it passes through a previously drilled or punched hole in a piece of metal. They are available in various head types to join thin and thick pieces metal.

Blind rivets

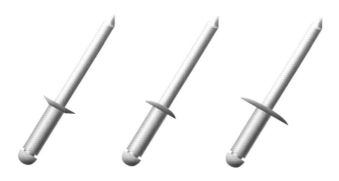

Blind rivets provide a way of joining two pieces of metal where there is access on only one side of the material. They are designed with a mandrel (metal stalk) which is drawn into the body of the rivet until the plies of the joint are tight. Shearing of the mandrel leaves a section which fills the pre-drilled hole. They are available in a range of materials and head designs. They are also used to avoid damaging previously finished pieces of work or on delicate materials.

Solid riveting

Solid rivets: 1. Snap head; 2. Universal head; 3. Flat head; 4. 90° countersunk head; 5. 60° countersunk head; 6. Raised countersunk head

Riveting creates permanent joints between pieces of metal. A hole is drilled through the two pieces of metal, a rivet is inserted through the hole and then a second head is created on the other side. Rivets are available in a wide range of materials and heads and it is important to select the correct one for the job. Considerations include ensuring that:

● The material the rivet is made of will not react with the parent metal causing corrosion.

● It can be closed easily.

● The final appearance of the rivet will meet the required standard.

Self-secured joints

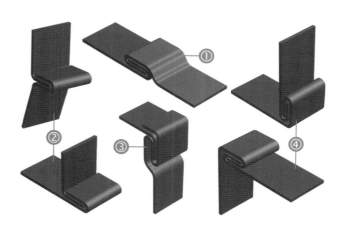

Self-secured joints: 1. Groove seam joint; 2. Paned down joints; 3. Pittsburgh lock; 4. Knocked up joints

Self-secured joints are created by folding and interlocking thin sheet metal edges so that they are made secure without any other joining processes being used. They are mainly used in fabrication and roofing with zinc sheets, using sheet metal less than 1.6mm thick. Some commonly used joints are the grooved seam, the paned-down joint, Pittsburgh lock, roll form and the knocked-up joint.

Adhesives

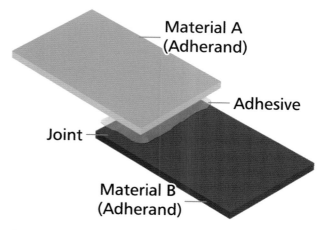

Adhesives

An adhesive is a material which sticks two pieces of material together. The materials being adhered can be similar or dissimilar. The bonding material is called the adhesive, the materials being stuck together are the adherands and the area of the material being adhered is called the joint. Adhesives fall into two basic groups: thermo-plastic and thermo-setting.

Thermo-plastic adhesives soften when heated and harden when cooled, and this cycle can be repeated. They have the advantages of relative lower cost and ease of application, but are not suitable for heavy loads. Typical thermo-plastic adhesives include acrylics, cellulosics, and rubber and resin-based types such as vinyl products.

Thermo-setting adhesives set to a permanent shape, need heating and pressure and will not re-soften. They are higher in cost and tend to be more complicated in their application. This range of adhesives includes the phenolics, epoxies, polyesters, polyurethanes and silicons. Thermo-setting adhesives can be supplied as a one part

adhesive which must be activated by external heat or as a two-part system which is chemically activated.

Quality Control

Once fabrication is complete, the product should be checked for tolerance, surface finish and standard of accuracy.

All specifications will include a plus and minus tolerance level and the finished product must be within this range. Surfaces must meet the specification; for example, flat surfaces should be true. Accuracy standards include checking that round products are perfectly round and have not distorted into an oval shape.

Sustainability

It is the fabricator's responsibility to ensure that the final product meets the required standards. Inaccurate fabrication can lead to the waste of a large amount of materials, cost and time.

CHECK YOUR KNOWLEDGE

1 What does pitch circle diameter refer to? Circle the correct answer.

a. the outside diameter
b. the insider diameter
c. the centre line between the inner and outer circles
d. the diameter of a hole

2 Which of these tools uses a chip forming process and which use a non chip forming process? Place a tick in the correct column.

Tool	Chip forming tools	Non chip forming tools
1 		
2 		
3 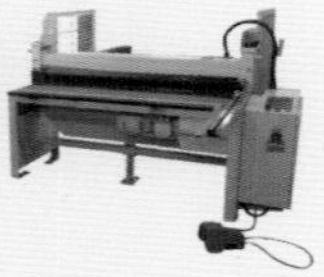		
4 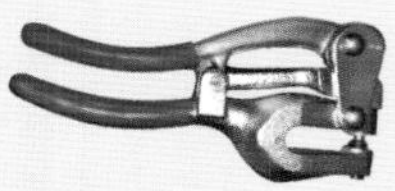		
5 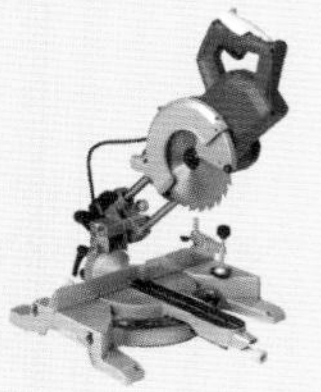		
6 		
7 		
8 		

3 Which of these alternative joining techniques would be used to join two pieces of metal that may need to be easily separated in the future? Circle the correct answer.

a. nuts and bolts
b. self-tapping screws
c. blind rivets
d. solid riveting
e. self-secured joints
f. adhesives

Summary

This concludes this chapter on metal fabrication.

You should now be able to list the tools used for measuring and marking out, material removal and forming. You should also be able to explain the techniques involved in these processes.

End test

1. **Which of these tools would be used in marking out and which would be used in material removal? Place a tick in the correct column.**

Tool	Marking Out	Material Removal
engineer's square		
snips		
combination set		
tape		
hacksaw		
chisel		
rule		
scriber		

2. **In metal fabrication, which datum would be most commonly used for marking out? Circle the correct answer.**

   ☐ a. datum edge

   ☐ b. datum surface

   ☐ c. datum point

   ☐ d. datum corner

3. **Which of the following terms are associated with marking out? Circle the correct answer.**

☐ a. progressive

☐ b. accumulative error

☐ c. chain dimensioning

☐ d. datum

☐ e. cumulative error

☐ f. co-ordinates

☐ g. standard

4. **Fold allowances are calculated using which dimension? Circle the correct answer.**

☐ a. material

☐ b. angle to be folded

☐ c. material thickness

☐ d. finished dimension

5. **Which of the descriptions shown match up with the cutting machines listed? Write a, b or c next to each description.**

☐ a. universal steel worker

☐ b. flypress

☐ c. whitney punch

   can be used for punching, shearing and notching

   can be used for shearing and piercing holes

   can be used for piercing holes or clearance holes

6. **Which of these statements are true regarding thermal cutting techniques? Circle the true statements.**

☐ a. The oxyacetylene gas cutting flame reaches up to a temperature of 3,500°C.

☐ b. The oxyacetylene gas cutting flame reaches up to a temperature of 20,000°C.

☐ c. Plasma gas cutting reaches up to a temperature of 3,500°C.

☐ d. Plasma gas cutting reaches up to a temperature of 20,000°C.

7. **What type of metals can these thermal cutting processes generally be used on? Write a or b next to each type of cutting.**

☐ a. ferrous metals

☐ b. ferrous & non ferrous metals

oxyfuel gas cutting

plasma cutting

8. **Resistance welding provides which of the following types of welds? Circle the correct answer.**

☐ a. spot

☐ b. tack

☐ c. block

☐ d. seam

☐ e. fusion

☐ f. projection

9. **Which of these tools or procedures can be used to control distortion? Circle the correct answer.**

☐ a. clamp

☐ b. hammering

☐ c. weld sequences

☐ d. wedges

☐ e. crimping

10. **Identify the non-thermal techniques of joining. Circle the correct answers.**

☐ a. self-secured joints

☐ b. soldering

☐ c. riveting

☐ d. brazing

Quality Control

10

Codes, Legislation and Standards

The many aspects of quality control

Quality control ensures a certain standard of confidence in a product. It does this by maintaining industry-led standards for performance, reliability, durability and availability. It is accompanied by a back-up service to ensure that all the customers' expectations have been met.

This chapter gives an introduction to the International Quality Assurance program which is produced by the International Organisation for Standardisation, ISO. The chapter is designed to give an understanding of the procedures and skills required to make goods that are fit for purpose and of a merchantable quality.

Quality control criteria

Quality Control Systems

Quality control is often depicted as a loop or cycle which goes through stages referred to as Plan, Do, Check and Act (PDCA). A PDCA circle is a recognised sequence for changing the way things are done in business. It was developed by Deming and it helps to keep continuous improvement on the right track.

Quality control cycle

- Plan. This could be to initiate a new process or improve an existing one. It should be based upon customer needs and be designed to fulfil the organisation's mission more effectively.
- Do. Engage the workforce, adopt best working practices to achieve the desired industry-led standards in order to maintain quality (fitness for purpose).
- Check. Review the gathered data to determine if the planned and implemented change has created the quality improvement intended.
- Act. Take action, either to implement the change or change the variables to see if the process can be made more effective, or 'standardise' the new successful process.

The PDCA circle should not be considered a constant burden, but rather an indication that the organisation is still responding to meet the ever-changing needs of the customer.

This constant reviewing of the product helps to maintain quality, gives a competitive edge and reduces wastage.

There are a number of quality control systems in existence.

ISO 9001

ISO 9001 is a group of standards that relate to quality management systems. They are designed to help businesses ensure they meet the needs of customers and other stakeholders and are produced by the International Organisation for Standardisation (ISO). These standards are not specific to any industry, product, goods or service. For the commercial world these standards are almost compulsory, especially when dealing with multinationals, large

Activity

You have been given the responsibility to oversee a manufacturing project to produce a new welding table which has the facility to allow the welder to work in all positions and maintain stability. Using the PDCA loop, indicate the areas that would come under the various stages. For example purchasing of consumables would come under the planning section. You are only required to give headings with a brief description.

Plan

_____
_____
_____
_____
_____
_____

Do

_____
_____
_____
_____
_____
_____
_____

Check

_____
_____
_____
_____
_____
_____

Act

_____
_____
_____
_____
_____

companies and government institutions. To be awarded certification a company's operations and internal quality systems must be verified by an independent third party carrying out an on-site audit to check compliance. To remain certified, the company must pass regular audits, usually every two years. Failure to comply means removal of certification or some form of action planning to meet compliance. The ISO 9000 certification brings recognition and credibility and provides a structure on which a total quality management (TQM) system can be built.

ISO 9001

Kaizen

Kaizen is a Japanese concept which continually looks at the production process at all stages. All employees at whatever level contribute to this process by seeking and addressing any issues which could be improved. This engagement of all staff in the process shows a commitment to improve the process for the benefit of all. Kaizen is a culture of sustained continuous improvement focusing on eliminating waste in all systems and processes of an organisation; it begins and ends with people.

There are two elements that construct Kaizen, improvement for the better and continuity. Lacking one of these elements would not be considered Kaizen.

It is not easy to implement the Kaizen philosophy in a culture that is not keen to adopt it. What follows is a list of basic tips for encouraging the Kaizen culture:

- Discard conventional fixed ideas.
- Think of how it can be done, not why it cannot be done.
- Do not make excuses, start by questioning current practices.
- Do not make excuses, do it straight away, even if it is for only 50% of targets.
- If you make mistakes, correct them right away.

- Do not spend money for Kaizen, use your wisdom.
- Wisdom is brought out when faced with hardship.
- Ask 'why' five times and seek root causes.
- Seek the wisdom of ten people rather than the knowledge of one.

Kaizen quality control process

Kanban

Kanban is a Japanese concept of holding a minimum amount of stock to meet demands currently placed. The advantage of this system is that stock levels are kept low which helps increase cash flow to the business. All movement throughout the factory is controlled by these Kanbans. Since they specify item quantities, no defects can be tolerated. For example if a defective component is found when processing a production order using Kanban, then obviously the quantity specified on the Kanban cannot be produced. Hence the importance of automation; the system must detect and highlight defective items so that the problem that caused the defect to occur can be resolved. Employee participation is an essential part of the process, drawing on their knowledge and experience to make suggestions for improvements, co-operate in changes and be involved in the improvements within the production system.

Kanban replenishment is simple and can use different methods to trigger re-stocking, such as Kanban cards.

The benefits of such a system are:

- reduced cycle times;
- lower set-up times;
- smoother production flow;
- higher productivity;
- less inventory of raw materials, work-in-progress and finished goods cost savings;
- reduced space requirements;
- improved relationships with suppliers.

Lower stock levels allow for a better use of cash, which is especially important during downturns in industrial output or global recession. This money can be reinvested in determining new markets and creating the climate for goods.

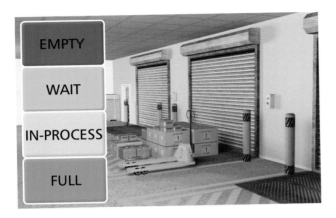

Kanban quality control process

Benchmarking

Benchmarking is the process of comparing a business's processes and performance to industry leaders or best practices from other industries. Performance indicators that are typically measured include quality, time and cost.

During the process of benchmarking, companies learn how well the industry leaders perform and, more importantly, the business processes that explain why these firms are successful. Benchmarking also helps to identify training and equipment needs in order to be competitive.

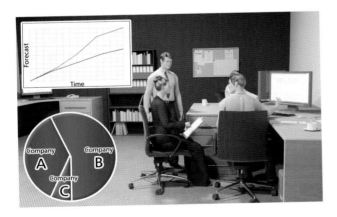

Benchmarking

Total Quality Management (TQM)

Total quality management (TQM) is a process of continuously improving quality (CIQ) by focusing on the requirements of customers. It centres on engaging all involved in the process from engineers to production staff, to contrib-

ute and set up improvements which will be of benefit to everyone. This gives a competitive edge which ensures recognition and reputation in the global market. The advantages of using a TQM programme can be summarized as follows:

- It makes an organisation more competitive.
- It establishes a new working culture which enables growth and longevity.
- It provides a working environment in which everyone can succeed.
- It reduces stress, waste and friction.
- It helps team building and promotes partnership and co-ordination.

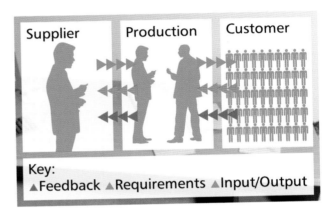

Total quality management

Materials Standards

The materials used in welding and fabrication are covered by quality control standards of their own which brings a conformity or compliance to the process that is traceable.

Documentation of standards include: mill certificates, manufacturer's consumables descriptions and materials safety data sheets.

Example of a purchase order

Activity

Describe the advantages of using the following:

Kanban

_____

_____

_____

_____

_____

Kaizan

_____

_____

_____

_____

_____

ISO 9000

_____

_____

_____

_____

TQM

_____

_____

_____

_____

_____

Mill Certificate

Example of a mill certificate

Mill certificates are documents issued by steel manufacturers to trace materials by batch number. Typical information given would include:

- a unique cast or batch number;
- a composition of the material (carbon content and alloying elements);
- the mechanical properties (hardness, yield and impact values);
- the heat treatments that have been carried out (annealed, tempered, hardened, etc.);
- forming characteristics;
- pre-heating or post-heating requirements.

This piece of paperwork is the basis of most of the design procedures, manufacturing processes and selection of appropriate welding processes to meet the desired specification. When the plate is delivered to the fabricator, an inspector checks the plate number against the mill certificate to show that the steel conforms to the specification to which the steel was ordered. When the plate is cut up into parts to be fabricated, the plate number, or some other identifying number, is transferred to each part considered to be of sufficient importance and this is in turn is recorded on the component drawing. This incorporates 'traceability' into the manufacturing process.

E-Learning

Use the e-learning programme to download a sample mill certificate.

Manufacturer's Consumables Descriptions

Example of a consumable definition

Each manufacturer supplies their own range of consumables such as filler materials, fluxes, and shielding gases and they all conform to a recognised standard such as ISO.

All manufacturers as part of their own quality control procedures issue details which confirms composition, compatibility, mechanical properties and to which standards they conform.

E-Learning

Use the e-learning programme to download a sample manufacturer's consumables description.

Health and Safety
Materials Safety Data Sheet

Example of a Materials Safety Data Sheet (MSDS)

Any material supplied which may have some safety consideration is covered by the use of Material Safety Data Sheets or MSDS. They govern factors including how to use them safely, what to do in the event of an incident, health risks and additional information for further advice.

E-Learning

Use the e-learning programme to download a sample MSDS.

Vendor Rating

This involves rating the vendor of materials for quality, reliability, and conformance to given standards.

Pricing factors include:

- Competitive pricing. The prices paid should be comparable to those of vendors providing similar product and services.
- Price stability. Prices should be reasonably stable over time.
- Price accuracy. There should be a low number of variances from purchase-order prices on invoices received.
- Advance notice of price changes. The vendor should provide adequate advance notice of price changes.
- Sensitive to costs. The vendor should demonstrate respect for the customer's bottom line and show an understanding of its needs.
- Billing. Are vendor invoices are accurate? The average length of time to receive credit memos should be reasonable. Estimates should not vary significantly from the final invoice. Effective vendor bills are timely and easy to read and understand.

Quality factors include:

- Compliance with purchase order. The vendor should comply with terms and conditions as stated in the purchase order.
- Conformity to specifications. The product or service must conform to the specifications identified in the request for proposal and purchase order.
- Reliability. Is the rate of product failure within reasonable limits?
- Reliability of repairs. Is all repair and rework acceptable?
- Durability. Is the time until replacement is necessary reasonable?
- Support. Is quality support available from the vendor? Immediate response to and resolution of the problem is desirable.

- Warranty. The length and provisions of warranty protection offered should be reasonable. Are warranty problems resolved in a timely manner?

Delivery factors include the following:

- Time. Does the vendor deliver products and services on time? Is the actual receipt date on or close to the promised date? Does the promised date correspond to the vendor's published lead times? Also, are requests for information, proposals and quotes swiftly answered?
- Quantity. Does the vendor deliver the correct items or services in the contracted quantity?
- Lead time. Is the average time for delivery comparable to that of other vendors for similar products and services?
- Packaging. Packaging should be sturdy, suitable, properly marked and undamaged. Pallets should be the proper size with no overhang.
- Documentation. Does the vendor furnish proper documents (packing slips, invoices, technical manual, etc.) with correct material codes and proper purchase order numbers?
- Emergency delivery. Does the vendor demonstrate extra effort to meet requirements when an emergency delivery is requested?

A vendor rating system helps minimise subjectivity in judgment and makes it possible to consider all relevant criteria in assessing suppliers. It provides feedback from all areas in one package, which can be convenient. A system can provide more control of the vendor base, facilitate better communications with vendors and help to build vendor partnerships. It can improve quality by establishing continuous review standards for vendors, thus ensuring continuous improvement of vendor performance. A vendor rating system can also make it easier to correct identified performance weaknesses.

E-Learning

Use the e-learning programme to download a sample purchase order and inventory control.

Welding Codes

Because welding is now a critical activity which may have a bearing on whether a structure fails in service, guidelines were introduced to control the parameters of the procedure and specify particular operating characteristics. Therefore for components which have a specific operating function which requires certification, welder codings or certification have been established which identify the stringent conditions under which the operator has achieved success and is therefore covered by some form of insurance.

Welding codes are a means of assessing and maintaining industry recognised standards for welders. They cover the welder and the employing company for any work carried out to this standard. This in turn is validated by insurance companies.

If the welder passes a welding code, they are usually coded for two years, subject to working at this standard. If they fail, they may need further training before attempting the test again.

Awarding bodies include the American Society of Mechanical Engineers, European Norm, The International Organisation for Standards, British Standards and Lloyds Registry.

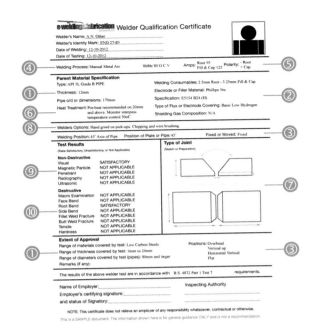

Example of a welder's certificate

To gain a code, a welder must complete a test to a designated weld procedure sheet. These are test documents that are approved by a number of validating bodies and dictate the range of work, the material and thickness range and welding positions that the welder is approved for. The sheet contains all of the weld parameters which must be followed.

E-Learning

Use the e-learning programme to download a sample completed welding procedure sheet.

Welder's certificate: 1. Materials and range (Thickness range); 2. Consumables; 3. Position range; 4. Welding process; 5. Welding variables; 6. Heat treatment; 7. Diagram (Visuals); 8. Welder's option; 9. Non-destructive testing; 10. Destructive testing

Information that is contained in the weld procedure sheet includes:

Materials Specification and Range

This stipulates the material to be used in the test and the operational range of materials that the welder will be covered for, if successful. For example, low carbon steels in thicknesses up to a specified dimension.

Consumables

This lists the designated consumables conforming to recognised standards that must be adhered to, for example an E5154 electrode. This must be followed or the certification will be invalid

Position Range

This identifies the position in which the procedure will be carried out but it also identifies the other weld positions that the welder will be approved for if the test is completed successfully. For example a vertical test piece in plate will cover the welder for the flat and horizontal/vertical welding positions as well.

Thickness Range

This indicates the thickness range of material the welder will be covered for. Typically the welder will be covered from half the thickness to twice the thickness of the size specified on the weld procedure sheet. For example if a weld is carried out in 6mm plate the welder is covered from 3mm to 12mm thickness range.

Welding Process

This defines which welding process, for example manual metal arc welding, that the welder is being coded for and will only cover them for that process.

Welding Variables

This indicates any weld variables that are to be used, such as voltage, amperage, wire feed rate, shielding gas flow rate, back purging flow rate and consumables. The values quoted are normally within a range statement to allow for some variation on machines.

Heat Treatment

For some weld procedures, some form of heat-treatment may be required in order to achieve a strong weld deposit. Typical heat-treatments would be a pre-heat temperature to give an even temperature balance, inter-pass temperature control (measuring the temperature between runs) on multiple weld deposition and possibly some form of post-heating to reduce stresses.

Diagram

The diagram indicated on the weld procedure will show the weld joint and sequence of welds required to complete the joint. It will also show the edge preparation of the root face, root gap and included angle if the joint is a butt joint.

Welder's Options

Welder's options usually refers to wire brushing, and interpass cleaning of a multiple weld joint or the chipping off of slag.

Visuals

This refers to the component parts such as the root penetration of the welded joint that will need to be visually examined against internationally set standards. In the case of a butt joint the maximum root penetration for most codes is 3mm. Other visual features that can be observed would include leg length on a tee-fillet weld, weld face, undercut, underfill, cold lapping, misalignment, surface porosity and inclusions.

Non-Destructive Testing

Non-destructive testing refers to tests that are carried out on the completed welded joint which will not result in any damage to the joint. Common non-destructive tests include: dye penetrant, magnetic particle, radiographic and ultrasonic inspection techniques.

Non-destructive testing (NDT) is used to test welds for surface defects such as cracks, arc strikes, undercuts, and lack of penetration. Internal or subsurface defects can include slag inclusions, porosity, and unfused metal in the interior of the weld.

An active visual inspection schedule can reduce the finished weld rejection rate by more than 75%. Visual inspection can easily be used to check for fit-up, inter-pass acceptance, welder technique, and other variables that will affect the weld quality. Minor problems can be identified and corrected before a weld is completed. This eliminates costly repairs or rejection.

Visual inspection should be used before any other non-destructive or mechanical tests are used to eliminate (reject) the obvious problem welds. Eliminating welds that have excessive surface discontinuities and will not pass the code or standard being used saves preparation time.

Destructive Testing

The destructive testing will be dictated by the standard but it may also be a requirement of a company for their quality control documentation. Typical destructive tests that are carried out include: bend tests, ductile (the ability to be pulled) fracture and nick-break tests.

Activity

You are required to undergo a welder coding, and as part of that process the weld you produce will be subjected to bend tests and non-destructive testing. State what these tests will determine and how they support the coding and your professional status.

_____

_____

_____

_____

_____

_____

_____

_____

_____

_____

_____

_____

_____

_____

Production Monitoring

To ensure the integrity of a product, it is vital that production is monitored at all stages and that the best use of staff and equipment is made.

Sustainability

Monitoring will ensure that production flows smoothly, sufficient quality controls are incorporated to highlight any discrepancies and wastage is reduced to a minimum.

Project Planning

In order to manage a project effectively, all activities from the initial concept to the finished product need to be planned and monitored. The aim is to maximise the use of resources, avoid waste, maintain quality control and achieve milestones.

When planning a project, visual representations such as Gantt and flow charts are a good way of indicating progress and the effective use of machines and labour.

Visual representation is also used with sampling to indicate the upper and lower tolerance of a production run, as in statistical process charts which can help to identify and rectify rejects and reduce wastage.

Gantt Charts

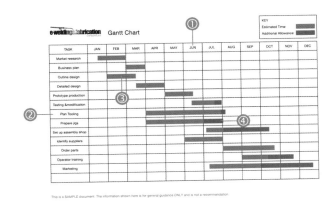

Gantt chart: 1. Horizontal axis (Timescale); 2. Vertical axis (Tasks); 3. Estimated time; 4. Additional allowance

Activity

Produce a flow chart for the setting up of a welding plant of your choice, indicating any secondary actions such as insulation check, purging, etc.

A Gantt chart consists of a horizontal axis showing the time-scale and a vertical axis which shows the tasks that make up the project. The total length of the timeline shows the length of the actual project. This will change as tasks are amended. For example, suppose that a delivery is late and this delays the start of another task. This may then have an effect on the rest of the project unless resources can be reallocated to make up the time that has been lost.

Gantt charts are useful tools for planning and scheduling projects. They allow you to assess how long a project should take and what resources are needed. They also show the order in which tasks need to be carried out and make it easier to manage the dependencies between tasks.

Flow Charts

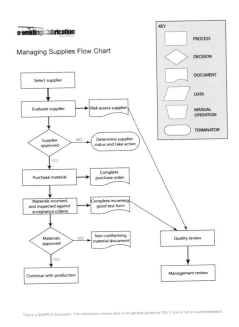

Example of a flow chart

Flow charts are designed to put in place a logical sequence of activities. These charts use recognised standard symbols to represent certain functions such as process, decisions and termination points.

Monitoring and Inspection

Inspection forms an integral part of any production process. The key stages include goods inward, production, and the completed product. Typical goods inspection would include the following:

- raw materials (such as sheet, plate, bar) which are received prior to entering production;

- bought in components (such as nuts, bolts, sub-assemblies);
- pre-manufacture equipment – tools, jigs, fixtures, to be used in manufacture.

A goods inwards department would normally have a specific quality inspector in place to ensure all goods are up to specifications.

Sampling

The mechanism by which this inspection is carried out in production is called sampling. It would be very expensive to provide a 100% check against every aspect of every component or service. To reduce the cost, a sample is taken at regular intervals and checked. If the sample is within specification then production will continue. The sample is usually a percentage of the whole batch, which is decided by the quality control manager. If the sample is found to be drifting from the specification, an adjustment can be made to ensure that the quality is maintained.

If the sample fails to reach acceptable levels, procedures are put in place to identify the factors that cause failure and address them until the required quality level has been achieved.

Goods inwards

Inspection methods

Goods outward

Sampling is the main method of inspecting products to ensure they are of sufficient quality. There are a number of sampling techniques, including 100% sampling. This is usually only carried out on new products or services.

Methods of sampling: 1. Spot check; 2. Random sampling; 3. Process sampling; 4. Batch sampling

Spot Check

A spot check is a one-off check to ensure that quality procedures are in place and working efficiently.

Random Sampling

Random sampling is where many checks are carried out over a period of time but without any set timescale to ensure that other quality procedures are in place and working.

Process Sampling

Process sampling is where operators are responsible for checking their own production to ensure it meets company and customer specifications.

Batch Sampling

Batch sampling is the most common method of sampling. This involves testing a selected amount of the entire product. If the majority of the sample conforms to the design specification results then the whole batch will be accepted.

For example, if a sample of 6 items in a batch of 100 components are tested and the majority conform to the design specification then the whole batch is accepted. However if a significant number fail to reach the specification level then a larger sample is taken. If they also fail, all the batches are rejected and on the new run 100% inspection is carried out to identify how the defects are occurring.

Permit to Work

A permit to work is a document that specifies the work that will be carried out and the precautions that need to be taken. It is produced for any situation where particularly hazardous conditions exist, such as entry into and working within confined spaces, working on a live production or installation and maintenance that may involve welding and cutting operations.

A permit to work is not simply permission to carry out a dangerous job. It is an essential part of a system which determines how that job can be carried out safely and it helps communicate this to those doing the job. It should not be regarded as an easy way to eliminate hazard or reduce risk. Remember that the issue of a permit does not, by itself, make a job safe – that can only be achieved by those preparing for, supervising and carrying out the work. In addition to the permit to work system, other precautions may also need to be taken, such as process or electrical isolation or access barriers, and these will need to be identified in task risk assessments before any work is started. The permit to work system should ensure that authorised and competent people have thought about foreseeable risks and put in place suitable precautions. Those carrying out the job should think about their own safety and take the precautions for which they have been trained and made responsible.

Example of a permit to work

Sample Case Studies

Contractors were engaged to demolish redundant oil storage tanks in a tank farm on an oil blending and storage site. A pump house was still in operation in the vicinity of the redundant tanks and the occupier was aware of the fire risk. A method of work was agreed with the contractors which involved cold cutting those parts of the tanks nearest to the pump house and taking them to a safe place on site for hot cutting into smaller pieces. A permit to work was not issued and the agreed procedures were not documented. The contractors did not follow the agreement and began hot cutting the tanks close to the pump house. Flammable vapours from the pump house were ignited and the resulting fire caused considerable damage to the plant. Five firemen were taken to hospital suffering from the effects of the fumes. A permit to work should have been issued for this job and the work monitored by the client to make sure the contractor stuck to the agreed method.

A fitter was scalded by an escape of high-pressure steam from an open pipe. Two fitters were carrying out work on the pipes under a permit to work. The first fitter thought the job was complete and returned the permit to the process operator who opened the steam valve. The second fitter had not completed his part and was still working on the open pipe. The permit to work system did not contain a signing off procedure.

Permit to work systems should be considered whenever it is intended to carry out work which may adversely affect the safety of personnel, plant or the environment.

Copies of a permit to work should be clearly displayed at the work site, or in a recognised location near to the work site. If this is not practicable, such as when a job is carried out in a number of locations, then the permit should be kept in the central or main control or permit co-ordination room, with additional copies at any local control rooms. In addition, a copy of the permit should be kept with the issuing authority or with the area authority if that person is not located at the worksite or control room.

Handover

If work is carried over to another shift, perhaps because the job takes longer than expected, then a shift handover procedure should be in place. This should ensure that the incoming shift is aware of any outstanding permit-controlled jobs, the status of those jobs and the status of the plant. Work-in-progress should be left in a condition that can be reliably communicated to, and understood by, the oncoming shift. A permit log, permit file or display boards are ways of recording ongoing permits. It is essential that there is good communication between incoming and outgoing issuing and performing authorities and it is recommended that the incoming issuing authority signs to allow the continuation of a permit.

Testing and Inspecting

All work produced is based upon meeting some form of standard. Inspection is an integral part of any manufacturing operation as a means of ensuring that only items made in accordance with the specification and any drawings are released for use. Inspections are made at various stages of the production process so that any discontinuities are detected early to reduce wastage and reduce any repair costs. In the case of welded fabrication these inspections would take in to account the material, specification, dimensional accuracy and surface quality. In the case of welding consumables, inspection looks at specification, cleanliness, storage and damage.

In engineering there are several techniques to ensure the work is kept within acceptance levels. They includes dimension and distortion control.

Dimensional Control

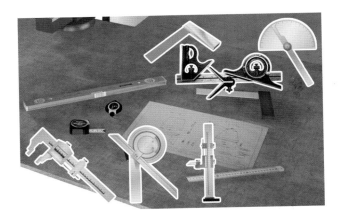

Dimension control

Dimensional control is carried to make sure that a produce conforms to the original design specification. Methods of doing this could include using a rule or laser to measure accuracy.

All measuring, whether on a part or on the drawing, is in essence an estimate, because no matter how accurate the measurement is, there will always be a more accurate way of taking it. The more accurate the measurement, the more time it takes. To save time while still making an acceptable part, dimensioning tolerances have been established. Most drawings state a dimensioning tolerance: the amount by which the part can be larger or smaller than the stated dimensions and still be acceptable. Tolerances are usually expressed as plus (+) and minus (–). If the tolerance is the same for both the plus and the minus, it can be written using the symbol ±. In addition to the tolerance for a part, there may be an overall tolerance for the completed weldment.

If products are found to have incorrect dimensions then it can cause time consuming and expensive remedial work.

Distortion Control Techniques

Distortion is the way a material deviates from the design specification. It can occur in many different ways and is usually caused by expansion and contraction of the material. It can also be caused by general wear or a mechanical object not operating properly.

When metal is subjected to a source of heat it will increase in size due to expansion taking place throughout its mass. This is referred to as co-efficient of linear expansion and will differ for a range of materials. But if the heat is applied to a small localised area only, the expansion will be local and uneven. The surrounding metal which has remained comparatively cool will tend to exert a force to prevent expansion of the heated metal and if the yield point of the metal has been reached during the heating cycle, permanent deformation will take place. The surrounding cold metal also offers resistance during cooling of the heated area and 'contractional stresses' will be set up which will also contribute to distortion. The amount of distortion has a marked effect on the amount of structural strain that will remain in the metal after cooling. If any restraint has been placed upon the metal to control distortion, then residual stresses may be produced, which will remain after the metal has cooled and the structure will be considered to be in a strained condition.

Distortions: 1. Longitudinal distortion; 2. Transverse distortion; 3. Angular distortion

Angular Distortion

When a root run is deposited in a single vee-butt joint, the weld deposit will have undergone expansion during the welding operation and will now contract as it cools down. This shrinkage will draw the edges of the welded plates together.

If a second run is made, the contractional pulling force is opposed by the now solid first deposit. Now the force at the top of the vee tries to pull the plate edges together and the solidified weld metal at the bottom opposes this force which gives rise to 'angular' distortion along the joint.

In a T-fillet weld, angular distortion results in shrinkage across the face of the weld with a reduction in the angle between the upright and base plate. The golden rule governing angular distortion states, that the more runs deposited, the greater the risk of distortion. Therefore the use of pre-setting is recommended, this being dependent upon the number of runs, thickness of plate and the welding process being used.

Longitudinal distortion

This occurs along the length of the weld with a 'bowing' effect such that the original length is reduced. For example, in the case of a butt welded joint in material 4-7mm thick the amount of longitudinal shrinkage is 0.25mm per metre length of weld. For material 8-10mm thick the shrinkage is 0.30 mm per metre length of weld. If the length is less critical it is common practice to cut and weld oversize and machine back to the design specification.

Transverse distortion

This results in shrinkage across the face of the weld with a 'lifting' of the edges and a reduction in the width of the plate dimensions. The amount of distortion is proportional to the material thickness.

Sustainability

If we know how a material will react to heat input and the rate at which it will contract, we can introduce systems into the production process to try to reduce potential problems and minimise distortion. This will lead to less time spent on correctional procedures, less wastage and more effective use of skilled labour and equipment.

Tacking

Tacking is dependent on the requirements of the work piece and the welding process being used. In general, it consists of making tack welds between the parts to be joined, or welding auxiliary pieces to the main parts of the work piece, which are removed after the weld has been completed

The distance between the tacks will vary with the type of metal being welded and the rate of travel. With metals that have a high co-efficient of thermal expansion and when the rate of travel is slow, the tacks should be close together.

Pre-Setting

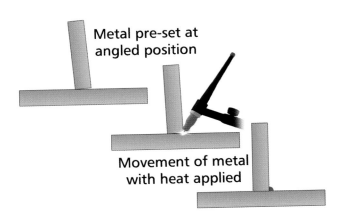

Pre-setting

Pre-setting is a distortion control technique which is de-signed to counteract the movement of metal when heat is applied to it. It involves placing components so that they will be pulled into the correct position by the weld. By using opposing forces it allows the movement of the metal to bring the component back into alignment and therefore reduce wastage.

Pre-setting of fillet welded joints can be a problem as it can result in a bad fit-up when the vertical is rocked away from the horizontal base plate, leaving a gap. In this case it may be necessary to use some form of restraining mechanism such as clamping or gussets which can be removed on completion of the weld. If pre-setting is to be used, then consideration must be given to the amount of angular distortion that is likely to occur. Factors which may affect this include the speed of travel, number of runs, type of edge preparation and heat input.

The amount of pre-setting which should be given to the plates before welding to compensate for angular distortion is a matter for experience. However, there are data sheets which give the average number of degrees of distortion which takes place under certain conditions.

Control of the Gap

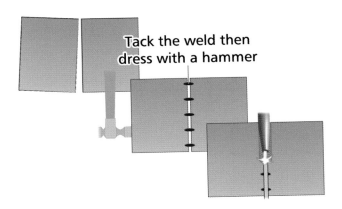

Control of gap

By understanding the expansion and contraction behaviours of common engineering materials we are able to predict the direction of movement when heat is applied.

When welding, by allowing expansion to exist at the front of the weld and contraction to work at the back of the weld it is possible to control the gap. By using the stresses that build up during heat input and providing a thermal balance into the weld we can reduce the distortion. This is done by allowing thermal movement at the front of the weld and the stresses of contraction to realign the joint.

Weld Sequences

Progressive Weld Direction

Weld sequences

When welding any component it is important to be able to predict how the material will react to heat input and cooling. By using welding sequences we can distribute the heat input in such a way that we produce a uniform heat distribution and reduce stresses which can produce distortion.

Pre-Heating

Pre-heat the metal to produce a thermal balance

Pre-heating

When welding a thick material or materials with a high thermal conductivity, pre-heating may be required to produce a thermal balance within the material. This ensures that the sudden heat input from the welding process is minimised and distortion is reduced.

Jigs, Fixtures and Wedges

Jigs, fixtures and wedges

Jigs and fixtures are devices which are used to restrain the metal during tacking or welding. They should be designed for easy access of plates and extraction of welded components. Wedges are designed to control the gap and prevent it closing up.

Post-Heating

Post-heat to relieve residual stresses

Post-heating

Post-heating is usually carried out to reduce residual stresses (stresses which reside within a structure) which have built up during welding and which could bring about the failure of the weld. These stresses may be the result of mechanical working, rapid cooling or the mass of the material; post-heating will redistribute the stresses within the structure and help to reduce distortion.

Back-to-Back Assemblies

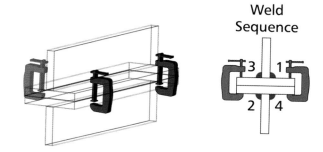

Back to back assembly

Back to back assemblies are where two assemblies are clamped together. A weld is then put in on the top plate followed by a weld on the bottom plate to counteract the heat input from the first weld. This produces an equal thermal distribution in the plates and reduces distortion and wastage.

Weld Defects

In all welding techniques there are a number of weld defects and discontinuities that can be identified once a weld is complete.

Remember that discontinuities are irregularities that are within acceptable limits and do not bring about failure of the component. A defect is a discontinuity which exceeds acceptance levels and renders the component subject to failure.

You have read about potential defects, and their causes and remedies, in the chapters on the various welding processes. The following chart summarises this information for you.

E-Learning

Use the e-learning programme to view this information in a flip book.

Porosity

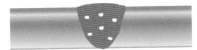

○ Gas Pockets

Porosity

Relevant to: Oxyacetylene, MMA, MIG and TIG welding

Created when gas becomes trapped in the weld deposit as the metal cools. This may be scattered in small clusters or along the entire length of the weld. These voids left in the weld cause it to be weakened. Porosity may be internal, on the surface of the weld bead or both.

Wormhole porosity is the name given to elongated gas pockets and is usually caused by sulphur in the steel, grease on the surface of metal or moisture which becomes trapped in the weld joint. Wormhole porosity can seriously reduce the strength of the weld.

Causes:

- incorrect filler rod/wire, electrode;
- damp or contaminated filler rod/wire, electrode;
- surface contamination (grease or oil);
- atmospheric contamination;
- lack of shielding gas;
- poor operator technique.

Remedies:

- Use correct consumables.
- Store filler rods/wires, electrodes appropriately.
- Keep plate surfaces clean and free from contamination.
- Check flow rates and seals.
- Improve operator techniques.

Inclusions

⌣ Non-metallic Materials

Inclusions

Relevant to: Oxyacetylene, MMA, MIG and TIG welding

Created when foreign matter such as the electrode, oil, grease or mill scale becomes trapped within the solidifying weld deposit as irregular pores. Inclusions cause a weakening of the weld and often serve as crack initiation points. Inclusions can include slag from MMA, oxide inclusions from surface coatings such as aluminium, magnesium or zinc, the wrong flame variation with oxyacetylene or tungsten in TIG welding.

Causes:

- unclean filler or parent metals;
- accidental contact of nozzle/electrode with weld pool;
- when weld is not cleaned between runs;
- damp or contaminated filler rod/wire, electrode;
- current set too high;
- poor operator technique.

Remedies:

- Keep plate surface, filler rods and wires clean.
- Avoid contact of nozzle/electrode with weld pool.
- Clean previous deposit.
- Store filler rods/wires, electrodes appropriately.
- Use correct current settings.
- Improve operator techniques.

Lack of Root Penetration

Lack of root penetration

Relevant to: Oxyacetylene, MMA, MIG and TIG welding

Failure of the weld metal to extend into the root of a joint.

Activity

Identify three distortion control techniques and give a sketch and brief description of how they work.

Causes:

- incorrect joint preparation and set up;
- too small gap;
- speed of travel is too quick;
- not enough heat applied.

Remedies:

- Ensure correct preparation and set up.
- Use a large enough gap.
- Adjust speed of travel.
- Increase amount of heat applied.

Lack of Side Wall Fusion

Lack of side wall fusion

Relevant to: Oxyacetylene, MMA, MIG and TIG welding

Lack of fusion between weld metal and parent metal at the side of the weld and on the interrun deposition.

Causes:

- incorrect alignment of joint edges;
- not enough heat applied;
- speed of travel is too quick;
- incorrect current settings;
- poor operator technique.

Remedies:

- Set up joint edges correctly.
- Increase amount of heat applied.
- Adjust speed of travel.
- Use correct current settings.
- Improve operator techniques.

Undercut

Undercut

Relevant to: Oxyacetylene, MMA, MIG and TIG welding

Created when metal is removed from a joint without being replaced by weld material. This is commonly found at the toe of a run or in previously deposited weld metal. Under-cutting causes a weaker joint at the toe of the weld which may result in cracking.

Causes:

- incorrect equipment used e.g. nozzle size;
- speed of travel is too quick;
- insufficient weld deposition;
- incorrect current settings;
- poor torch, gun or electrode manipulation.

Remedies:

- Use correct equipment for the job.
- Adjust speed of travel.
- Use correct consumables and ensure deposition is sufficient.
- Use correct current settings.
- Improve operator techniques.

Underfill

Underfill

Relevant to: Oxyacetylene, MMA, MIG and TIG welding

Created when the weld metal is insufficient to produce the required deposit as stated in the specification. For a fillet weld it occurs when the weld deposit has an insufficient throat thickness.

Causes:

- incorrect equipment / consumables used e.g. nozzle size;
- speed of travel is too quick;
- poor torch, gun or electrode manipulation.

Remedies:

- Use correct equipment and consumables for the job.
- Adjust speed of travel.
- Improve operator techniques.

Excessive Weld Reinforcement

Excessive weld reinforcement

Relevant to: Oxyacetylene, MMA, MIG and TIG welding

Created when the weld metal deposited is excessive and leaves the weld protruding on the surface of the weld.

Causes:

- incorrect equipment / consumables used e.g. diameter of the filler wire;
- speed of travel is too slow;
- not enough heat applied;
- poor operator technique.

Remedies:

- Use correct equipment and consumables for the job.
- Adjust speed of travel.
- Increase amount of heat applied.
- Improve operator techniques.

Excessive Root Penetration

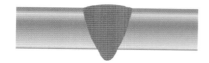

Excessive root penetration

Relevant to: Oxyacetylene, MMA, MIG and TIG welding

Produced by excessive weld metal protruding through the root of a fusion weld.

Causes:

- incorrect equipment / consumables used e.g. type of filler wire;
- speed of travel is too slow;
- incorrect edge preparation or too large a gap;
- incorrect current settings;
- poor operator technique.

Remedies:

- Use correct equipment and consumables for the job.
- Adjust speed of travel.
- Prepare edges and root gaps appropriately.
- Use correct current settings.
- Improve operator techniques.

Misalignment of Plate

Misalignment of plates

Relevant to: Oxyacetylene, MMA, MIG and TIG welding

Created by failing to align the plates after tacking and prior to welding, giving a stepped appearance.

Causes:

- failure to dress the plates prior to welding.

Remedies:

- Tacking at regular intervals.
- Dress the plates prior to welding.

Poor Weld Profile/Dimension

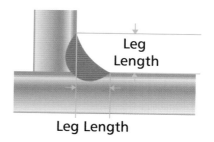

Poor weld profile/dimension

Relevant to: Oxyacetylene, MMA, MIG and TIG welding

Caused by failure to maintain design specifications.

Causes:

- incorrect equipment / consumables used e.g. gas pressures;
- incorrect current settings;
- speed of travel is incorrect;
- poor manipulation of electrode, torch or gun;
- failure to observe weld.

Remedies:

- Use correct equipment and consumables for the job.
- Use correct current settings.
- Adjust speed of travel.
- Improve operator techniques.
- Observation of weld pool characteristics/side wall fusion.

Spatter

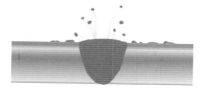

Spatter

Relevant to: MMA and MIG welding

Created by a surface deposition adjacent to the weld which is not fully fused into the surface of the material.

Causes:

- incorrect current settings;
- excessive arc length;
- incorrect parameters set e.g. inductance;
- poor manipulation of electrode or gun.

Remedies:

- Use correct current settings.
- Appropriate arc length for the job.
- Set parameters according to the job.
- Improve operator techniques.

Stray Arcing

Stray arcing

Relevant to: MMA, MIG and TIG welding

Created when an arc is struck outside of the weld zone and may produce a hardened zone which may bring about ultimate failure of the weld.

Causes:

- striking an arc outside the weld zone;
- poor operator technique.

Remedies:

- Ensure all strikes are within the weld/fusion zone.
- Improve operator techniques.

WormHoles

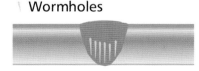
Wormholes

Wormholes

Relevant to: MMA, MIG and TIG welding

Created by possible surface or below surface contaminants which rise up through the weld metal.

Causes:

- contaminants within the base metal or on the surface.

Remedies:

- Clean all surfaces and filler materials prior to welding with a proprietary solvent cleaner.

Plate Generated Problems

Not all welding problems are caused by the weld metal, the process or the welder's lack of skill in depositing that metal. The material being fabricated can be at fault too. Some problems result from internal plate defects that the welder cannot control. Others are the result of improper welding procedures that produce undesirable hard metallurgical structures in the heat-affected zone. The internal defects are the result of poor steelmaking practices. Steel producers try to keep their steels as sound as possible, but mistakes do occur in steel production and the problems they give rise to are blamed, too frequently, on the welding operation.

Lamination

Located toward the centre of the plate, laminations are caused by insufficient cropping (removal of defects) of the ingots. The slag and oxidised steel in the ingot are rolled out with the steel, producing the lamination. Laminations can also be caused when the ingot is rolled at too low a temperature or pressure. Laminations differ from lamellar tearing in that they are more extensive and involve thicker layers of non-metallic contaminants.

Delamination

When laminations intersect a joint being welded, the heat and stresses of the weld may cause some laminations to become delaminated. Contamination of the weld metal may occur if the lamination contained large amounts of slag, mill scale, dirt, or other undesirable materials. Such contamination can cause wormhole porosity or lack-of-fusion defects.

Lamellar Tears

Lamellar tears appear as cracks parallel to and under the steel surface. In general, they are not in the heat-affected zone and they have a step-like configuration. They result from thin layers of non-metallic inclusions that lie beneath the plate surface and have very poor ductility. Although barely noticeable, these inclusions separate when severely stressed, producing laminated cracks. These cracks are evident if the plate edges are exposed.

Non-Destructive and Destructive Testing

Some standards only call for visual and destructive testing; other standards require visual, destructive and non-destructive testing. Where both destructive and non-destructive testing is called for, the non-destructive tests are carried out first. If the weld fails this test then there is no requirement to carry out the destructive tests.

Destructive Testing

Destructive testing is carried out on a weld to ensure that it meets the specified standard. This involves the removal of small sections of the weld metal from the joint which is then bent or fractured to check weld integrity.

This type of testing checks that sufficient fusion has taken place in both the root and side wall of the joints. It can also highlight any errors such as an incorrect type of consumable being used, insufficient heat input and poor operator technique.

Nick Break Test

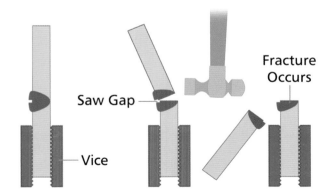

Nick break test

The specimen is supported on either side of the weld and then struck with a hammer. The joint will require a small cut in it to initiate fracture. The fractured surface is then examined to check whether penetration has reached the root of the weld.

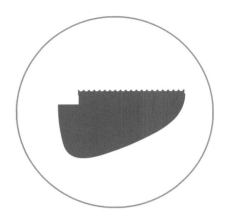

Fractured surface to be examined

The test is carried out on butts in plate or mild steel tubes. The specimen is prepared by saw-cutting each end of the weld to a depth of 1.6mm and saw-cutting across the face of the weld to a depth of 1.6mm. The specimen is then placed in a vice and broken open. The broken weld will show any defects that may be present in the weld such as slag inclusions, porosity, internal cracks, and poor root penetration.

Root and face bend tests

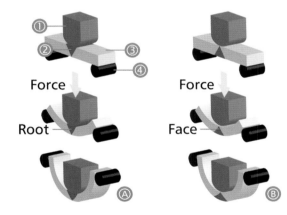

Root and face bend tests: A. Root bend test; B. Face bend test; 1. Load; 2. Weld; 3. Test piece; 4. Rollers

Root and face bend tests are applied to the root and face of the specimen. They are designed to ensure that the weld will remain intact when bent through a specified angle, from 90 to 180°. This ensures that the penetration and side wall fusion is sufficiently strong enough for service conditions as laid down by the standard.

The weld is first ground level with the parent material and then bent in a jig.

Activity

Identify the following weld defects and their possible causes and remedies.

	Name of defect	Cause	Remedy
Gas Pockets			
Non-metallic Materials			

The code being applied for, such as ISO, BS4872, EN287 or ASME, will specify the radius of the bend that the weld must achieve without failing.

Bend tests are carried out to check the integrity of a weld deposit and can also be used to validate consumables. A standard test piece for butt welds would be 300mm long by 100mm wide and from this, approximately 25mm in from each end, should be cut two pieces 37mm long. These test coupons are then bent over a former, through 90°-180° (dependent upon code or standard), having a diameter equal to 4 x thickness of plate. Prior to bending, the upper and lower surfaces of the weld may be ground flush with the surface of the plate. The sharp corners of the weld are then filed to a radius not exceeding one tenth of the thickness of plate. Both specimens must be bent at right angles to the weld (transverse), one with the root in tension and the other with the face in tension. These are known as face and root (reverse bend) bend tests and must show no signs of cracking.

When the thickness of plate exceeds 10mm an alternative bend test is used, known as the side bend test. This entails placing the former longitudinally along the cross-section of the weld, so that the whole cross-section is now subjected to the load applied. Typical defects determined by this test are lack of side wall fusion, under-bead cracking, lamellar tearing, and inclusions.

Tee-Fillet Test

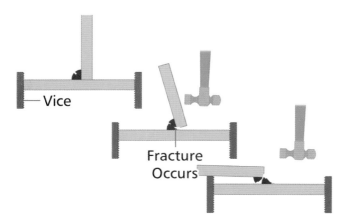

Tee-fillet test

In the Tee-fillet test, the specimen is placed with two edges in a vice and a blow with a hammer is then struck from the back of the weld face side until fracture occurs. To help initiate the fracture a saw cut of specified depth is placed upon the centreline of the face of the weld.

Examination of the fracture will reveal whether full penetration of the root and side walls has been achieved. This will be indicated by a 'ragged' bottom edge indicating that the original edge was penetrated by the weld and confirms both the strength and integrity of the weld deposit.

Ragged Edge

Fractured surface to be examined

The test specimen should be 300mm in length and the material width should not be less than 50mm in width. Set up for welding by tack welding in the usual manner (tack welds may be on the sides to be welded). Distortion or misalignment should be corrected prior to the test weld being deposited. The test weld must match the parent metal thickness and should be deposited in one run; the only exception to this is the overhead test piece. The central 50mm portion of the test piece may then be removed by saw cutting to a depth of 1.6mm along the length of the 50mm weld face and by moving one flange of the weld back and forth until it is broken open. The specimen is then examined for lack of root penetration, slag inclusion or any other oxide inclusions. The specimen should exhibit a 'ragged edge' fracture, indicating good root penetration and side wall fusion. The remaining end pieces may then be polished and 'macro-etched'.

Ductile Fracture Test

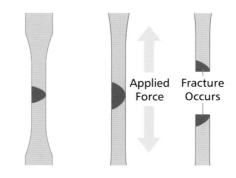

Applied Force   Fracture Occurs

Ductile fracture test

The ductile fracture test is carried out to determine at what point the fracture of the component will take place.

A weld specimen with a notch in the weld is pulled apart to indicate under what loads the structure will fail or maintain weld strength and integrity.

Fractured surface to be examined

Many codes call for additional test pieces to be taken at pre-determined locations, amongst these is the reduced section tensile test piece or ductile test in which a specimen is machined to designated standards and then tested in a tensile testing machine until fracture occurs.

Non-Destructive Testing

Non-destructive testing is carried out to ensure that the component or weld is free from any discontinuity which could affect its performance in service. The tests will not result in any damage to the completed welded joint.

In production, depending on the type of component being made, testing is usually carried out on a sample of so many per batch. If a structural component is being produced then the testing may be carried out on each one.

Non-destructive testing is regulated by ISO standards for discontinuity tolerances. If the component fails the test a decision is then made whether to scrap it, monitor it, or carry out some form of remedial work.

Dye Penetrant Testing

Dye penetrant testing

Dye penetrant testing is used for surface or near surface defect detection. It uses a low viscosity liquid which is drawn into small gaps by capillary attraction. It is applied by spray, brush or immersion in the liquid.

This process has an allotted time period to allow the liquid to fill any discontinuities, after which any remaining surface liquid is cleaned up with a dry cloth or solvent wipe. A contrasting developer is then sprayed onto the joint and bleed back occurs by reverse capillary attraction. This highlights the location of the discontinuity.

Penetrant inspection is used to locate minute surface cracks and porosity. Two types of penetrants are now in use: colour-contrast and fluorescent versions. Colour-contrast penetrants contain a coloured (often red) dye that shows under ordinary white light. Fluorescent penetrants contain a more effective fluorescent dye that shows under ultraviolet light.

The following steps should be followed when a penetrant is used:

- The first step is pre-cleaning. Suspected flaws are cleaned and dried so that they are free of oil, water, or other contaminants.
- The test surface is covered with a film of penetrant by dipping, immersing, spraying, or brushing which draws the penetrant into the flaw by capillary attraction.
- After a designated time period has elapsed, the test surface is then gently wiped, washed, or rinsed free of excess penetrant. It is dried with cloths or hot air.
- A developer is applied to the test surface to act as a blotter to speedup the process by which the penetrant seeps out of any flaws by reverse capillary attraction in to the developer.
- Depending upon the type of penetrant applied, visual inspection is made under ordinary white light or ultra-violet light. In the latter case, the penetrant fluoresces a yellow-green colour, which clearly defines the defect.

Magnetic particle inspection

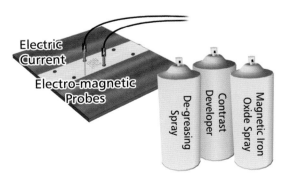

Magnetic particle inspection

Magnetic particle inspection is used for surface or near surface defect detection. It works on the principle that if you induce an electric current into a ferrous metal the edges of a fracture will take up opposite polarity. If a fluid containing magnetic iron oxide is then applied the fault will be revealed by a bridge of magnetic iron oxide indicating the lines of magnetic flux.

Magnetic particle inspection uses fine ferromagnetic particles (powder) to indicate defects open to the surface or just below the surface on magnetic materials. A magnetic field is induced in the part by passing an electric current through or around it. The magnetic field is always at right angles to the direction of current flow. Magnetic particle inspection registers an abrupt change in the resistance in the path of the magnetic field, such as would be caused by a crack lying at an angle to the direction of the magnetic poles at the crack. Finely divided ferromagnetic particles applied to the area will be attracted and outline the crack. For some applications you may need to test in two or more directions.

Ultrasonic inspection

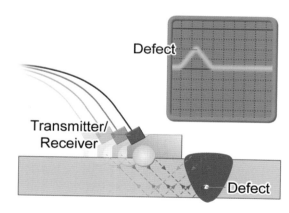

Ultrasonic inspection

A signal is sent through the material and is picked up by an oscilloscope after a time delay that corresponds to the thickness of material. If there is a defect present, the signal will be received more quickly and will indicate the depth at which the defect lies.

Sound is directed into the part from a probe held at a pre-selected angle or in a pre-selected direction so that flaws will reflect some energy back to the probe. These ultrasonic devices operate much like depth sounders, or sonar. The speed of sound through a material is a known quantity. The equipment measures the time taken for a pulse to return from a reflective surface. Internal computers calculate the distance and present the information on a display screen so that an operator can interpret the results. A typical wave formation would show the wave going into the material, and then a flat line corresponding to the thickness of material, with a second wave signal recording off the back wall of the plate. Any break in the flat line would indicate a defect and the height of the signal will determine the depth and location.

Radiographic inspection

Radiographic inspection exists in two forms: X-ray and gamma ray.

X-ray is somewhat limited to the thickness range and is directional, which may mean several X-rays required on one component. As the thickness of the material increases the sharpness of the x-ray film and the ability to clearly detect defects decreases.

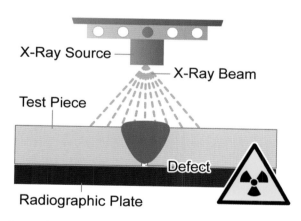

Radiographic inspection: X-ray

Gamma ray works on a radioactive isotope which gives out gamma rays with a 360° spectrum which can penetrate deeper and the whole joint can be screened in one exposure. This makes it the preferred choice on site work although it requires the area to be cordoned off during testing. Any defect or discontinuity would show up as a difference in density or shading in the film.

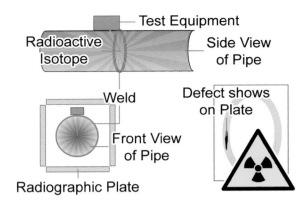

Radiographic inspection: Gamma ray

Radiographic inspection is a method for detecting flaws inside weldments. Radiography gives a picture of all discontinuities that are parallel (vertical) or nearly parallel to the source. Discontinuities that are perpendicular (flat) or nearly perpendicular to the source may not be seen on the X-ray film. Instead of using visible light rays, the operator uses invisible, short-wavelength rays developed by X-ray machines, radioactive isotopes (gamma rays) and variations on these methods. These rays are capable of penetrating solid materials and reveal most flaws in a weldment on an X-ray film or a fluorescent screen. Flaws are revealed on films as dark or light areas against a contrasting background after exposure and processing.

CHECK YOUR KNOWLEDGE

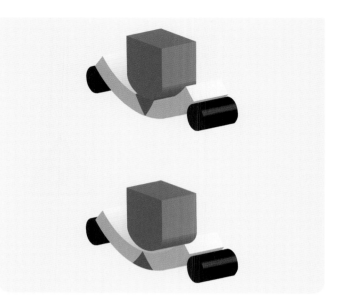

1   What is the purpose of a standard? Circle the correct answer.

   a.   to meet manufacturers recommendations
   b.   to comply with an internationally recognised body
   c.   to guarantee the work against litigation
   d.   to make sure all workers are protected

2   Which of the following are recognised approved procedures for sampling? Circle the correct answer.

   a.   batch sampling
   b.   spot check
   c.   standard sampling
   d.   process sampling
   e.   random sampling
   f.   shift sampling
   g.   numerical sampling

3   Which of these diagrams shows a root bend test and which shows a face bend test? Write RB or FB next to the diagrams.

Summary

To produce a product of a consistent quality that is 'fit for purpose' and complies with the design specification and relevant standards, you need to plan your procedures, incorporate inspection and testing at regular intervals, review the results and incorporate any necessary changes into the production process.

This concludes this chapter on quality control. You should now be able to explain the applicable codes, legislation and standards associated with welding and fabrication and demonstrate an understanding of production monitoring. You should also be able to explain the testing and inspection methods used to check the quality of welding and fabrication.

End test

1. **Add the following words to the diagram to represent the quality control model.**

   Plan

   Review

   Do

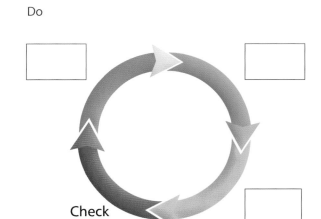

   Check

2. **Match these terms to their definitions. Write a or b next to the definitions.**

   ☐ a. Kaizen

   ☐ b. Kanban

   A focus on gradual and continuous improvement
   Just-in-time stock replenishment

3. **On which of the following would a vendor rating be based when the order was made? Circle the correct answer(s).**

   ☐ a. speed of delivery

   ☐ b. location to manufacturer

   ☐ c. quality of product

   ☐ d. meeting specified dimensional controls

   ☐ e. reliability

   ☐ f. financial status

   ☐ g. large supplier

4. **Which of the following awarding bodies provide standards for welding codes? Circle the correct answer.**

   ☐ a. NASA

   ☐ b. ASME

   ☐ c. Lloyds Registry

   ☐ d. British Standards

   ☐ e. American National

   ☐ f. European Commission

   ☐ g. European Norm

5. **What flow chart symbols should be used on each part of the process shown? Write a, b or c next to each symbol.**

   ☐ a. record all findings from sampling

   ☐ b. is the product to be scrapped or remedial work

   ☐ c. remove all sharp edges

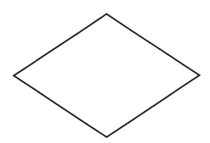

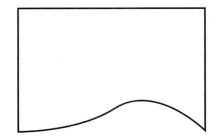

□ c. porosity

□ d. undercut

□ e. lack of root penetration

6. What can a Gantt chart show a production manager? Circle the correct answer(s)

□ a. current workload

□ b. holiday periods

□ c. purchase order numbers

□ d. equipment use

□ e. skilled labour use

□ f. storage

7. Which of the following would be considered to be distortion control techniques? Circle the correct answer(s)

□ a. pre-setting

□ b. weld sequences

□ c. hammering

□ d. pressing

□ e. taper spacing

□ f. time control

8. Identify each of the weld defects from the graphics shown. Write a, b, c, d or e next to the diagrams.

□ a. lack of side wall fusion

□ b. inclusions

Gas Pockets

Non-metallic Materials

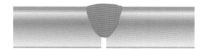

9. **Which of these are destructive testing methods and which are non-destructive testing techniques? Put a tick in the correct columns.**

Testing method	Destructive testing	Non-destructive testing
dye penetrant		
nick break		
Radiographic		
root and face bend test		
tee-fillet test		
Ultrasonic		

10. **What details would be revealed when using a dye penetrant or magnetic particle testing? Circle the correct answer.**

☐ a. all defects

☐ b. visual defects only

☐ c. surface or near surface defects

☐ d. limited defects

Answer section

Answers to Check your Knowledge

Chapter 2

Check your Knowledge 45

1   c
2   a, e, f and g
3   a
4   d, a, e, c, b
5   a and d
6   a, b and c
7   d

End test 46

1   b
2   d
3   b
4   d
5   b
6   b
7   b
8   5, 1, 3, 4, 2, 5, 3, 1, 2, 1, 3, 4, 5, 3, 4, 1
9

Class A	Class B	Class C	Class D
Textiles	Oil	Acetylene	Aluminium
Wood	Paint	Propane	Magnesium
	Petrol		

10   a
11

Damaged plug	Must be replaced
No clamp in plug to hold outer sheath of a flexible cable	Must be firmly clamped
Cable joined with strip connector	Must be joined with proper cable connector
No guard on lamp	Must have a guard
Piece of equipment which should not be used in a wet environment	Must not be used in a wet environment
Piece of equipment where casing shows signs of burning/overheating	Must be labelled 'DO NOT USE'

12   b
13   True, False, False, True, False, True
14   b, d, e, f and h
15   c
16   True, False, False, True
17   a

Chapter 3

Check your Knowledge 68

1   a, b, d and e
2   c and e

3   a, c, d and f
4   b

End test 69

1   a. record
     b. Review
     c. exercises
     d. work
2   b, c and e
3   a. False
     b. True
     c. True
4

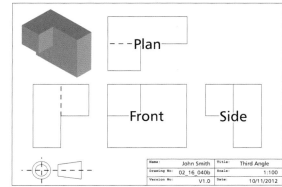

5   a. True
     b. False
     c. True
     d. True
6   c

Chapter 4

Check your Knowledge 108

1   a, b, c and g
2   a
3   b, a, c
4   c, a, b

End test 110

1   c
2   1) Nozzle
     2) Torch
     3) Pressure Regulator
     4) Flashback Arrestor
     5) Oxygen Hose

     6) Oxygen Cylinder
     7) Acetylene Hose
     8) Acetylene Cylinder
3   b
4   Steps 1, 4, 5, 6, 3, 2, 7
5   a, c, e
6   More acetylene than oxygen
7   c, a, b
8   a
9   b, a, d, c
10   c and d, a and e, b and f

Chapter 5

Check your Knowledge 140

1   b, d and e
2   b
3   c and d
4   c, a, b

End test 141

1   a
2   1) Earth Connection
     2) Electrode
     3) Electrode Holder
     4) Power Source
     5) Welding Return Clamp
     6) Welding Lead
     7) Welding Return Lead
3   b
4   6, 8, 4, 5, 9, 2, 1, 3 and 7

PROCEDURE	STEP
Insert electrode into holder and hang up holder	**6**
Turn power on	**8**
Connect welding lead to the negative terminal of the power source	**4**
Ensure work piece is independently earthed	**5**
Set current to an appropriate setting for the job	**9**

PROCEDURE	STEP
Connect welding return lead to the positive terminal of the power source	2
Ensure power supply is off	1
Connect welding return lead to work piece using the welding return clamp	3
Check electrode is not touching work table	7

5 1) Electrode Coating
   2) Electrode Filler Wire
   3) Gas Shield
   4) Slag
   5) Weld Deposit
   6) Weld Pool
6 c
7 b
8 d
9 b, a, d, c
10 a, c and d

Chapter 6

Check your Knowledge 171

1 a, e and g
2 a, d, e and f
3 c
4 a, c, b

End test 172

1 b
2 c
3 1) Shielding Gas Cylinder
   2) Regulator and Flow Meter
   3) Wire Feed
   4) Power Supply
   5) Welding Cable Assembly
   6) Welding Gun
   7) Welding Return Lead
4 d
5 Inert Gas Shield: Argon, Helium, Argon + Helium
   Active Gas Shield: Argon + Oxygen, Carbon Dioxide, Argon + Carbon Dioxide, Argon, Carbon Dioxide + Oxygen, Helium + Argon + Carbon Dioxide

6 a. No
   b. Yes
   c. No
   d. Yes
   e. No
   f. No
7 c
8 d, a, c, b
9 b
10 d

Chapter 7

Check your Knowledge 203

1 b, d and f
2 c
3 b
4 b, a, c

End test 204

1 b
2 1) Foot pedal
   2) Power source
   3) Regulator and flow meter
   4) Shielding gas system
   5) Torch
   6) Welding return lead
3 c, a, d, b
4 a, c, d and e
5 b
6 c
7 d
8 a
9 a and d
10 b

Chapter 8

Check your Knowledge 228

1 d, c, e, a
2 a
3 a, b and d

End test 229

1   c, a, b, d
    Hardness = A material's ability to resist indentation, cutting and abrasion.
    Brittleness = A material's ability to resist being significantly deformed when it cracks or breaks.
    Ductility = A material's ability to be drawn out along its length, bent or twisted under a tensile load without fracture occurring.
    Toughness = A material's ability to resist shock and impact loading.
2   c
3   c
4   b
5   c
6   a, c, b
7   a and f, c and d, b and e
8   Chromium and Nickel
9   b and e
10 d, c, a, b

Chapter 9

Check your Knowledge 271

1   c
2   Chip forming tools: 5, 6, 7, 8
3   a and b

End test 272

1

Tool	Marking Out	Material Removal
Engineer's Square	✓	
Snips		✓
Combination Set	✓	
Tape	✓	
Hacksaw		✓
Chisel		✓
Rule	✓	
Scriber	✓	

2   a
3   a, c, d, e and f

4   c
5   a, b, c
6   a and d
7   a, b
8   a, d and f
9   a, c and d
10 a and c

Chapter 10

Check your Knowledge 303

1   b
2   a, b, d and
3   Root bend test, face bend test

End test 304

1

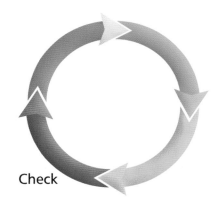

Check

2   a, b
3   c, d and e
4   b, c, d, and g
5   b, c, a
6   a, b, d and e
7   a, b and e
8   c, d, b, a, e
9

Testing method	Destructive testing	Non-destructive testing
Dye penetrant		✓
Nick break	✓	
Radiographic		✓
Root and face bend test	✓	
Tee-fillet test	✓	
Ultrasonic		✓

10 c

Glossary

Absorbent A substance used to remove moisture from the air such as silica gel crystals.

Absorption Soaking up of substances into the base whether this is skin or some metallic material.

Active gas An inert shielding gas into which a small percentage of another gas is mixed to improve performance characteristics such as increased surface deposition.

Adherand The surface that adhesive is spread upon.

Adhesive The bonding agent used to join materials and metals.

Affinity Attraction for something i.e. affinity for oxygen.

Air bending Three point bending process which leaves an air gap at the underside of the bend.

Allergies Reaction to a substance such as dust, vapours, etc.

Alloy Two or more elements, one of which must be a metal, are used commercially to improve mechanical properties and extend the range of provision.

Alpha brass 70/30 Brass comprising 70% Copper, 30% Zinc which can be cold worked.

Ambient Comfortable temperature such as room temperature 68°–72°C.

Angular A reduction in the angle of bend or joint.

Annealing A form of heat treatment which results in a softening of the structure and recrystallisation.

Apex The top of two or more lines joining one another at a predetermined angle.

Arc blow A magnetic effect brought about by the flow of electricity in a conductor, where the magnetic lines of flux can affect weld deposition. Normally associated with Direct Current (DC) they can have the same effect as two bar magnets of the same polarity being brought together, they deflect from one another.

Arc energy Is the name given to energy that is released and absorbed by the parent metal, when an electrical arc is established between an electrical conductor and the work piece, which results in heat being generated.

Arc eye A painful condition of the eye brought about by exposure to radiated light in an arc welding process. Conditions include headache, nausea, and a feeling of hot sand in the eyes. This normally passes off within 24 hours of exposure.

Arc length The distance of the conducting arc energy from the end of the electrode or tungsten to the work piece. Applicable in MMA, MIG, and TIG.

Arc wander The misdirection of the electron flow from a tungsten electrode as a result of improper grinding.

Arrest System Designed to arrest someone falling from a height.

Asphyxiation The removal of a normal breathing zone.

Austenitic A crystalline state in Stainless steels in which chromium and nickel are present.

Autogenous weld A weld that is made entirely from the parent metal with no additional filler wire.

Autonomation A process in which tolerances can be monitored automatically.

Back electromotive force A resistance to the flow of electricity as a result of the cable being coiled. This produces a heating effect similar to that associated with filament lamps and electric bar heaters.

Back purging The application of an inert shielding gas to the underside of a weld on materials that are subject to oxidation.

Backfire A miniature explosion caused by a blockage of the welding nozzle orifice. This is indicated by a popping sound.

Backing bar/strip Can be permanent or just to limit the amount of penetration (control of root profile) on a weld deposit.

Balled end Typical formation on a tungsten electrode when using a zirconiated electrode with Alternating Current (AC).

Bar The name given to a quantity of gas under pressure in the SI metrication units.

Barrel Is the shank of a bolt which is either produced in the as-drawn condition or machined to close tolerances.

Bars Chill bars are used to conduct the heat away from the weld zone and prevent burnthrough.

Bauxite The ore from which aluminium is extracted.

Benchmarking Best practice within a discipline or industry.

Bend tests Carried out to ensure weld integrity and strength under applied forces.

Beta brass 60/40 Brass which contains 60% copper 40% Zinc and which is somewhat brittle and needs heat treatment in order to form the material.

Bird's nest The result of constantly feeding electrode wire in a blocked MIG torch. This occurs on the input side of the feeder unit and should be dealt with as soon as possible to prevent further damage to the wire feed unit.

Bisect To equally divide a line or angle.

Black barrel Common form of universal bolt used with loose tolerances.

Blanking Cutting out shaped blanks either mechanical or manually on a fly-press.

Bleedback A reverse capillary attraction process which highlights the presence of defects.

Blind rivet Common rivet used in manufacturing in which a mandrel fractures off leaving the head in the rivet.

Blowback The temporary loss of gas control, which may result in a small explosion caused by weld metal droplets blocking the end of the nozzle.

Bossing A pear shaped wooden mallet used for hollowing and raising.

Box & Pan Forming machine in which the top blade is made of fingers which can be removed in order to assist forming of boxes or pan shaped objects.

Boxwood A parallel wooden mallet designed for shaping and dressing sheet metal.

Braced Giving strength and rigour to a component.

Braze weld A surface deposition technique similar to fusion welding, but is not considered a fusion process as it relies on the formation of an inter-metallic bond between the component layers.

Brazing Relies on capillary attraction to draw a fluid filler material through close fitting joints. This action is similar to a vacuum.

Brittleness A property in which there is a reduced degree of toughness, tensile strength, and ductility, likely to fracture easily with little deformation.

Burnback Occurs when the wire feed speed is insufficient to meet the voltage being used. This results in the wire balling up and fusing to the contact tip causing blockage of the filler wire.

Burnthrough The collapse of the leading edges of a welded joint.

Capillary attraction A vacuum effect which draws materials through closely fitting surfaces.

Carburising A flame in which there is an excess of Acetylene gas typified by a long feathered inner cone flame. Used for depositing hard surfacing materials.

Castings Components which are produced by hot molten metal being poured into a predetermined shaped mould to produce consistent components.

Ceriated A high temperature resistant metal used as an electrode in Tungsten Inert Gas Shielded Welding (TIG).

Cherry picker Originally used for harvesting fruit, these machines are increasingly being used as a mobile working platform for construction and engineering uses.

Chip forming A process in which some form of particle is produced in the cutting process.

Codings An industry led and internationally recognised way of assessing a person's skill performance.

Co-efficient of linear expansion The effect of expansion in a linear direction.

Coining A forming technique in which the material is pressed into a forming tool to take up the exact form of the bottom tool, and this removes all elasticity in the material.

Cold lapping A surface deposit which has not fully fused into the parent metal.

Cold shortness Fracturing of a material as direct result of too high a percentage of phosphorous.

Cold working Is a means of imparting strength by rolling or forming.

Collet Copper construction sleeve, used to hold the tungsten and conduct electricity to the tip of the electrode when placed in a TIG welding torch.

Columnar Long needle like grain structure as result of rapid cooling.

Composites Are two or more materials joined together with some form of bonding agent such as glass reinforced plastic (GRP) or carbon fibre.

Compressive strength The ability of a material to resist the compressive force being exerted on the material.

Compressive Is an applied force which works over a designated cross-sectional area.

Concave A weld appearance which is curved inwards with a reduced throat thickness and extended leg length.

Concentric Two circles which have a common axis, such as a washer.

Concise Precise instructions.

Conducive Good reaction to a particular situation.

Conductivity The ability of a material to conduct both heat and electricity.

Configuration Joint shape.

Conformity Complying with a given standard or tolerance.

Contamination A reduction in purity of a component or material by atmospheric gases, fluids, scale, oil or grease. This can be surface or internal and could lead to failure in service.

Convex A weld appearance which is curved outwards with an increased throat thickness.

Copper acetylide An explosive compound formed when 70% copper or above, is in contact with neat acetylene gas.

Corrosion resistance The ability of a material to resist attack by corrosive mediums and maintain structural integrity within extreme service conditions.

Corrosive A material or condition which results in another material being chemically attacked.

Coupling distance The distance that the cutting torch is held up at, in relation to the surface of the material.

Crater cracking A crack which appears due to the cross-sectional area of the weld deposit being insufficient to withstand the heating and cooling stresses of the material.

Crowned surfaces The curved surfaces of a planishing hammer, designed to remove possible surface indentation when using the hammer.

Cryogenic A temperature state which exists at minus degree, for example -50°C.

Crystalline A natural formation which exhibits certain physical properties, exists in many forms and forms the structure of materials.

Cumulative error A build of error usually encountered when marking out.

Cupro-nickel A copper-nickel alloy which is extensively used in coinage and for corrosion resistant properties.

Dampening An absorption of loading as is the case with many machine beds.

Datum A reference point from which all dimensions should be referred to.

De-burr The removal of any sharp edges on metal.

Decomposition A breakdown of the components which make up the gas, liquid or solid.

Dedicated Specifically designed for a purpose.

Defect A discontinuity which exceeds acceptance levels and renders the component subject to failure.

De-lamination A lamination which opens up during the application of heat or work hardening.

Deoxidiser An element included either in the material, shielding gas or filler wires to reduce the effects of oxygen and other atmospheric gases.

Deposition A lack of fusion between weld metal and the parent metal at the side of the weld and on the inter-run deposition.

Developer A contrasting coloured dye used to highlight a defect.

Deviates Moves away from a given standard or tolerance.

Differentiate Being able to recognise differences and make judgements on merits.

Discontinuity Is a form of defect that is within acceptable tolerance limits and does not bring about failure of the component.

Dispel Remove source.

Double curvature A forming process in which material is shaped in two directions, for example car bonnets.

Drag lines Vertical cut lines associated with thermal cutting processes.

Drag technique A technique in which the electrode is moved in the opposite direction to travel.

Dressing The shaping and alignment of metals by use of a hammer.

Drooping characteristic Associated with MMA and TIG machines which require a high open circuit voltage to initiate the arc, but once established the voltage falls off to an operating range which is much lower.

Dross The adhering metal oxide normally found on the underside of a thermal cut component.

Ductile test A stretching of a reduced section of weld metal to determine its failure point.

Ductility The ability to be drawn out along its length, twisted or formed without fracture taking place.

Duplex Is a material in which the metallurgical structure consists of a mixture of 50% ferrite and 50% austenite, which conveys high strength and good corrosion resistance.

Duralumin An aluminium-copper alloy containing 4% copper, which is hard and durable, often used for high strength structures where the strength to weight ratio is low such as aircraft.

Duty cycle The amount of time that a machine can operate on maximum amperage. A 60% duty cycle machine can operate for six out of ten minutes at maximum amperage.

Dwell The time spent on a location in order to ensure fusion.

Earth A common bonding point in order to ensure safety within an electric circuit.

Economiser Used to minimise the use of gas in non-welding periods, and as a safety feature preventing unmanned lit flames.

Elasticity The ability of a material to stretch under a load and yet return to its original length upon removal of the load.

Electrolytic corrosion A condition in which materials will erode each other in the presence of an electrolytic material such as moisture. This reaction can occur between all metals that make up the galvanic series. All metals possess a charge. Those with a higher charge when in contact with one which is lower in the series will corrode the inferior metal.

Electromagnetic forces Forces attracted to one another by virtue of their magnetic flux.

Electromotive forces Energising forces produced by the generation of electricity.

Embrittle To bring about failure of a product.

Engine Divided Precision engraving of measurement scales to very high degrees of accuracy.

Equi-axed Small rounded crystals or grains which have good mechanical properties.

Ergonomic Designed around an individual.

Erosion The breakdown of a material as a result of oxidation, corrosion or operating conditions.

Exothermic reaction A reaction in which heat is given off.

Exotic metals Metals that are highly susceptible to oxidation, such as titanium and vanadium.

Extrusion A forming process in which the material is pushed through a shaped die to produce a specific component.

Face bend test A destructive testing process in which a coupon is taken from the weld deposit and machined ready to apply tensile pressure to the weld face to determine weld integrity.

Fatigue A reduction in operating capacity as a direct result of physical constraints and exertions. It can be associated with personnel and materials under loads.

Ferritic A material in which iron (ferrous) is the main constituent.

Ferro-magnetic A predominately Iron material which is capable of being magnetised.

Finite Limited resource.

Fire Marshal Someone designated to co-ordinate activities in the event of a fire.

Flame retardant Material treated with chemicals to reduce the possibility of flammability.

Flammable Will react very easily to bring about combustion of the material as direct result of some reaction.

Flange A matting face component which is either welded or screw threaded onto pipe in order to join straight and angular sections of pipe or rectangular sections of components.

Flashback A condition in which the flame travels back up through the torch and hoses towards the gas cylinders. Often depicted by a high squealing sound with black soot and sparks being emitted from the torch.

Flat characteristic A volt-ampere curve associated with constant voltage machines used for MIG welding. The volt-ampere curve shown is one of a straight line as opposed to a drooping characteristic curve associated with MMA and TIG.

Flow chart A diagrammatic representation of a production schedule or fault finding technique.

Flux A chemical cleaning agent which may also assist the flow characteristics of a filler material or form the basis of a silicate coating to retard the cooling rate as in Manual Metal Arc welding.

Forgings Hot metal products produced by pressurised hammers to make the metal flow to the desired specification.

Formal Specific or designated way of doing things.

Fulcrum point A pivotal point for the application of force.

Fusion face The face on which fusion occurs.

Fusion The thermal joining of two or more metals to make a solid deposition of metal.

Galvanic corrosion A form of electrolytic corrosion in which metals with a higher voltage will corrode a metal with a lower voltage.

Gantt chart A diagrammatic representation in which processes, equipment and workforce are being used to gain a measure of timescale to produce the product.

Gas energy A thermo-chemical reaction in which gases form to produce combustion and liberate heat while being supported by atmospheric oxygen.

Gas lens A mechanism which makes the gas shield directional and allows a greater electrode extension.

Gouging A material removal technique in which material is removed by specially shaped nozzles in thermal cutting procedures.

Grain growth An enlargement of the grain structure by absorption of neighbouring grains under the action of a prolonged heating cycle.

Grains A crystalline structure which can exist in several forms.

Graphite A carbon rich material which is present in many different forms in steels and cast irons.

Gunmetals Bronzes containing 88% copper, 10% tin and 2% zinc are often referred to as gunmetals.

Hafnium Hafnium is a shiny, silvery, ductile metal that is corrosion-resistant and chemically similar to zirconium, used for plasma cutting electrodes.

Hard soldering A process which is similar to brazing and is used for refrigeration pipework.

Hardening A form of heat treatment in which the material is heated to a pre-determined temperature and quenched in water, oil or brine (salt water) to give a high degree of hardness and resisting surface indentation or wear.

Harmful Can have an effect on your wellbeing.

Harness A supporting and restraining piece of equipment used when working at heights that allows operators to work freely.

Hazard Something with the potential to cause you some harm.

Heat affected zone (HAZ) An area either side of the weld zone which has an impact on the mechanical properties of the metal.

Heat sink A zone on the metal which is designed to reduce and allow heat to be absorbed and subsequently reduce burnthrough.

Hermaphrodite Neither one form or another and is associated with callipers, sometimes referred to as 'odd-leg' since one leg is stepped and pushed against a datum edge while the other leg holds a scribing point. Used for parallel marking out.

Hide A cow hide mallet used to prevent surface indentation when forming components.

High frequency A high voltage spark train used to initiate the arc in TIG welding.

High strength friction grip A machined bolt used with tight tolerance control which can be tightened to a per-determined pressure to exert forces on the plies that make up the joint.

Hollowing The shaping out of a bowl like structure.

Hot shortness Fracturing of a material as direct result of too high a percentage of sulphur.

Humidity A temperature rise brought about by limited airflow, confined spaces or atmospheric pressure.

Hydrogen cracking The presence of hydrogen in the underbead of the weld which will travel through the grain structure resulting in failure of the material.

Hygroscopic An affinity for moisture, will rapidly absorb moisture.

Impact strength The ability of a material to resist an impact load.

Inching The slow movement of a forming tool or wire drive mechanism as in MIG, under the direct control of the operator.

Included angle The angle created on the combined edge preparation prior to welding.

Inclusion An addition to the metal which does not combine with the base metal. Typical inclusions include gas cavities, oil and grease.

Incompatible Does not combine with the parent metal.

Inductance The control of current surges to bring about operational requirements, reduces spatter deposition.

Induction An introduction to an organisation or process.

Inert A gas which does not readily combine with other gases and prevents atmospheric contamination.

Ingestion The consumption of a substance which could impact on your health e.g. food and drink. This could be caused by not washing your hands prior to eating.

Inhalation The breathing in of some form of hazardous substance that could impact on your health.

Injector A mechanism in which a high pressure gas is used to draw another gas through the system.

Interface The contact point between component parts.

Intermetallic bond The formation of a layer which contains the filler material and some surface material.

Intermetallic A material which is formed by contact between the filler material and the parent metal.

Interpass A series of runs which overlap and are fused together.

Interrun deposition A series of deposits in a multiple layer weld.

Inverter A highly sophisticated machine which maximises current and voltage in a reduced packaging by the use of electronic components.

Irritant Something which causes a reaction such as dusts, chemicals, or vapours.

Isometric Is a three dimensional view of an object.

Isotopes A radioactive material capable of penetrating material with a 360° range of rotation.

Joggling A step-like formation put on the edges of plates so that the plates can overlap one another but still retain one surface alignment.

Kaizen A Japanese philosophy which engages all involved in the production of components.

Kanban A Japanese philosophy in which minimum stock is held and is demand led to allow for cash flow and efficiency.

Kapok A coarse cotton wool like material which is used to line acetylene cylinders and retain acetone liquid to stabilise the gas. Is also used in the manufacture of furniture as padding.

Kerf The width of the cut in thermal cutting processes.

Keyhole Formation of a leading edge in a welded joint.

Lamellar tear A step-like fracture that occurs in the underbead of a weld deposit.

Laminar flow The action of a gas being in the same direction as the electrode, running parallel to the electrode.

Lamination An oxide or scale inclusion as the result of hot rolling plate and sections.

Lanthanated A high temperature resistant metal used as an electrode in Tungsten Inert Gas Shielded Welding (TIG).

Lanyard This is an arrest mechanism used in conjunction with a harness to safeguard people working at heights.

Latitude The amount of movement within pre-determined specifications.

Leader Lines These are projection lines which denote some form of manufacturing process or detail.

Leg length The distance from the point of contact along the members to a designated distance linked to thickness of plate.

Litigation Legal prosecution for failure to maintain, safeguard or produce goods or services to minimum standards as laid out in contracts or sales of goods act.

Longitudinal The linear length of a product.

Machineability The ability with which a material can be easily machined.

Macro-etch An examination of the structure of the material using an etchant to reveal structural detail viewed using up to five magnifications.

Magnetic flux The result of the flow of electrons when transmitting electricity or existent magnetic field.

Magnetic particle A non-destructive testing technique used to detect surface or near surface defects.

Malleability The ability of a material to be shaped and formed under an applied load in all directions without fracture occurring.

Mandatory Must be done (government legislation).

Mandrel A steel parallel bar or spindle used to dress material over, or as part of a blind rivet assemble.

Martensitic A structure which exhibits a needle like grain formation which can be hardened by heat treatment and is often used for cutting implements.

Material Safety Data Sheet (MSDS) Issued by a manufacturer who supplies any form of goods which have some hazardous issues.

Maximum Exposure Levels (MELS) Maximum exposure levels that operators can be exposed to hazardous substances within a working day.

Mill scale The oxide layer present after hot rolling steel components.

Minerals Elements found in ores and the earth's crust.

Mixer Mechanism used to mix gases prior to burning in combustion.

Mobile elevated working platforms (MEWPS) An alternative method to reach high locations without fixed scaffolding.

Monel A copper-nickel alloy used extensively in corrosive environments.

Morse taper A designated taper designed to match the inside of the drilling machines shaft (quill).

Mould A container or characteristic of flux coatings in MMA which shape solidifying metal.

MSDS Manufacturer's Safety Data Sheets issued with a substance that may have hazardous implications attached to it. Sometimes referred to as COSHH sheets.

Muntz metal An alloy used extensively in soft water areas to resist de-zincification of the brass alloy.

Nesting Close grouping of components designed to get the maximum usage of the material with minimum distortion.

Neutral line A distinct distance within the thickness of plate in which the tensile and compressive stresses are equal and allow the material to flow to shape without fracturing. This also gives a point around which material calculation can be based to make allowance for the material thickness and calculate finished dimensions.

Neutral A condition in which both gases are equal to provide a welding flame.

Nibblet A half-moon residue of using a portable cutting tool in material removal process.

Nick-break A destructive test used to check weld integrity.

Non-assertive Not entirely confident or self-assured in putting their point forward.

Non-chip forming Material removing process in which the material is severed without any residue by using a shearing action.

Normalising A heat treatment process involving heating to a pre-determined period and rapidly cooling to restore toughness and tensile strength.

Nugget A formation at the interface of the plies making up the joint under the action of two spot welding electrodes.

Oblique A two-dimensional view of an object.

Occupational Exposure Levels (OEL) Typical levels that operatives can be safely exposed to in a working day.

Open circuit voltage The voltage required to initiate the arc process.

Ores Naturally formed materials containing metallic elements.

Orifice The hole or opening on nozzles.

Orthographic Projection A formal diagrammatic presentation of an object for manufacturer, erection or dismantling.

Oscilloscope A machine which records sound waves generated and received, and displays them on a screen as a wave formation.

Outriggers Designed to provide stability to a mobile platform or truck when loading/unloading.

Oxidation The reaction of a hot body to the presence of oxygen.

Oxidising A substance with the ability to intensify/ raise the temperature of a chemical reaction between substances.

Ozone A gas produced in the weld zone, as a direct result of the breakdown of atmospheric gases.

Packing A blockage in the bore of a gas nozzle as a result of using the inferior equipment to clean a nozzle.

Parameters Variables which are under the control of the operator.

Paramount High degree of importance.

Penetrant A low viscosity fluid designed to flow between close fitting components by capillary attraction.

Penetration The furthermost point of fusion.

Permit to work Designed to be used under controlled operations which have associated risks attached to them such as welding and cutting operations.

Phosgene Produced by the breakdown of de-greasing agents in the weld zone or near vicinity. This gas has major implications for the respiratory system and should be controlled at all times- first world war mustard gas.

Photo-electric A system which employs a light beam to secure the safety of operators while a machine is in use, break the beam, and the machine cuts out.

Pig Iron The rawest form of iron which is high in impurities and gets its name from the metal ingots that it is poured into during the production of steel.

Pinch force A magnetic effect upon an electrical conductor which results in separation and transportation of the metal globule across the arc.

Pitch Circle Diameter (PCD) This is a common datum between two concentric circles and is often used to determine drill holes for flanges.

Planishing The removal of high spots on shaped components.

Plasma Plasma is created by an arc in an ionized gas that has electrons and positive ions whose charges are nearly equal. These charged particles conduct the electrons across the gap between the work and an electrode.

Plastic stage A stage between solid and liquid in which forming and joining can take place.

Plasticity The ability of a material to flow to shape under a load and retain that shape when the load has been removed.

Plate A form of metal product which is flat and uniform in shape, and is in excess of 3mm thick.

Polarity A terminal point at source in an electrical circuit which can be positive, negative: direct current (DC) or alternating as in an Alternating Current (AC) circuit.

Porosity Gas entrapment within the weld deposit. These can come in a range of shapes and sizes.

Porous A structure which will allow material to pass through it.

Pre-heating The heating of a material to a pre-determined temperature to reduce temperature gradient within the material and prevent cracking occurring.

Process annealing A stage within a forming process where there is a need to carry out a heat treatment process and bring about re-crystallisation of the structure in order to continue further forming.

Progressive marking Marking off a designated datum so that all measurement are taken from a designated point.

Prohibitory Restricts and upholds the law.

Projection A raised portion on a component that forms the focus for heat input and ultimately collapses and forms part of the projection welded joint.

Proven Has a track record for consistency.

Pulse echo A signal which passes through a material and is reflected back.

Purging The removal of atmospheric gases from pipelines or hoses.

Push technique The movement of the torch electrode in the same direction of travel.

Radiographic A non-destructive testing technique used to detect internal flaws in components.

Raising The shaping of sheet metal in order to produce a designated profile.

Reactive metals Metals that react with oxygen such as titanium and vanadium.

Ream to enlarge a hole to a specific dimension for accuracy.

Reasonably Practicable Measure taken in order to ensure safety as well as being able to function.

Reciprocating The upwards and downwards movement of blades or punches for material removal.

Re-crystallisation A heating process in which the grain structure is relieved, the distorted grain arrangement is allowed to reform back to its original form and which helps to remove residual stresses.

Rectifier A component which has the ability to change polarity from AC to DC.

Reducing zone A zone within the flame in which surface oxides are removed.

Refractory A high temperature resistant surface.

Residual stresses Stresses which reside within a material as a result of forming and joining processes.

Retrofit Designed to be fitted as an auxiliary after assembly.

Risk The likelihood that something will happen and the degree of severity.

Root bend test designed to test weld integrity.

Root face The machined square edge face designed to give control over heat input and deposition of the weld deposit

Root gap Designated gap to ensure penetration of the weld joint.

Run-on, run-off tags Designed to prevent inclusions at the beginning and termination of a weld deposit.

Rutile A surface coating consisting of minerals from the earth.

Sampling A quantitive method of checking product specification and quality.

Scavenging agents Chemical substances designed to clean the surface of the metal and ensure good fusion of the weld deposit.

Scissor lift A mobile elevated working platform which uses a scissor action to raise and lower the platform.

Scoured A roughing of the surface in order to gain a certain advantage.

Scribing Marking lines out on metal or other materials.

Seating The contact surface on nozzles, welding torches, and cutters.

Sections Shaped forms of metal which impart strength with reduced weight.

Septicaemia Blood poisoning.

Shear strength The ability to resist a shearing action.

Sheet Metal up to 3mm in thickness.

Side bend test Designed to test weld integrity.

Silicate (slag) The by–product of the electrode coating which forms a protective coating over the solidifying weld metal.

Slag inclusion A silicate inclusion coming from the electrode coating.

Slip rolls The rolls on a roller designed to allow for extraction of rolled components.

Slope angle The angle that the torch/electrode is held in relation to the metals surface.

Snifting The rapid opening and closing of the gas valve in order to expel any contaminants prior to fitting gauges and assembling equipment.

Solution treated A heat treatment process designed to take hard elements in solution in order that forming can be carried out.

Sonar The sending out and receiving of sound waves in order to detect the presence of an object.

Spalling Breakdown of the surface coating due to excess moisture content.

Spatter Small weld metal droplets produced by an extended arc length or high welding currents.

Spheroidal Small round balls of Graphite.

Spontaneous An immediate reaction.

Spring back The elastic nature of certain materials upon removal of a load.

Stabilised Elements added to a filler wire or material to form alternative compounds and therefore stabilise the structure.

Standardisation Conforming to a recognised standard.

Statistical Process Control (SPC) A way of defining acceptance and rejection tolerances to control production.

Step-down transformer A transformer in which the output side of the machine has a reduced number of windings to that of the input side. This results in a reduced voltage but an increased amperage range.

Stickout The amount the electrode wire or tungsten electrode sticks out past the contact tip or ceramic nozzle.

Stiles The parallel sides of a set of ladders into which the rungs are located and fixed.

Stringer A weld bead that is deposited in a straight line with no side to side movement.

Stub end The residue of an electrode.

Surface deposition A deposition of filler material to increase hardness, resist abrasion, and wear resistance.

Susceptibility The likeliness of something to occur.

Sweating The formation of minute pools of molten metal.

Sweeten To introduce oxygen into a confined space to remove odours or to increase the air content. A highly dangerous activity as it is likely to produce spontaneous combustion in the presence of a heat source.

Swing beam Folders designed with weighted arms which swing outwards and upwards to form material.

Tacking A small fusion of the parent metal at discrete distances in order to assist joining and distortion control. A tack can be made with or without filler wire.

Taper spacing The control of the leading edges in order to reduce distortion.

Teflon A plasticised coating material used for its low frictional properties.

Tempering A heat treatment process designed to reduce the degree of hardness and impart toughness.

Tensile strength Resistance to a pulling force, as in the case of some bolts (high tensile bolts) and cables.

Tensile A pulling force.

Thermal conductivity The ability to carry heat.

Thoriated A high temperature resistant metal used as an electrode in Tungsten Inert Gas Shielded Welding (TIG).

Throat The furthermost point of penetration to the centre of a line touching the toes.

Tilt angle The angle that bisects the angle of the joint.

Tinning A surface coating of tin in order to produce an inter-metallic bond in soldering.

Toes The points where the weld touches the plate.

Tolerance An allowance for dimensional control.

Torsional strength The ability to resist a twisting force.

Total Quality Management A total quality management programme which involves all aspects of a company.

Toughness The ability to resist an impact load.

Toxic Poisonous substance.

Traceability Capable of being recorded and retrieved.

Trailing shield A device used to ensure that the cooling weld metal is protected from atmospheric contamination.

Trammels A method of producing circular arcs when marking out large radiuses.

Transferred arc A source of ignition in plasma arc cutting.

Transition The surface profile across the components.

Transverse The distance across the width of the material.

Trueness Maintaining dimensional accuracy.

Tungsten A metallic material capable of withstanding high temperatures.

Turbulence Uncontrolled air movement brought about by too high a gas flow rate or air movement.

Turned barrel Machined barrel bolt which is also machined under the head and is used in fine tolerance jointing.

Ultrasonic The sending out and receiving of pulse echoes in order to establish material and weld integrity.

Underbead An area immediately underneath a weld bead deposit.

Undercut The gouging effect of too high a current and insufficient dwell on the parent metal or speed of travel.

Underfill Insufficient filling of a weld deposit.

Vaporisation The effect of excessive current which brings about decomposition.

Vapours Fumes given off by a substance.

Vendor rating Designed to have a comparison between providers of components based on reliability, quality and conformance to designated standards.

Vernier A Fine limit measurement system used in callipers, height gauges protractors and depth gauges.

Viscosity The flow rate, and ease of flow of a fluid.

Weaving The manipulation of the electrode/torch to produce a wide weld deposit.

Weld face The point at which fusion into the parent metal takes place.

Weld integrity The strength of the weld able to withstand service conditions.

Weld reinforcement Extra weld metal to help distribute the stresses on the welded joint.

Weld zone The area that includes the weld deposit and the heat affected zone.

Weldment A deposit made up of parent and filler metal.

Wetting The increased surface deposition.

Witness marks A series of dot marks defining the outline of a component.

Work-hardening The rolling or manipulation of a material which results in an elongated grain structure.

Wormholes Formed by entrapped gases giving rise to pores to the surface of the weld deposit somewhat similar to chimneys.

Wrought Iron An almost carbon free form of iron which can be cold formed as in garden gates.

Yield point The point at which a material loses its elastic limit and takes on some form of permanent deformation.

Zig-Zag entry A distortion control technique used in thermal cutting to ensure that a wedge is formed to stop the component moving.